# Natural Hazards in the Asia–Pacific Region

## Geological Society books refereeing procedures

GEOLOGICAL SOCIETY SPECIAL PUBLICATION NO. 361

# Natural Hazards in the Asia–Pacific Region: Recent Advances and Emerging Concepts

EDITED BY

J. P. TERRY
National University of Singapore

and

J. GOFF
University of New South Wales, Australia

2012
Published by
The Geological Society
London

# THE GEOLOGICAL SOCIETY

The Geological Society of London (GSL) was founded in 1807. It is the oldest national geological society in the world and the largest in Europe. It was incorporated under Royal Charter in 1825 and is Registered Charity 210161.

The Society is the UK national learned and professional society for geology with a worldwide Fellowship (FGS) of over 10 000. The Society has the power to confer Chartered status on suitably qualified Fellows, and about 2000 of the Fellowship carry the title (CGeol). Chartered Geologists may also obtain the equivalent European title, European Geologist (EurGeol). One fifth of the Society's fellowship resides outside the UK. To find out more about the Society, log on to www.geolsoc.org.uk.

**The Geological Society Publishing House** (Bath, UK) produces the Society's international journals and books, and acts as European distributor for selected publications of the American Association of Petroleum Geologists (AAPG), the Indonesian Petroleum Association (IPA), the Geological Society of America (GSA), the Society for Sedimentary Geology (SEPM) and the Geologists' Association (GA). Joint marketing agreements ensure that GSL Fellows may purchase these societies' publications at a discount. The Society's online bookshop (accessible from www.geolsoc.org.uk) offers secure book purchasing with your credit or debit card.

To find out about joining the Society and benefiting from substantial discounts on publications of GSL and other societies worldwide, consult www.geolsoc.org.uk, or contact the Fellowship Department at: The Geological Society, Burlington House, Piccadilly, London W1J 0BG: Tel. +44 (0)20 7434 9944; Fax +44 (0)20 7439 8975; E-mail: enquiries@geolsoc.org.uk.

For information about the Society's meetings, consult *Events* on www.geolsoc.org.uk. To find out more about the Society's Corporate Affiliates Scheme, write to enquiries@geolsoc.org.uk.

Published by The Geological Society from:
The Geological Society Publishing House, Unit 7, Brassmill Enterprise Centre, Brassmill Lane, Bath BA1 3JN, UK

The Lyell Collection: www.lyellcollection.org
Online bookshop: www.geolsoc.org.uk/bookshop
Orders:   Tel. +44 (0)1225 445046, Fax +44 (0)1225 442836

The publishers make no representation, express or implied, with regard to the accuracy of the information contained in this book and cannot accept any legal responsibility for any errors or omissions that may be made.

**British Library Cataloguing in Publication Data**

A catalogue record for this book is available from the British Library.
ISBN 978-1-86239-339-4
ISSN 0305-8719

**Distributors**
For details of international agents and distributors see:
www.geolsoc.org.uk/agentsdistributors

Typeset by Techset Composition Ltd, Salisbury, UK
Printed by MPG Books Ltd, Bodmin, UK.

# Contents

# Living with natural hazards in the Asia–Pacific region

JAMES R. GOFF[1]* & JAMES P. TERRY[2]

[1]*Australia–Pacific Tsunami Research Centre, School of Biological, Earth and Environmental Sciences, University of New South Wales, Sydney, 2052 NSW, Australia*

[2]*Department of Geography, National University of Singapore, AS2, 1 Arts Link, Kent Ridge, Singapore 117570*

*\*Corresponding author (e-mail: j.goff@unsw.edu.au)*

Many might say that it could not be a worse time to live in the Asia–Pacific region. In the past few years we have not only experienced the 2004 Indian Ocean tsunami, but also the 2006 Java, 2007 Solomon Islands, 2009 New Zealand, 2010 Chilean and the 2011 Tōhoku (Japan) earthquakes and tsunamis. We should not forget either the seemingly endless list of other natural hazards such as tropical cyclones and typhoons (e.g. 2010 Fiji and Philippines), volcanic eruptions (2010 Indonesia), river floods (2010 Pakistan), wildfires (2009 Australia), amongst many others.

For a variety of reasons, an increasing number of people in the Asia–Pacific region are either choosing to live, or are finding themselves living, at the coast (Sieh 2006). This in itself is not a problem except when they are exposed to hazards such as tsunamis and cyclones. It is in this coastal zone, though, that we have seen the recent effects of devastating natural hazards. The value of the work carried out by natural hazards researchers has recently been brought to the forefront of public awareness. It is not always easy to recognize the hazards that a low-lying coastal area faces either because there may be no previous historic records of large-magnitude, destructive tsunamis from which we might learn valuable lessons (Satake & Atwater 2007) or because people are, for various reasons, unaware of the area's geological past (Normile 2011).

As we write this editorial, the ongoing troubles faced by the Fukushima nuclear power plant are broadcast to us daily. While it is true that the first reactor was completed there in 1971, an expert panel reviewed the plant's sesimic resistance in 2008 (Normile 2011). By this time Japanese scientists were well aware of the Jogan tsunami of 869AD, an event that they concluded could recur at about 1000 year intervals. This had not been factored into the orginal design plans for the Fukushima plant, but the opportunity existed to address this issue in 2008 – it was not (Normile 2011). The people of Japan and the rest of the world are now living with the aftermath of that decision.

If there is one thing that is evident from the work that we do on geological hazards, it is that it is all too easy to base estimates of magnitude and frequency on extrapolations from historical data. These forecasts, based generally on a few centuries of data at best, are completely inadequate for the big events that have simply not occurred in historic time. For some types of climatic and hydrological hazards, homogenous and robust datasets are of much shorter duration, so any trends are difficult to identify with confidence (Terry & Gienko 2010; Terry & Wotling 2011).

The implications for such oversights have proven to be catastrophic and it is only through a combination of geological, climatic and numerical modelling research, combined with more traditional historical studies, that we can hope to guard against such events catching us off guard in the future. An interesting case in point relates to palaeotsunami work carried out in New Zealand over the past 10 years or so that has consistently pointed to there having been a large event affecting the northern coasts of the country in the fifteenth century (e.g. Nichol *et al.* 2003; Walters *et al.* 2006; Goff 2008; Goff *et al.* 2010). This signifcant body of literature was largely ignored until recent numerical modelling work found 'an intriguing similarity in distribution and scale' of modelled runup heights with those of the palaeotsunami data (Power *et al.* 2011). Why is this so important? Palaeotsunami researchers have long proposed that the most likely source for this event was from a large subduction zone event on the Tonga–Kermadec trench to the north of New Zealand. Until recently, however, numerical modellers and geophysicists did not feel that this was plausible despite warnings from key researchers that 'simple geophysical hypotheses about maximum earthquake size at subduction zones, and about patterns of earthquake recurrence, appear to be of limited value in the long-term forecasting of the time and size of great subduction zone earthquakes' (Satake & Atwater 2007, p. 368). This point has been re-emphasized

*From*: TERRY, J. P. & GOFF, J. (eds) 2012. *Natural Hazards in the Asia–Pacific Region: Recent Advances and Emerging Concepts.* Geological Society, London, Special Publications, **361**, 1–2, http://dx.doi.org/10.1144/SP361.1

following the 2011 Tōhoku earthquake and tsunami (Normile 2011).

How long do we have to wait for the next disaster to realize the truth in this statement?

Researchers of natural hazards have an obligation to work together, to consider *all* available data. It is not necessarily easy to work in multidisciplinary groups, but the ascendancy of one branch of natural hazards research does little to help our understanding of the big picture. We are entering a period of marked climate change and appear to be facing a time of increased seismic activity (Ammon *et al.* 2010). There is little time available for natural hazards researchers to recognize the need for, and value of, true multidisciplinary studies; but, in the absence of a combined physical and human sciences approach to our work, we will doubtless fail to deliver appropriate information effectively. Socially oriented hazards research demonstrates over and over that even where a community does have a better understanding of natural hazards, abandoning a particularly hazardous place may not be desirable or possible for a wide range of reasons (Ambler 2000). Following the 2011 Tōhoku tsunami, a vast number of Japanese communities will rebuild in exactly the same place – the challenge for natural hazards researchers is to provide useful and meaningful data to ensure that these communities are as safe as they can be.

This Special Publication represents a snapshot of the burgeoning natural hazards datasets emerging from the Asia–Pacific region. This is the kind of information that will prove vital to ensuring that humans can live safely with natural hazards into the future.

# References

AMBLER, J. 2000. *Attacking Poverty While Improving the Environment: Towards Win–Win Policy Options.* Poverty and Environment Initiative, Social Science Research Council, New York.

AMMON, C. J., LAY, T. & SIMPSON, D. W. 2010. Great earthquakes and global seismic networks. *Seismological Research Letters*, **81**, 965–971.

GOFF, J. R. 2008. *The New Zealand Palaeotsunami Database*. NIWA Technical Report, **131**. National Institute of Water & Atmospheric Research, Auckland (ISSN 1174-2631).

GOFF, J. R., PEARCE, S., NICHOL, S. L., CHAGUÉ-GOFF, C., HORROCKS, M. & STROTZ, L. 2010. Multi-proxy records of regionally-sourced tsunamis, New Zealand. *Geomorphology*, **118**, 369–382.

NICHOL, S. L., LIAN, O. B. & CARTER, C. H. 2003. Sheet-gravel evidence for a late Holocene tsunami run-up on beach dunes, Great Barrier Island, New Zealand. *Sedimentary Geology*, **155**, 129–145.

NORMILE, D. 2011. Scientific consensus on great quake came too late. *Science*, **332**, 22–23.

POWER, W., WALLACE, L., WANG, X. & REYNERS, M. 2011. Tsunami hazard posed to New Zealand by the Kermadec and southern New Hebrides subduction margins: an assessment based on plate boundary kinematics, interseismic coupling, and historical seismicity. *Pure and Applied Geophysics*, doi: 10.1007/s00024-011-0299-x.

SATAKE, K. & ATWATER, B. F. 2007. Long-term perspectives on giant earthquakes and tsunamis at subduction ones. *Annual Review of Earth and Planetary Science*, **35**, 349–374.

SIEH, K. 2006. Sumatran Megathrust earthquakes – from science to saving lives. *Philosophical Transactions of the Royal Society*, **364**, 1947–1963.

TERRY, J. P. & GIENKO, G. 2010. Climatological aspects of South Pacific tropical cyclones, based on analysis of the RSMC-Nadi (Fiji) regional archive. *Climate Research*, **42**, 223–233.

TERRY, J. P. & WOTLING, G. 2011. Identifying rain-shadow influences on river flows and flood magnitudes across the central massif divide of La Grande Terre island, New Caledonia. *Journal of Hydrology*, **404**, 77–86, doi: 10.1016/j.jhydrol.2011.04.022.

WALTERS, R. A., GOFF, J. R. & WANG, K. 2006. Tsunamigenic sources in the bay of plenty, New Zealand. *Science of Tsunami Hazards*, **24**, 339–357.

# The special vulnerability of Asia–Pacific islands to natural hazards

JAMES P. TERRY[1]* & JAMES R. GOFF[2]

[1]*Department of Geography, National University of Singapore, AS2, 1 Arts Link,
Kent Ridge, Singapore 117570*

[2]*Australia–Pacific Tsunami Research Centre, School of Biological, Earth and Environmental
Sciences, University of New South Wales, Sydney, 2052 NSW, Australia*

*\*Corresponding author (e-mail: geojpt@nus.edu.sg)*

Even a cursory glance at any map of the Asia–Pacific region makes a striking impression – in addition to the continental mainland, the region encompasses a truly vast expanse of ocean throughout which are dispersed thousands of islands. Some islands are clustered together relatively near continental coastlines, while others are remote and isolated. Indeed, the majority of Asia–Pacific states are island territories (Table 1). Island sizes range from substantial landmasses such as Sumatra (473 481 $km^2$) and Honshu (227 963 $km^2$), with populations numbering tens of millions, to tiny specks of land like far-flung Pukapuka atoll in the Northern Cook Islands, covering barely 3 $km^2$ but supporting a small community nonetheless. Astonishing physical diversity is also apparent, from rugged volcanic mountains reaching high elevations, to flat coral islets emerging just above sea level. The Asia–Pacific region is also unique since it contains all five of the world's nations that are entirely atolls – Kiribati, The Maldives, The Marshall Islands, Tokelau and Tuvalu.

Owing to a variety of influences and challenges across both geophysical and geographical spheres, many Asia–Pacific islands are inherently more vulnerable than continental locations to natural hazards (ICSU 2008a; Goff et al. 2011). The majority of Asia–Pacific islands owe their origins to plate-boundary tectonics along the 'Pacific Ring of Fire', meaning that many are volcanically and/ or seismically active (Nunn 1994). Furthermore, recently erupted volcanic materials of mixed composition are unstable and prone to mass movements (Goff 2011). Even on ancient volcanoes, slope susceptibility to failure is enhanced by deep chemical weathering under humid climates to produce weak residual soils (saprolite). Heavy precipitation events typical of wet maritime regimes, especially those in monsoon or cyclone belts, then act as effective triggers for mass movements and may generate large responses in island fluvial systems leading to serious floods (Fig. 1) (ICSU 2008b; Terry et al. 2008a, b). For low-lying shorelines, tsunamis and storm surges are a clear menace, and coastal populations face grave risks if warnings are inadequate (Ziegler et al. 2009) or if there is no higher ground providing opportunities for immediate evacuation, as tragically seen in the April 2011 Tohoku tsunami.

Geographical influences on the hazard vulnerability of Asia–Pacific islands are associated primarily with their relative remoteness and inaccessibility. For nation states administering widely dispersed islands over great oceanic distances, transport networks are costly to maintain and may be unreliable as a result. For example, the outlying atolls of Tuvalu and Kiribati are serviced infrequently by government ships as not all have airstrips. Reliable communications are a similar challenge in upland areas of very large islands – such as in the central highlands of Borneo and New Guinea. There, scattered rural communities

**Table 1.** *Selected island nations of the Asia–Pacific region*

| Examples of nations or territories comprising islands only | |
| --- | --- |
| Cook Islands | New Zealand |
| Federated States of Micronesia | Niue |
| Fiji | Papua New Guinea |
| French Polynesia | Philippines |
| Guam | Singapore |
| Indonesia | Solomon Islands |
| Japan | Sri Lanka |
| Kiribati | Taiwan |
| Maldives | Tokelau |
| Marshall Islands | Tonga |
| Nauru | Tuvalu |
| New Caledonia | Vanuatu |

| Examples of continental nations with offshore islands and/or significant island populations | |
| --- | --- |
| Australia | Malaysia |
| China | Myanmar |
| India | Thailand |
| Korea | Vietnam |

From: TERRY, J. P. & GOFF, J. (eds) 2012. *Natural Hazards in the Asia–Pacific Region: Recent Advances and Emerging Concepts.* Geological Society, London, Special Publications, **361**, 3–5, http://dx.doi.org/10.1144/SP361.2

live in relative isolation from more developed towns nearer the coast. When natural hazards strike inaccessible places, government authorities are hampered in making rapid assessments of the scale or severity of the impacts and evacuation efforts are delayed. Likewise, the distribution of emergency food, medicines and temporary shelter for people in need of assistance takes time.

Economic marginalization and dependency on natural resources are other key factors. Island populations generally benefit less from national funding programmes and major development projects, and may be divorced from mainstream activities in urban conurbations. In consequence, many islanders necessarily follow traditional subsistence lifestyles, such as in (parts of) Fiji, Indonesia, Malaysia, The Philippines and Sri Lanka, and are heavily dependent on what their local environments provide (forest products, freshwater resources, food gardens, coral reefs, mangroves and coastal

fisheries) for sustenance. This dependency increases their exposure when a natural disaster damages the health and productivity of crucial ecosystems, threatening food security, livelihoods and income, thereby prolonging the period of post-disaster recovery. Yet, the remarkable resilience of (small) island societies (Gough *et al.* 2010) is easy to admire, and should offer lessons for urban and mainland dwellers elsewhere.

In light of these and similar considerations, not only is continuing systematic research necessary to improve our understanding of the origin, frequency and intensity of natural hazards, but in particular more attention should explore the impacts and responses of hazards in the Asia–Pacific islands. Scientific momentum must also reinforce disaster preparedness, risk management and adaptation. Improved mitigation of natural disasters has already been identified as a priority issue by island states (World Bank 2009), but this requires a better grasp of natural hazard trigger mechanisms, physical processes, characteristics and behaviour. One daunting hurdle to overcome is the lack of monitoring and surveillance on numerous islands, and the resulting poor or patchy records of historical events. Thus, although national governments and

**Fig. 1.** Wrecked bridge over the Sigatoka River (top) and the inundation of Ba town by the Ba River in Fiji, January 2009, which was the wettest first month in more than a century at several locations in western Fiji. Floods were caused by persistent rain associated with a number of intense synoptic-scale weather features in the region, including an active monsoonal trough, an enhanced South Pacific Convergence Zone, two tropical depressions and a tropical cyclone (FMS 2009). Flood magnitude–intensity relationships in many Asia–Pacific island rivers remain poorly understood owing to a lack of consistent hydrometric gauging. Photographs are courtesy of the Fiji Meteorological Service.

**Fig. 2.** Large-scale engineering works aimed at containing volcanic debris flows on Mount Sakurajima, southern Japan (top), and modern seawalls protecting coastal housing development (post-2004 Boxing Day tsunami) in Penang, Malaysia (bottom). Such types of hazard protection measures are expensive for poorer nations and may not be appropriate for all island settings.

local authorities alike accept the need to formulate appropriate (and culturally acceptable) disaster management plans and hazard adaptation measures (Fig. 2), many struggle to do so in the absence of robust data and meaningful scientific advice.

We hope that the contributions presented in this Special Publication showcase recent valuable findings in natural hazard research in the Asia–Pacific and also go a small way towards promoting the scientific imperative for future work in this region.

## References

FMS 2009. *Fiji Islands Climate Summary, January 2009*, Volume 30, No. 1. Fiji Meteorological Service, Nadi.

GOFF, J. 2011. Evidence of a previously unrecorded local tsunami, 13 April 2010, Cook Islands: implications for Pacific island countries. *Natural Hazards and Earth Systems Science*, 11, 1371–1379.

GOFF, J., CHAGUÉ-GOFF, C. ET AL. 2011. Palaeotsunamis in the Pacific. *Earth-Science Reviews*, 107, 141–146, doi: 10.1016/j.earscirev.2010.10.005.

GOUGH, K. V., BAYLISS-SMITH, T., CONNELL, J. & MERTZ, O. 2010. Small island sustainability in the Pacific: introduction to the special issue. *Singapore Journal of Tropical Geography*, 31, 1–9.

ICSU 2008a. *Science Plan on Hazards and Disasters: Special Vulnerability of Islands*. International Council for Science (ICSU), Regional Office for Asia and the Pacific, Kuala Lumpur.

ICSU 2008b. *Science Plan on Hazards and Disasters: Earthquakes, Floods and Landslides*. International Council for Science (ICSU), Regional Office for Asia and the Pacific, Kuala Lumpur.

NUNN, P. D. 1994. *Oceanic Islands*. Blackwell, Oxford.

TERRY, J. P., GARIMELLA, S. & LAL, R. 2008a. A study of floodplain growth in the Labasa River sugarcane belt of northern Fiji: rates, influences and contributing processes. *Geographical Research*, 46, 399–412.

TERRY, J. P., KOSTASCHUK, R. A. & WOTLING, G. 2008b. Features of tropical cyclone-induced flood peaks on Grande Terre, New Caledonia. *Water and Environment Journal*, 22, 177–183.

WORLD BANK 2009. *Preparedness, Planning, and Prevention. Assessment of National and Regional Efforts to Reduce Natural Disaster and Climate Change Risks in the Pacific*. The World Bank, Washington, DC.

ZIEGLER, A. D., WONG, P. P. & GRUNDY-WARR, C. 2009. Still vulnerable to killer tsunamis. *Science*, 326, 1188–1189.

# Flood generation during the SW monsoon season in northern Thailand

HAN SHE LIM[1]* & KANOKPORN BOOCHABUN[2]

[1]*Department of Geography, National University of Singapore, 1 Arts Link, Kent Ridge, Singapore 117570*

[2]*Research and Applied Hydrology Group, Hydrology Division, Office of Hydrology and Water Management, Royal Irrigation Department. 811 Samsen, Bangkok 10300, hailand*

*Corresponding author (e-mail: geolhs@nus.edu.sg)*

**Abstract:** This paper analyses the annual floods for the city of Chiang Mai in northern Thailand using a relatively long dataset (1921–2009) to study the mechanisms behind flood generation in this region. Four floods of different magnitudes were chosen for the empirical analysis. Daily rainfall, flow and baseflow data are analysed together with information about tropical storm occurrence–frequency and El Niño Southern Oscillation (ENSO) events to identify the occurrence and causes of floods. We found that floods are caused by a variety of factors but the most extreme floods are often caused by a combination of wet catchment conditions and heavy rainfall due to monsoonal effects or tropical storms. Tropical storms play a variable role in that their occurrence in the earlier part of the monsoon season may only wet up the catchment and have no part to play in the peak-flow generation. However, heavy rainfall due to tropical storms during the later part of the monsoon season may result in extreme floods. Typhoon Damrey (2005) is such an example as a 100 year flood event occurred after the passage of this typhoon across northern Thailand. Flood forecasting and management therefore need more high-resolution information about rainfall patterns and tropical storm activity.

Seasonal flooding is a regular feature of the monsoon climate and its occurrence signals the beginning of the rice-growing season when plentiful rains arrive. Communities living in monsoonal regions have learned to live with floods but there is now a growing perception that floods are hazards that need to be controlled (Manuta & Lebel 2005). Floods are common in north Thailand because this region experiences the highest seasonality in rainfall distribution within Thailand (Boochabun *et al.* 2004). In addition, the complex interactions between rainfall and large-scale climatic circulation systems, such as the El Niño Southern Oscillation (ENSO) and tropical storms, make peak-flow generation a highly variable and complex process. For instance, monsoon rainfall generally decreases during El Niño years while the opposite occurs during a La Niña year (Rasmusson & Carpenter 1983; Kripalani & Kulkarni 1997). Yet, high rainfall occurred during an El Niño year in 2002, resulting in serious flash floods in certain parts of northern Thailand (Singhrattna *et al.* 2005).

This paper examines floods that occur in Chiang Mai, the main city in northern Thailand and the second largest city in Thailand. Floods occur regularly in the city but have recently been causing more damage as urban development encroaches into the floodplain. The gauging record for this city is relatively long for this part of the world (1921–present) and includes flow data for many floods that occurred in the recent past. The growing importance of flooding in this city is reflected in the academic literature. Wood & Ziegler (2008) examined sedimentation patterns for a 100 year flood that caused serious flooding in the city in 2005. Duan *et al.* (2009) used the HEC-RAS (Hydrologic Engineering Center's River Analysis System) model and satellite imagery to map and model the extent of flood inundation for the same event. Their analysis showed that the flood depth was up to 1.68 m in the floodplains, and that several schools, hospitals and factories were found to be located in areas that are categorized as having a high flood risk. As an attempt to contribute to the growing literature on flood studies in Thailand, this paper examines a series of Chiang Mai city floods of different magnitudes in order to understand the occurrence and causes of floods in this city through an analysis of the hydrological response behaviour and the climatic factors that drive flood generation. The case-study floods chosen are caused by different mechanisms in order to highlight the complexities surrounding the generation of floods in northern Thailand.

*From*: TERRY, J. P. & GOFF, J. (eds) 2012. *Natural Hazards in the Asia–Pacific Region: Recent Advances and Emerging Concepts.* Geological Society, London, Special Publications, **361**, 7–20, http://dx.doi.org/10.1144/SP361.3

## Study site

The Ping River flows through Chiang Mai city and flow is gauged at the P1 gauging station (18°47′09″, 99°00′29″). The catchment above the P1 station drains an area of 6355 km² (Fig. 1). The Ping River originates within the mountainous area of northern Thailand, with steep mountains that go up to an elevation of 2000 m and valleys that lie below 500 m. This river basin is underlain by older Palaeozoic gneiss and foliated granitic rocks, Palaeozoic sediments and volcanics, Mesozoic granitic rocks, and Tertiary continental basin-fill sediments (Wood & Ziegler 2008). The catchment was previously covered by subtropical forests that have been slowly converted to agricultural land use, which includes upland rice, irrigated crops, flower farms and commercial greenhouses on the hillslopes and floodplains of the catchment. The width of the river at the P1 gauging station is approximately 110 m. The floodplain is about 3 km wide, extending to about 1–1.5 km on either side of the river bank (Wood & Ziegler 2008). The annual peak stage levels at P1 show that the river overflows its bank once water levels rise above an

elevation of approximately 3.7 m above sea level, which seems to be a common occurrence according to the data shown in Figure 2.

The climate of the catchment is classified as tropical monsoon (Aw) according to the Köppen system. The average annual temperature ranges from 20 to 34 °C (Thanapakpawin *et al.* 2006). The annual long-term rainfall is approximately 1200 mm (Wood & Ziegler 2008). The rainfall distribution is highly variable on an annual and seasonal basis. This is because the region is located at the interface of two dominant regional climatic systems: the Indian SW monsoon and the ENSO system.

The SW monsoon lasts from approximately late April–early May to October–November (Matsumoto 1997). It occurs as warm air from the Indian Ocean moves towards Thailand around late April–early May. At this time the Inter-Tropical Convergence Zone (ITCZ) moves quickly from south to north Thailand, bringing fresh rains to the study area in early May. By June, the ITCZ has moved further northwards to southern China, so north Thailand is relatively dry during this period. In August, the ITCZ moves southwards again and lies over

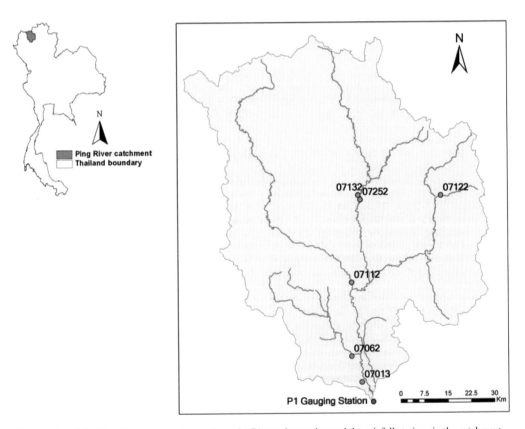

**Fig. 1.** Map of the Ping River catchment area above the P1 gauging station and the rainfall stations in the catchment.

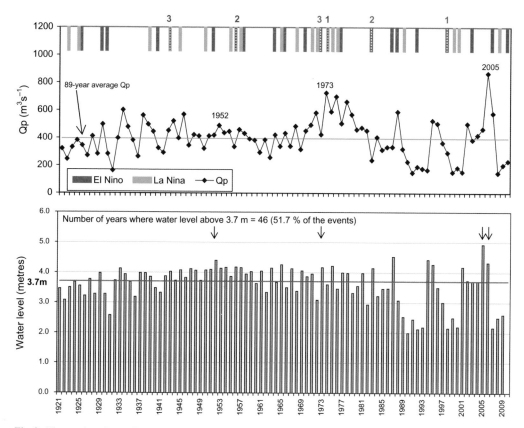

**Fig. 2.** Time-series of annual peak flows ($Q_p$) and water level at the P1 gauging station, 1921–2009. Threshold level of 3.7 m indicates bankful conditions. Bars with hashing and numbers 1, 2 and 3 indicate the top three ENSO events in terms of their severity. (Source of data: Royal Irrigation Department.).

northern Thailand. Peak rainfall occurs during this month or in September. The end of the monsoon period occurs approximately in October when the ITCZ moves further south. This is followed by the winter season, which is dominated by the NE monsoon that lasts from mid-October to approximately April or early–mid May (Thai Meteorological Department 2002). Cyclones and other forms of climatic disturbances in the form of monsoon depressions and typhoons also influence rainfall activity in this catchment. Tropical cyclones originate from the east of the catchment over the western North Pacific Ocean or the South China Sea and pass through or close to north Thailand from May to October. Peak activity occurs around the months of September and October (Thai Meteorological Department 2002). Seasonal rainfall can account for as much as 92% of the annual rainfall. The hydrological regime of the Ping River reflects the seasonal rainfall distribution as 70% of annual total flow occurs during the rainy season (Thanapakpawin *et al.* 2006).

**Data and methods**

The empirical analysis of flood generation is based on an analysis of annual peak-flow data derived from analysing daily flow data from the P1 gauging station. Annual peak flow, $Q_p$, is used as an indicator of flooding, especially if it corresponds with overbank flow (Fig. 2). Confirmed reports of flooding are based on news sources and information from the Royal Irrigation Department office in Chiang Mai.

Daily rainfall and baseflow data are analysed together with information about tropical storm occurrence and ENSO events. Daily rainfall is the simple average of rainfall data from six stations located throughout the P1 catchment (Fig. 1). Data on tropical cyclones are obtained from the Thai Meteorological Department (TMD). Cyclone is the term given to tropical cyclones originating from the Indian Ocean and the South Pacific (west of longitude 160°), while typhoons refer to tropical cyclones originating in the Pacific Ocean. In this paper, tropical cyclone is used as a generic term to refer to either typhoons or cyclones; however, the terminology adopted by the TMD is used to refer to specific events in relation to the floods. The ENSO events (El Ninõ or La Ninã) are identified using the method developed by the Japan Meteorological Agency (JMA). The Southern Oscillation Index (SOI) was not used because it is relatively noisy (Bove *et al.* 1998). The JMA Index is a 5 month running mean of spatially averaged sea-surface temperature anomalies over the tropical Pacific in the region 4°S–4°N, 150°W–90°W (ftp://www.coaps.fsu.edu/pub/JMA_SST_Index/). An El Ninõ or La Ninã event occurs when the JMA Index is greater than 5 °C or at least 5 °C below average for at least six consecutive months (including October, November and December), respectively.

Baseflow represents an integrated measure of catchment wetness. Baseflow data for the P1 gauging station was obtained using the Baseflow Index Program (BFI) version 4.15 available on the World Wide Web (http://www.usbr.gov/pmts/hydraulics_lab/twahl/bfi/). Baseflow separation is based on the Institute of Hydrology (UK) Standard method of baseflow separation (Institute of Hydrology 1980).

Flood frequency analysis was conducted on the 89 year-flow dataset to identify the return periods of various flood events (Fig. 3). (The return period of the flood events in this study was calculated using the Weibull formula, which is the most commonly used method to calculate return periods; see Brutsaert 2005, p. 515 for a fuller explanation. The return period, $T(x)$, is calculated as $T(x) = (n+1)/m$, where $n$ is the number of years of

record and $m$ is the rank of an individual flood event. The largest event in an annual maximum flow series will have a rank of 1 (i.e. $m = 1$).) A range of different floods that occurred in Chiang Mai city (in 1952, 1973, 2005 and 2006) were identified. These floods represent events of different magnitudes and were also caused by different mechanisms. The 2005 flood is the largest flood recorded within the 89 year period. The second largest flood on record occurred in 1973. The 1952 flood is included because local accounts stated that large parts of Chiang Mai city were inundated. Finally, the 2006 flood is included as a comparative example against the 2005 flood, as floods occurred in both years but may have been caused by different mechanisms. Their close temporal proximity reduces the impact of land-use change or changes in channel capacity in influencing flood generation and subsequent flood behaviour.

To examine the interactions between rainfall, flow and baseflow (i.e. catchment wetness) in causing floods, the normalized cumulative flow, baseflow and rainfall values for each day of any month are plotted together to show the relative increase in each of these three variables over the course of a month. The normalized cumulative value for each day is obtained by dividing the daily value of a particular variable by its cumulative value observed for each month. The following indices for peak flows for the selected years could be obtained.

- $Q_p$ – annual peak-flow value.
- $Q_p/Q_{p\ longmean}$ – represents the annual peak flow as a function of the long-term average for the 89 year period.

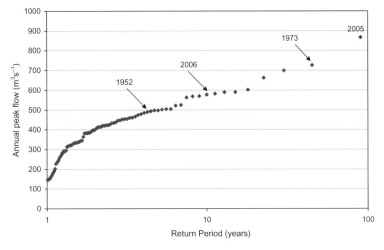

**Fig. 3.** Flood frequency graph for the P1 gauging station, 1921–2009. The floods analysed are highlighted. (Source of data: Royal Irrigation Department.)

- API-7 – the 7 day antecedent rainfall prior to each flow peak; it provides an indication of recent rainfall activity prior to the peak flow.
- $RF_p$ – refers to the maximum daily rainfall occurring within the API-7. It provides an indication of the rainfall intensity in relation to the daily flow.
- BF at $Q_p$ – refers to the baseflow value when $Q_p$ occurs.
- $BF/BFp$ – refers to the ratio of baseflow when $Q_p$ occurs to the annual peak baseflow value. It provides an indication of how wet the catchment is when $Q_p$ occurs.
- $BF/Q_p$ – ratio of baseflow to $Q_p$. This value provides an indication of whether baseflow or quickflow processes dominate in the production of $Q_p$ (following Hibbert & Cunningham's 1967 definition of baseflow and quickflow, see Gregory & Walling 1973). (According to Hibbert & Cunningham 1967, a storm hydrograph can be separated by a line into a quickflow and a delayed flow component. The quickflow component generally represents rapid runoff, while the delayed flow generally represents runoff from slow sources or from baseflow (Gregory & Walling 1973).)

## Results

### When will it flood?

Rainfall patterns show a bimodal distribution. Higher rainfall is observed around the month of May and peaks in September following the movement of the ITCZ over northern Thailand (Fig. 4). Baseflow is highest in September owing to the continuous rainfall in the previous months. Peak flows and, therefore, floods are likely to occur in late August or September when heavy rainfall falls on a wet catchment. Furthermore, the increased frequency distribution of tropical cyclone activity in September implies that heavy rainfall associated with this storm activity results in favourable conditions for flooding to occur (Fig. 5).

### Flood-generating mechanisms

The analysis of floods that occurred in two consecutive years, in 2005 and 2006, show the different mechanisms influencing flood generation of this catchment (Figs 6 & 7).

Three floods occurred in 2005 (Figs 3 & 7). This is a 100 year event. Two of the three floods are related to tropical storm activity. The earliest flood was due to a tropical depression (14–16 August) (Table 1); Tropical Cyclone Vicente (20–22 September) and Typhoon Damrey (30 September) caused the subsequent two floods. Typhoon Damrey, in particular, caused massive flooding as it swept westwards across the IndoChina peninsula as a tropical depression around 27 September (Wood & Ziegler 2008). The annual peak flow for 2005 was the highest annual peak flow $(867 \text{ m}^3 \text{ s}^{-1})$ recorded for the 89 year data record.

The normalized cumulative flow, baseflow and rainfall plots for August showed flows increasing significantly in response to heavy rainfall on 12 August 2005 (106 mm) (Fig. 8a, b). By contrast, the annual peak flow observed on 30 September was caused by continuous rainfall due to Tropical Cyclone Vicente (19 September, 26.2 mm) and Typhoon Damrey (27 September, 39.6 mm). Both flow and baseflow increased gradually throughout September in response to continuous rainfall (Fig. 8c). This corresponded to a period of rapid increase in flow and catchment wetness conditions (Fig. 8a). In fact, Typhoon Damrey occurred at a time when the P1 catchment was very wet, as the baseflow to annual baseflow peak $(BF/BF_p)$ was

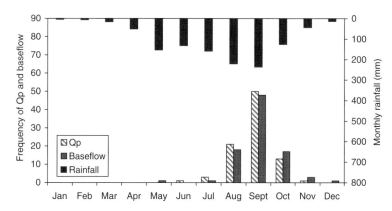

**Fig. 4.** Long-term monthly distribution of annual peak flow, rainfall and baseflow, P1 gauging station, 1921–2009.

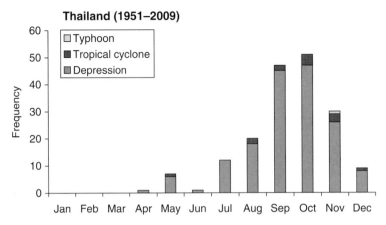

**Fig. 5.** Monthly distribution of tropical storms over Thailand. (Source of data: Thai Meteorological Department.)

relatively high compared to the baseflow during the August high flow (Table 2). The relatively low API 7-day value (107.2 mm) also showed that this flood was not caused by a single heavy rainfall event (Table 2). The main 2005 flood was, therefore, caused by continuous typhoon-bearing rainfall occurring over a wet catchment that was already previously wetted up by another tropical cyclone and heavy monsoon rainfall.

The 2006 event is ranked ninth on the list of annual peak flows and has a 10 year return period (Fig. 3). In this case, monsoon rainfall appears to have been the sole cause of the floods in 2006, unlike the main 2005 flood. The annual peak flow occurred earlier in the monsoon season compared to its 2005 counterpart; 1 August 2006. Subsequent high flows were recorded on 2 September, 23 September and 10 October. The cumulative graphs showed that the 1 August and 2 September flow peaks were a result of heavy rainfall approximately

2 days prior to the recorded $Q_p$ (43.7 mm on 30 July and 34.8 mm on 31 August) (Fig. 9). The subsequent peaks in late September and October were a result of continuous rainfall during the period prior to each recorded peak flow (Fig. 9d). The annual peak flow on 1 August occurred when the catchment was about 65% wet $(BF/BF_p = 0.65$; Table 2). The peak was therefore caused by 2 days of relatively heavy rainfall on 30 and 31 July, which resulted in an annual peak flow that was 1.5 times that of the long-term average (Fig. 9b, Table 2).

### Role of tropical cyclones

The role of tropical cyclones in causing floods is examined in this subsection using the floods that occurred in 1952 and 1973 as examples. Tropical cyclones occurred in both years but their effect on the annual peak flow and flood generation was quite different.

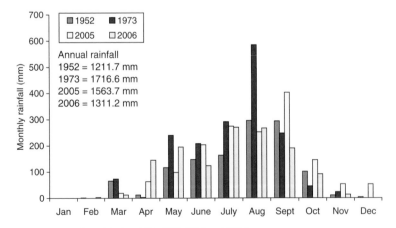

**Fig. 6.** Monthly distribution of rainfall for 1952, 1973, 2005 and 2006.

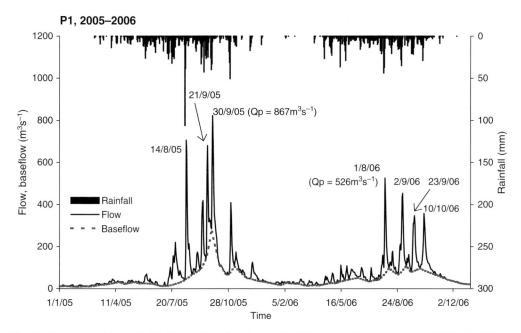

**P1, 2005–2006**

**Fig. 7.** Time-series of daily rainfall, flow and baseflow for the Ping River at the P1 gauging station, 2005 and 2006.

In 1952, two typhoons (Typhoon Louise and Typhoon Nora) made landfall near the Ping River catchment (Table 1). These typhoons did not result in the annual peak flow for the year (Tables 1 & 2, Fig. 10). The annual peak flow was, in fact, caused by high rainfall (62.1 mm on 19 September) that was not related to any tropical cyclones. The resulting annual peak flow was 1.2 times the long-term average and is ranked 21 in the 89 year period. Historical accounts tell of extensive flooding of the city of Chiang Mai. Flow and baseflow increased gradually over the course of August and September, even though there were certain days that experienced more rainfall owing to the effects of the two typhoons, Louise and Nora (Fig. 10c, d). The role of the two typhoons appears to have been to wet up the catchment, given the high $BF/BFp$ value when the impacts of Typhoon Nora were felt by the P1 catchment ($BF/BFp = 0.99$; Table 2). The annual peak flow on 22 September was then caused by a single heavy rainfall event (19 September) on already wet catchment soils (Fig. 10d).

The 1973 flood is, by contrast, more severe than the one that occurred in 1952, being ranked second in magnitude over the 89 year record based on the annual peak-flow data (45 year return period).

**Table 1.** *List of tropical cyclones and peak-flow characteristics for the four floods studied*

| Type of storm | Name | Date | Where it landed | Date of $Q_p$ occurrence | $Q_p$ $(m^3\ s^{-1})$ | API-7* (mm) | $Q_{p}$ rank[†] |
|---|---|---|---|---|---|---|---|
| Typhoon | Louise | 29 August 1952 | Nan | 1 September 1952 | 396 | 83 | – |
| Typhoon | Nora | 8 September 1952 | Chiang Rai | 10 September 1952 | 450 | 110.6 | – |
| Typhoon | Anita | 9 July 1973 | Nan | 13 July 1973 | 308 | 83.9 | – |
| Tropical cyclone | Jones | 23 August 1973 | Nan | 25 August 1973 | 726 | 117.7 | 2 |
| Tropical cyclone | Vicente | 19 September 2005 | Nan/Chiang Rai | 21 September 2005 | 679.5 | 122 | – |
| Tropical cyclone | Damrey | 27 September 2005 | Nan | 30 September 2005 | 867.2 | 64.1 | 1 |

Note that the criterion for inclusion into the table is that the date of $Q_p$ occurrence must be within 5 days of the date of the tropical storm entering Thailand
*API-7 is the amount of rainfall recorded during the week prior to $Q_p$ occurring. It is calculated as the weekly sum of rainfall starting from the date that the tropical storm arrived at Thailand.
[†]The ranking is given only if the tropical cyclone was the cause of the annual peak for a year.

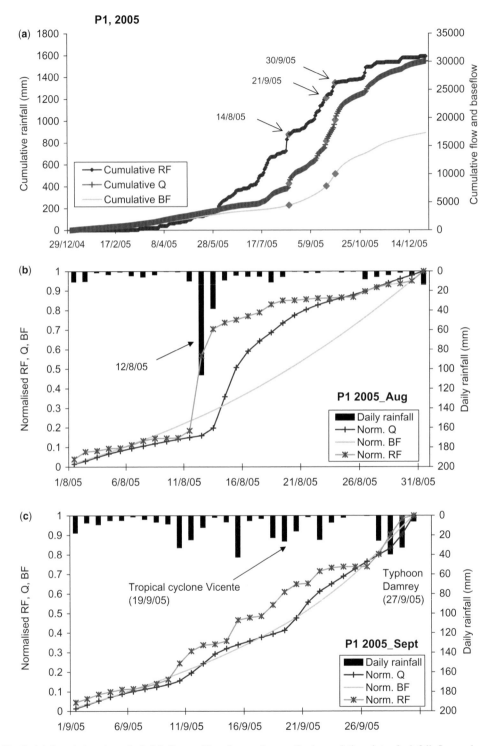

**Fig. 8.** (a) Cumulative plots of rainfall, flow and baseflow, and normalized cumulative plots of rainfall, flow and baseflow for (b) August and (c) September 2005, Ping River at P1 gauging station. The red diamonds in (a) refer to the days when a spike in flow occurs.

**Table 2.** *Summary of the annual peak-flow, rainfall and baseflow for the four floods studied*

| | $Q_p$ $(m^3 s^{-1})$ | $Q_p/Q_p$ longmean* | API-7[†] (mm) | $RF_p^{‡}$ (mm) | BF at $Q_p$ $(m^3 s^{-1})$ | BF/ $BF_p^{§}$ | BF/ $Q_p$ |
|---|---|---|---|---|---|---|---|
| **2005** | | | | | | | |
| Monsoon (14 August) | 706.5 | 1.8 | 164.1 | 106.0 | 46.4 | 0.16 | 0.07 |
| Tropical Cyclone Vicente (21 September) | 679.5 | 1.7 | 122.0 | 42.6 | 172.6 | 0.61 | 0.25 |
| Typhoon Damrey (30 September) | 867.2 | 2.2 | 107.2 | 39.6 | 255.0 | 0.89 | 0.29 |
| **2006** | | | | | | | |
| Monsoon (1 August) | 577.3 | 1.5 | 131 | 43.7 | 71.5 | 0.65 | 0.12 |
| Monsoon (2 September) | 454.1 | 1.1 | 123.1 | 34.8 | 87.3 | 0.80 | 0.19 |
| Monsoon (23 September) | 346.8 | 0.9 | 101.6 | 21.3 | 85.5 | 0.78 | 0.25 |
| Monsoon (10 October) | 357.6 | 0.9 | 80 | 28.8 | 88.0 | 0.80 | 0.25 |
| **1952** | | | | | | | |
| Typhoon Louise (1 September) | 396 | 1.0 | 83.0 | 34 | 154.8 | 0.85 | 0.39 |
| Typhoon Nora (10 Sept) | 450 | 1.1 | 110.6 | 47 | 180.6 | 0.99 | 0.40 |
| Monsoon (22 September) | 490 | 1.2 | 93.6 | 62 | 162.5 | 0.89 | 0.33 |
| **1973** | | | | | | | |
| Typhoon Anita (13 July) | 308 | 0.8 | 83.9 | 40.8 | 69.5 | 0.19 | 0.23 |
| Tropical Cyclone Jones (25 August) | 726 | 1.8 | 184.4 | 114.3 | 276.5 | 0.76 | 0.38 |
| 30 August peak | 689 | 1.7 | 286.8 | 61.9 | 304.8 | 0.84 | 0.44 |
| Monsoon (21 September) | 624 | 1.6 | 113.3 | 34.2 | 314.9 | 0.87 | 0.50 |

*$Q_p$ longmean is the long-term mean annual peak flow based on the 89 year data record.
[†] API-7 is the sum of daily rainfall prior to the day that $Q_p$ occurs.
[‡] Highest daily RF within the API-7 period.
[§] $BF/BF_p$ refers to the ratio of BF valued when $Q_p$ occurred to the annual peak baseflow value for each year.

Typhoon Anita and Tropical Cyclone Jones crossed near to the Ping River catchment in 1952 (Table 1). Their landfall resulted in a significant increase in river flow (Fig. 11c, d). Tropical Cyclone Jones resulted in 1 day of heavy rainfall over the catchment (114.3 mm on 23 August) that led to the annual peak flow for the year (Fig. 11d). The limited impact of Typhoon Anita ($Q_p/Q_p$ longmean = 0.8) is related possibly to its early occurrence in the monsoon season when the catchment was still relatively dry ($BF/BF_p$ = 0.19; Table 2). However, the catchment had become relatively wetter by the time Tropical Cyclone Jones occurred, such that heavy rainfall resulted in an extreme annual peak (1.8 times the long-term average) (Table 2). In this case, it would seem that both heavy rainfall and wet catchment conditions played a role in flood generation, although the former seemed to have a greater role.

## Discussion

The empirical analysis of flood events that occurred in Chiang Mai highlights that the flood generation mechanisms vary on an annual basis. Here, we used the annual peak-flow data as an indicator of the magnitude of floods. The 1952, 1973 and 2005 floods were all influenced by tropical storm activity, whilst this influence was lacking in the 2006 floods. The most extreme floods experienced in this catchment were caused by a combination of common mechanisms of flood generation in this region; wet catchment conditions due to continuous monsoon rainfall or tropical storm activity (e.g. 1952) in addition to heavy rainfall from tropical storm activity (see Hirschboeck 1988). We see this happening in the case of the 1973 and 2005 floods. Furthermore, the P1 catchment exhibits a fast response time to rainfall that is an approximate 2 day delay period between rainfall and $Q_p$ for the four floods examined in this paper (Table 1). This could be a reflection of the mountainous topography and suggests that high-resolution data collection is necessary for the flood-monitoring programme of this catchment area.

The role of tropical cyclones in flood generation is highly variable and complex for the P1 catchment. Analysis of the four floods showed that the effect of tropical cyclones was to: (a) wet up the catchment, especially if they occur in the earlier part of the monsoon season (e.g. the 1952 flood); or (b) to act as a trigger for peak-flow generation as high rainfalls associated with these storm events tend to magnify the effects of other rainfall-generating mechanisms during the monsoon season (e.g. rainfall associated with southwesterly winds, tropical depressions). Previous studies showed that the formation of tropical cyclones is dependent on factors such as the occurrence and location of sea-surface temperature anomalies that are associated with ENSO events. For instance, cyclone formation

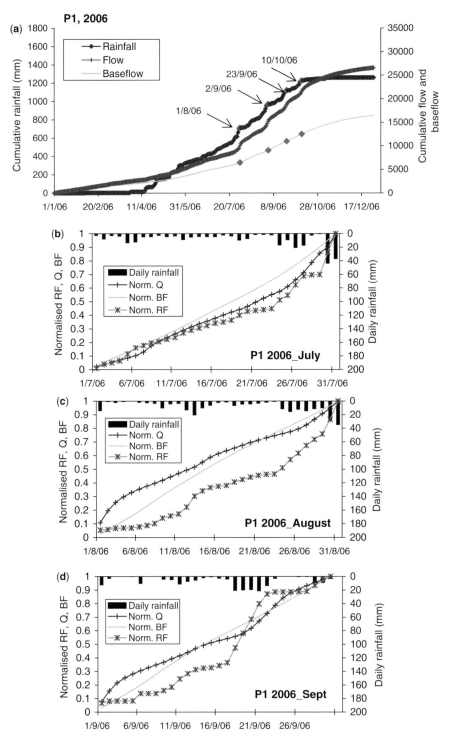

**Fig. 9.** (a) Cumulative plots of rainfall, flow and baseflow, and normalized cumulative plots of rainfall, flow and baseflow for (b) July, (c) August and (d) September 2006, Ping River at P1 gauging station. The red diamonds in (a) refer to the days when a spike in flow occurs.

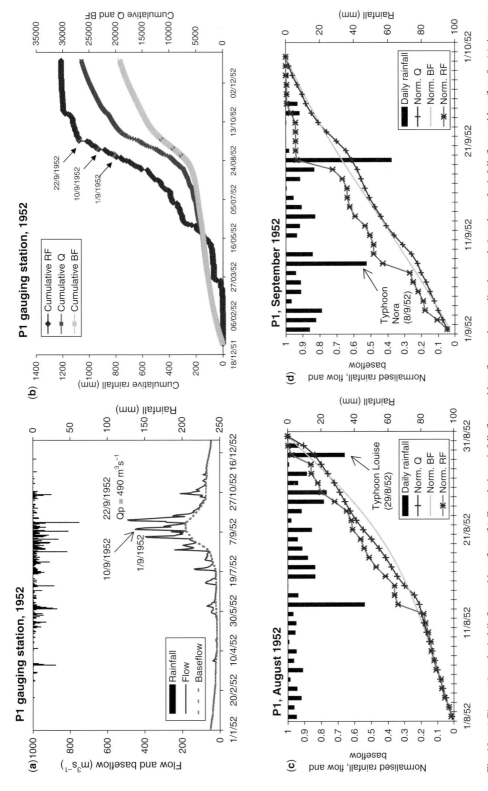

**Fig. 10.** (a) Time-series of rainfall, flow and baseflow. (b) Cumulative rainfall, flow and baseflow, and normalized cumulative plots of rainfall, flow and baseflow for (c) August and (d) September 1952, Ping River at P1 gauging station. The red diamonds in (b) refer to the days when a spike in flow occurs.

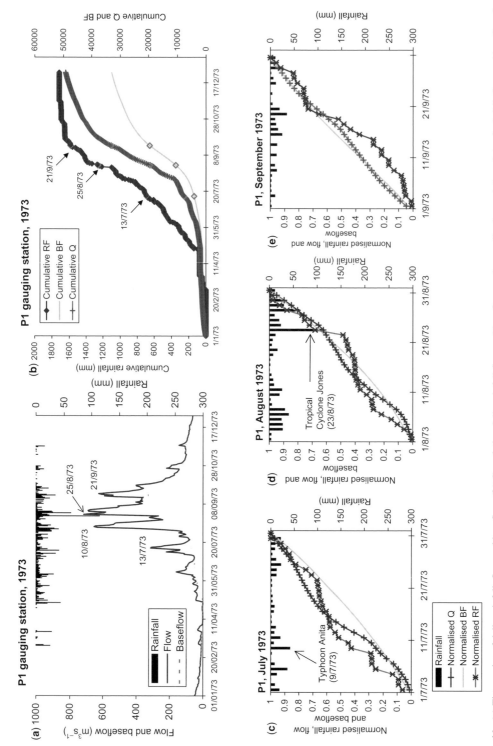

**Fig. 11.** (a) Time-series of daily rainfall, flow and baseflow. (b) Cumulative daily rainfall, flow and baseflow, and normalized cumulative plots of rainfall, flow and baseflow for (c) July, (d) August and (e) September 1973, Ping River at P1 gauging station. The red diamonds in (b) refer to the days when a spike in flow occurs.

was found to decrease between the months of September and November during an El Niño year (Elsner & Liu 2003; Wu *et al.* 2004). A further study of the relative role and impacts of tropical cyclone activity on flood generation in this catchment requires a closer examination of cyclone tracks landfalling in northern Thailand. In addition, the amount of rainfall associated with each tropical storm, its characteristics and timing of its landfall within the monsoon season as well as ENSO occurrence will provide more specific information on the relative role of tropical cyclones in flood generation for this catchment. In particular, the role of the mountainous terrain of this catchment may enhance the impact of tropical storms, especially through orographical rainfall enhancement – as shown elsewhere in Puerto Rico (see Smith *et al.* 2005).

The four flood events also allowed an analysis of the influence of ENSO activity on flood generation. No ENSO activity was reported for 1952 and 2005. The 1973 flood occurred during a La Niña year and the 2006 flood occurred during an El Niño year. In fact, the 1973 flood is located within a period in the early 1970s when there was an unusual persistence of La Niña activity and this year also experienced particularly strong La Niña conditions (Fig. 2). Monsoon rainfall in Thailand shows a generally negative correlation during El Niño years, while the opposite occurs during a La Niña year (Rasmusson & Carpenter 1983; Kripalani & Kulkarni 1997). Kripalani & Kulkarni (1997) claimed that rainfall exhibited distinct sequences of above and below normal rainfall, lasting 30 years in the case of Thailand, that are not forced by ENSO events. The impact of a La Niña event will be magnified if it occurs during a period of above-normal rainfall (i.e. these two forcings are phase-locked). According to these authors, above-normal rainfall occurred between approximately the mid-1930s until the end of the 1960s. The early 1970s occurrence of La Niña fell outside of this high rainfall period but, nonetheless, the persistence of several La Niña events over a short period of time in the early 1970s meant that the P1 catchment may well have been generally wetter compared to other years during the 89 year period. In fact, Table 2 shows that the $BF/Q_p$ values for 1973 high flows are generally higher (ranging between 0.23 and 0.50) for the same periods of time within the monsoon season compared to other years, such as 2005 and 2006, when the $BF/Q_p$ ratio is at a maximum of 0.29 (in 2005) (Table 2). The relatively higher $BF/Q_p$ values for the 1973 and, in addition, the 1952 high flows also suggest that baseflow formed a more significant component of peak-flow composition than in 2005 or 2006 when quickflow sources of runoff would have been more significant contributors to peak

flows (following the definitions of quickflow and baseflow adopted by Hibbert & Cunningham 1967 in Gregory & Walling 1973) (Table 2).

Floods can also occur owing to heavy monsoon rainfall even during an El Niño year (i.e. 2006). In 2002, flash floods were reported for some areas near the P1 catchment when monsoon rainfall coupled with heavy rainfall due to Tropical Cyclone Usagi occurred. This unexpected heavy monsoon rainfall during an El Niño year was attributed to the unusual shift in the location of sea surface temperature (SST) anomalies over the Pacific Ocean In 2002, ENSO activity was centred over the date line rather than the eastern Pacific Ocean. This led to above-normal rainfall over Thailand (Singhrattna *et al.* 2005). The influence of ENSO activity on flood generation is therefore highly complicated owing to complexities within the ENSO system, such as the location of SSTs and the relationship between ENSO and rainfall.

## Conclusion

The empirical study of four different flood events of different magnitudes in Chiang Mai city gave us the opportunity to analyse the different mechanisms of flood generation in northern Thailand using the Ping River catchment at the P1 gauging station as a case study. Floods occur regularly but the mechanisms behind their formation vary on an annual basis. Floods that affect the city can occur even during El Niño years when monsoon rainfall is generally expected to be lower. However, the most extreme floods experienced in this catchment are caused by a combination of factors that work together. The 2005 and 1973 floods are a result of heavy rainfall often due to tropical storms making landfall near the catchment area, especially when the catchment is already wetted up by monsoonal rainfall or prior tropical storms. As such, a complex interaction is observed between monsoonal rainfall and the number, timing and occurrence of tropical storms in causing more extreme floods at this site using just four examples of floods. Whilst climatic controls are important in flood generation, land-cover/land-use changes also feature as a potentially important force in flood generation given the rapid changes in land cover/land use in SE Asia (e.g. Schmidt-Vogt *et al.* 2009). Future work for this site looks at investigating trends in annual peak flows and the climatic variables that affect rainfall in northern Thailand, as well as an analysis of land-cover/land-use changes over time to identify the relative effects of these two forces on peak flow and flood generation. On a more practical basis, the fast response time of this relatively large catchment area implies that the continued monitoring of storm tracks by the Royal Meteorological

Department, and more detailed temporal and spatial monitoring of rainfall and flow patterns, are necessary for the successful flood monitoring and management for this catchment. This is especially true in the case of flash-flood monitoring and the development of warning systems using telemetry to convey real-time data to government agencies for flood monitoring and warning.

The authors would like to thank the Hydrology and Water Management Centre for Upper Northern Region Royal Irrigation Department (Chiang Mai) and the Thai Meteorological Department for providing the data for this paper. We also gratefully acknowledge financial assistance from the National University of Singapore Academic Research Fund (Tier 1) R-109-000-090-12.

# References

BOOCHABUN, K., TYCH, W., CHAPPELL, N. A., CARLING, P. A., LORSIRIRAT, K. & PA-OBSAENG, S. 2004. Statistical modelling of rainfall and river flow in Thailand. *Journal of the Geological Society of India*, **64**, 503–515.

BOVE, M. C., ELSNER, J. B., LANDSEA, C. W., NIU, X. & O'BRIEN, J. J. 1998. Effect of El Niño on US landfalling hurricanes, revisited. *Bulletin of the American Meteorological Society*, **79**, 2477–2482.

BRUTSAERT, W. 2005. *Hydrology: An Introduction*. Cambridge University Press, New York.

DUAN, M., ZHANG, J., LIU, Z. & AEKAKKARARUNGROJ, A. 2009. Use of remote sensing and GIS for flood hazard mapping in Chiang Mai Province, northern Thailand. *In*: ZHANG, J., LI, Z., CHENG, P & YAN, Q. (eds) *International Conference on Geo-Spatial Solutions for Emergency Mitigation and the 50th anniversary of the Chinese Academy of Surveying and Mapping*. Chinese Academy of Surveying and Mapping, Beijing, 203–208.

ELSNER, J. B. & LIU, K. B. 2003. Examining the ENSO-typhoon hypothesis. *Climate Research*, **25**, 43–54.

GREGORY, K. J. & WALLING, D. E. 1973. *Drainage Basin Form and Process: A Geomorphological Approach*. Edward Arnold, London.

HIBBERT, A. R. & CUNNINGHAM, G. B. 1967. Streamflow data processing opportunities and application. *In*: SOPPER, W. E. & LULL, H. W. (eds) *International Symposium on Forest Hydrology*. Pergamon, Oxford, 725–736.

HIRSCHBOECK, K. K. 1988. Flood hydroclimatology. *In*: BAKER, V. R., KOCHEL, R. C. & PATTON, P. C. (eds) *Flood Geomorphology*. Wiley, New York, 27–49.

INSTITUTE OF HYDROLOGY (UK) 1980. *Low Flow Studies*. Research Report 1. Institute of Hydrology, Wallingford, UK.

KRIPALANI, R. H. & KULKARNI, A. 1997. Rainfall variability over South-east Asia – connections with Indian Monsoon and ENSO extremes: new perspectives. *International Journal of Climatology*, **17**, 1155–1168.

MANUTA, J & LEBEL, L. 2005. Climate change and the risks of flood disasters in Asia: crafting adaptive and just institutions. In: *Human Security and Climate Change. An International Workshop*, Oslo, 21–23 June 2005. (Available at: World Wide Web Address: http://www.cicero.uio.no/humsec/papers/Manuta&Lebel.pdf.)

MATSUMOTO, J. 1997. Seasonal transition of summer rainy season over Indochina and adjacent monsoon region. *Advances in Atmospheric Sciences*, **14**, 31–245.

RASMUSSON, E. M. & CARPENTER, T. H. 1983. The relationship between Eastern Equatorial Pacific Sea Surface Temperatures and Rainfall over India and Sri Lanka. *Monthly Weather Review*, **111**, 517–528.

SCHMIDT-VOGT, D., LEISZ, S. J. ET AL. 2009. An Assessment of trends in the extent of swidden in southeast Asia. *Human Ecology*, **37**, 269–380.

SINGHRATTNA, N., RAJAGOPALAN, B., KUMAR, K. K. & CLARK, M. 2005. Interannual and interdecadal variability of Thailand Summer Monsoon Season. *Journal of Climate*, **18**, 1697–1708.

SMITH, J. A., STURDEVANT,, REES, P., BAECK, M. L. & LARSEN, M. C. 2005. Tropical cyclones and the flood hydrology of Puerto Rico. *Water Resources Research*, **41**, W06020, doi: 10.1029/2004WR003530.

THAI METEOROLOGICAL DEPARTMENT 2002. World Wide Web Address: http://www.tmd.go.th/climate/climate_04.html.

THANAPAKPAWIN, P., RICHEY, J., THOMAS, D., RODDA, S., CAMPBELL, B. & LOGSDON, M. 2006. Effects of landuse change on the hydrologic regime of the Mae Chaem river basin, NW Thailand. *Journal of Hydrology*, **334**, 215–230.

WOOD, S. & ZIEGLER, A. D. 2008. Floodplain sediment from a 100-year recurrence flood in 2005 of the Ping River in northern Thailand. *Hydrological Earth System Sciences*, **12**, 1–15.

WU, M. C., CHANG, W. L. & LEUNG, W. M. 2004. Impacts of El Niño Southern Oscillation events on tropical cyclone landfalling activity in the western North Pacific. *Journal of Climate*, **17**, 1419–1428.

# Marine inundation hazards in French Polynesia: geomorphic impacts of Tropical Cyclone Oli in February 2010

SAMUEL ETIENNE

*Université de la Polynésie française, CNRS – GEOLAB, UMR 6042 GEOLAB, BP 6570, 98702 Faa'a, Tahiti, French Polynesia (e-mail: samuel.etienne@upf.pf)*

**Abstract:** Marine inundation hazards in French Polynesia are various and unevenly distributed in the territory; they are strongly related to the physiography (topography, bathymetry, coral reef development) of these oceanic islands. Cyclones and tsunamis appear as predominant processes in the definition of coastal flooding risks for Polynesian people. This study examines the geomorphic impacts of Tropical Cyclone Oli, which struck the western part of French Polynesia in February 2010. Submarine reef erosion is quantified through coral colony degree of destruction and massive coral colony displacement. Sediment transport and beach retreat are quantified, and flow velocities at the coastline are estimated through boulder analysis. Erosion and resilience of a sandy bank (cay) at the reef margin is also considered on Tubuai Island through satellite image analysis and GPS field survey. Outer-reef slope angle appears as a major control factor for coral destruction, with vertical submarine cliffs relatively shielded compared to gentle slopes. Submarine boulder measurements provide valuable estimates of flow velocity profile with depth. Beachrock slab measurements also provide estimates of flow velocities at the reef–beach junction. Combining these different geomorphic markers might be a way to apprehend the flow velocity variation when the cyclone waves cross the coral reef.

For most countries of the world, marine inundation hazards have limited spatial impacts owing to the narrowness of the coastal strip. Exceptions to this are low-lying areas (e.g. Bangladesh (Mirza 2002) or Louisiana deltas (Houck 1985; Burkett *et al.* 2003)), where severe marine flooding can extend several kilometres inland, or specifically small islands such as atolls, which occasionally can be totally submerged (e.g. Dupon 1987, Yamano *et al.* 2007). Regarding the recent (post-World War II) concentration of demographic and economic centres in the coastal zone (enhanced by tourism development: Meur-Férec *et al.* 2008), these areas bear an increasing degree of risk especially for those affected by high-energy events such as cyclones, tsunamis or storms (Nott 2006). This paper examines the vulnerability of French Polynesia, a country of small islands in the South Pacific Ocean, to marine inundation hazards, with specific emphasis on cyclone geomorphic impacts, including the recent impact of Tropical Cyclone (TC) Oli in February 2010. Surveys were conducted on different islands of French Polynesia: reef damages, coral boulder transport and beach erosion were examined and mapped within 2 months of the meteorological event. Geomorphic resilience has also been estimated on Tubuai Island, which was directly affected by the cyclone. Post-storm studies have been really helpful in understanding the dynamics of atolls and other low-lying islands, especially in the Pacific (Scoffin 1993).

## Physical characteristics and vulnerability to marine inundation hazards of French Polynesia

French Polynesia is a vast territory located in the South Pacific Ocean, comprising five archipelagos and 121 islands (Fig. 1). Emerged lands represent less than 3500 km² disseminated over $5.5 \times 10^6$ km² of deep ocean (exclusive economic zone). Tahiti, the largest and most populated island, covers 1042 km². In January 2010, the population was estimated to be 267 000 (ISPF 2010), with a concentration of 75% in the Windward Islands (Tahiti and Moorea). People are generally located on low-lying coastal plains, apart from Tahiti where the volcano slopes have been recently colonized due to the spatial saturation of the coastal zone. These Polynesian islands can be classified into two physiographical categories: high volcanic and/or limestone islands with steep slopes (the highest summit is Mount Orohena in Tahiti, 2241 m); and low-lying islands (atolls), mainly represented in the Tuamotu Archipelago where land levels rarely exceed 10 m asl (metres above sea level). In some cases, uplifted atolls lead to the appearance of high limestone islands fringed with calcareous cliffs with altitudes reaching 100–150 m (e.g. Makatea, Rurutu).

Both island categories and intermediate stages are genetically linked as they represent one stage from the slowly emerging submarine volcano

*From*: TERRY, J. P. & GOFF, J. (eds) 2012. *Natural Hazards in the Asia–Pacific Region: Recent Advances and Emerging Concepts*. Geological Society, London, Special Publications, **361**, 21–39, http://dx.doi.org/10.1144/SP361.4

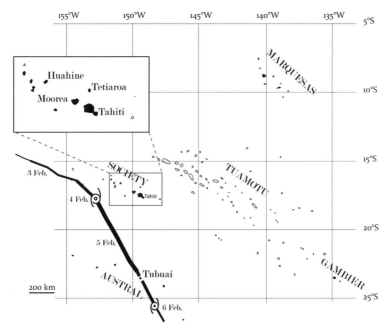

**Fig. 1.** Geographical map of French Polynesia and Tropical Cyclone Oli's track. The thickness of Oli's track is relative to the cyclone strength following the Saffir–Simpson scale (1–4 points).

(seamount stage) to the almost drowned island (atoll stage). During plate-tectonic-driven evolution, coral reefs appear and evolve with typical morphologies from fringing reef to barrier reef and, ultimately, atoll (Fig. 2). In the Austral Archipelago, the islands fed by the MacDonald hotspot are disrupted by the rejuvenation of some islands when passing a nearby second hotspot: this phenomenon heats the oceanic plate and leads to localized uplift, and the emergence of the coral reef (Rurutu and Rimatara). Tubuai Island is expected to undergo the same uplift – in few millions years – as it will come closer to the recently discovered Arago hotspot (Bonneville *et al.* 2002). Then the coral platform, especially those inherited from the Holocene sea-level highstand, supports the coastal plain, which is the main area of settlement in high islands. Elevation of coastal plains is very low, almost always below 10 m asl. In the Society Archipelago, Tahiti presents the characteristics of a high volcanic island with a narrow (200–1000 m width) fringing reef. Huahine is also a high volcanic island surrounded by a barrier reef (600–2000 m width) and separated from the mainland by a lagoon channel (300–400 m), except in its northern part where the reef is fringing and very narrow (50–60 m width in Maeva).

Considering these demographic and physical characteristics, marine inundation hazards represent major natural risks for Polynesian people: tsunami,

cyclones and cyclonic swell all contribute to varying degrees with respect to the archipelago concerned.

## Tsunami hazards

Tsunami is a major coastal hazard in the Marquesas Islands owing to their position in the centre of the Pacific Ocean and in the absence of protective coral reefs. In other archipelagos, historical tsunami run-up and inundation are very limited. Coral reefs were present around these islands during the last glacial maximum (LGM), with a sea level of about 120 m below the present level. During the post-LGM marine transgression, the coral reefs have caught up with the rising sea level but the growth phase has been punctuated by four drowning events associated with rapid sea-level jumps (Cabioch *et al.* 2008). The last reef generation, dated 9–9.6 ka, now stands between 55 and 60 m bsl (metres below sea level) and reef building has been replaced by the accumulation of non-reefal *Porites*. A sudden cooling of surface water in the eastern Equatorial Pacific linked to a significant release of glacial meltwater from the Andes' mountain glaciers has been suggested to explain this reduction in coral growth around the Marquesas Islands. Moreover, nearshore bathymetry allows the penetration of tsunami waves in narrow embayments where waves might be channelized: during

| Age (en Ma) | 1-0 | 3 | 4 | 6 | 8 | 12 | 25 | |
|---|---|---|---|---|---|---|---|---|
| Island | Macdonald | Marotiri | Rapa | Raivavae | Tubuai | Rurutu | Rimatara | Maria |
| Coastal geomorphology | seamount | no reef | fringing reef (narrow) | fringing reef and barrier-reef | fringing reef and barrier-reef | fringing reef and makatea | fringing reef and barrier-reef | atoll |
| Altitude | – 50 m | 113 m | 650 m | 437 m | 422 m | 389 m | 83 m | 3 m |
| Main geological event | Submarine volcanism (hot spot) | Subaerial volcanism | Volcano erosion, coral reef initiation | Subsidence, reef lateral growth | Subsidence | Rejuvenation when travelling near the Arago hot spot. Karst development on the uplifted atoll | Subsidence | Subsidence, atollisation |

coral

volcano

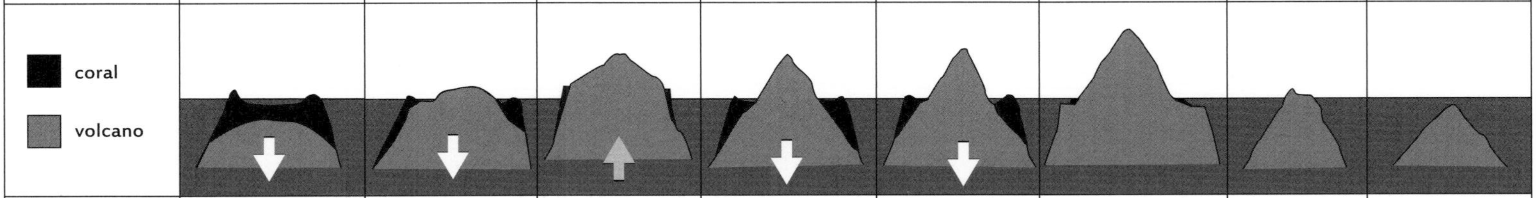

**Fig. 2.** Evolution series of oceanic volcanic islands from the submarine seamount stage to the atoll stage with reference to Austral Archipelagos (modified from Mottay 1976).

the North Pacific 2011 tsunami, recorded wave height reached 148 cm in Nuku Hiva, whereas it never exceeded 39 cm in the other archipelagos of the territory (PTWC 2011). Maximum inundation limit extends over 500 m from the coastline in flat areas (Schindelé *et al.* 2006). Maximum run-up might reach 18 m asl in some valleys of Ua Pou (e.g. Aleutian tsunami 1946). Usually, mean run-up is around 7 m at the coast but some in excess of 10 m have also been observed in Nuku Hiva (1946) and Hiva Oa (1946; Chilean tsunami 1960) (Schindelé *et al.* 2006). For comparison, maximum observed run-ups in Tahiti are less than 4 m. Tsunami might be also a major hazard for Rurutu (Austral) because it is an uplifted island (Fig. 2) and the population has settled in the vicinity of the coastline.

## Cyclone hazards

Cyclones represent the second type of major coastal hazard in French Polynesia, especially in the Austral archipelago where cyclone frequency is one event every 6–7 years (Larrue & Chiron 2010). They are usually restricted to the western part of the territory (west of 150° meridian); however, cyclones do encounter favourable growth conditions east of 150° meridian during El Niño Southern Oscillation (ENSO) periods (Terry & Etienne 2010), and may affect the Society and Tuamotu archipelagos. During the 1982–1983 ENSO event, five tropical cyclones and one tropical depression struck both archipelagos within 6 months (Dupon 1987). The situation was comparable during the 1997–1998 ENSO event: five tropical cyclones and four tropical depressions have been recorded in French Polynesia (Larrue & Chiron 2010). Contrary to tsunamis, cyclones are very rare in the Marquesas owing to the proximity of the Equator and the relatively cool waters, which are factors precluding cyclogenesis (Terry 2007; Larrue & Chiron 2010).

## Swell hazards

Cyclonic swell is a well-known and recurrent hazard in French Polynesia but still poorly documented. This kind of swell is generated by cyclonic activity outside the French Polynesia territory (usually west of the date line). Five swell systems concern French Polynesia, but the three dominant systems are associated with trade-wind surges coming from the SE (40%), the SSW (25%) and the NE (22%) (Gabrie & Salvat 1985). Cyclonic swell of 1.5–2 m at the coast occurs regularly in the Society Islands and this wave height has become the reference level for hazard mapping (Ministère du Développement Durable 2006). Swell height higher than 4 m tends to come from the SW and occurs during Austral winter. At the reef, it frequently reaches

**Table 1.** *Cyclonic swell amplitude in French Polynesia*

| Archipelago | Number of recorded events | Mean cyclonic swell height (m) | Extreme recorded height (m) |
|---|---|---|---|
| Marquesas | 1 | 7 | 7 |
| Gambier | 5 | 7–11 | 11 |
| Tuamotu | 11 | 4–12 | 15 |
| Society | 9 | 4–12 | 12 |
| Australes | 9 | 4–11 | 11 |

*Source:* Ministère du Développement Durable (2006).

8–10 m (e.g. in Teahupoo, Tahiti, also known as a world-famous surfing spot). On Rurutu, Moerai harbour was destroyed in December 1991 by cyclonic swell generated by TC Wasa, and the north coast of Tubuai also experienced damage to the coastal road (Fer 2000). In February 2005, cyclonic swell wave heights of 5–7 m were recorded in the Austral Islands as a consequence of TC Meena crossing the Cook Islands (APCEDI 2005). For the Tuamotu Archipelago, Laboute (1985) refers to maximum swell amplitude of 10–15 m during the 1982–1983 ENSO event and this is used as the height reference for Risk Management Planning (Ministère du Développement Durable 2006) (Table 1).

## Cyclonic Event Oli, February 2010

Tropical Cyclone Oli, lasting from 1 to 7 February 2010 (Fig. 1), was the fifth depressional system, and the second cyclone to occur in the SW Pacific Basin during the 2009–2010 season. Oli was the first tropical cyclone to affect the French Polynesia Islands in 2010, and the most severe storm since TC Zita and TC Arthur (both category 2 at their peak intensity), which affected the western part of the territory in January 2007. The initial depression developed north of Fiji waters, 3000 km from Tahiti. The system reached category 1 cyclone status (on the Saffir–Simpson scale) located near 16°S, 156.5°W (*c.* 750 km WNW of Tahiti, 450 km north of Mauke, Cook Islands) at 6 p.m local time on 2 February (6 a.m. UTC on 3 February). Twenty-four hours later, TC Oli reached category 2 with sustained winds over 80 knots (150 km h$^{-1}$) and following a NW–SE track towards Tahiti (300 km at its closest). During the night of 3–4 February, the cyclone strengthened rapidly and reached category 4 around midnight (1 min wind speed: 115 knots (210 km h$^{-1}$)). Its trajectory was then NNW–SSE and impacted directly over Tubuai Island. TC Oli hit this island in the morning of the 5 February

(5 p.m. UTC), but wind speed lowered and the cyclone had eased to category 2. Then the system followed a SE direction, weakened progressively and dissipated 500 km SE of Rapa.

During this meteorological event, the French High Commission (Haut-Commissariat de la République) adopted mitigation strategies based on the detection, tracking and forecasting of the cyclone by Météo-France. Emergency measures during the cyclonic paroxysmal phase included evacuation of atolls and travel restrictions. The army tried to evacuate several small islands (Scilly and Mopelia atolls), but often ran up against the refusal of the inhabitants to leave. The 35 inhabitants of Scilly refused to go aboard the helicopter, and in Mopelia only five inhabitants out of eight agreed to be transferred to Bora Bora. There, 279 homes have been damaged and six homes destroyed. Two people were injured on Maupiti by flying debris. On Bora Bora, Raiatea, Maupiti, Tahaa and Huahine the power supply was destroyed and many districts were flooded. Red alert was activated at 7:00 a.m. (local time) on 3 February on the Leeward Islands, 6:00 p.m. on the Windward Islands and at 12:30 p.m. on 4 February on the Austral Archipelago (HCR 2010). Damage was severe on Tubuai where 70% of buildings were affected by both the wind and wave effects, with 115 houses totally destroyed. One fatality was recorded there.

## Geomorphic impacts

### Methodology

Post-cyclone field surveys (Fig. 3) were conducted within 2 months of the event on Tubuai (15–19 February), Moorea (13–14 March), Tetiaroa (12–14 April) and Huahine (24–26 April). The coastline was surveyed all around Huahine and Tubuai, and places showing evidence of recent disturbance of the coast were selected for detailed investigation. Observations were more scattered in Moorea and Tetiaroa owing to, respectively, restricted access to the coastline (private properties) or the private status of the whole island. Scuba dive surveys were conducted in Moorea, Tahiti and Tubuai, where private diving operators were able to provide logistical facilities. Such facilities were not available in Huahine and Tetiaroa at the time of the survey.

Fresh coral boulders tossed on the reef flat were examined, and their location (GPS), dimensions (A-, B- and C-axis), orientation of the A-axis and rock characteristics were recorded. On the lagoon–beach contact, contemporary beachrock was often exhumed; beachrock slabs transported inland by the waves and fresh scars of missing pavement were measured (Fig. 4). Boulder measurements are used for flow velocity estimation following the equations of Nott (2003) and Nandasena et al. (2011) (hereafter NPT equations) (see Appendix I and II). The hydrodynamic equations derived by Nott (2003) are simple and useful tools for predicting the initial transport of a boulder by tsunamis or storm surges that have been very successful in the literature over the past decade. However, Nandasena et al. (2011) revised the equation for the submerged boulder scenario by rearranging the lift area of the lift force; the subaerial boulder scenario was also reconsidered by rearranging the lift area and omitting inappropriate use of inertia force; and, finally, the joint bounded scenario was revised by balancing force components in the lifting direction. On Huahine and Tubuai, beach erosion has been estimated in the horizontal and vertical directions. For horizontal retreat, pre-cyclone markers such as rip-rap revetment or rock armour have been used as evidence of the antecedent position of the beach top. Where this evidence was absent no measurement were carried out. Concordance of the position before the cyclone was checked on aerial photographs (Goggle Earth, IGN), satellite images (Quikbird) and by questioning local people. Vertical erosion (beach lowering) was estimated by measuring sand cliff height, exhumed roots and trees. Main coastal vegetation types at the rear of the beach were recorded (trees: *Casuarina equisitifolia*, *Cocos nucifera*; bush: *Crinum asiaticum*) to examine any possible correlation between erosion severity and vegetation types. When present, washover deposits were mapped with a GPS recorder and the thickness variation measured along a transect normal to the shoreline (Tubuai and Huahine).

Submarine semi-quantitative observations were also undertaken on the west coast of Tahiti (30 dives), the NW coast of Moorea (four dives), and the west and north coast of Tubuai (four dives). Diving sites were selected with respect to the main reef orientation compared to the direction of cyclonic wave approach (i.e. perpendicular or parallel), and to the outer-reef slope angle; that is, gentle (less than 25°) or steep (more than 60°). In Tahiti, the reef to the west of the Papeete Pass has been surveyed in detail (25 one h dives along a 2 km transect). The percentage destruction of corals was visually estimated using ground-cover abacus at regular depth intervals, down to 45 m below sea level (bsl). Chosen intervals were 2 m, and visual estimations were made with $\pm 1$ m range (e.g. at 10 m bsl, visual estimation of coral destruction stands for 9–11 m bsl). However, when rapid changes in coral destruction were observed, especially at great depth, 1 m intervals were used (see Table 2, Tapapatavae site). Massive coral

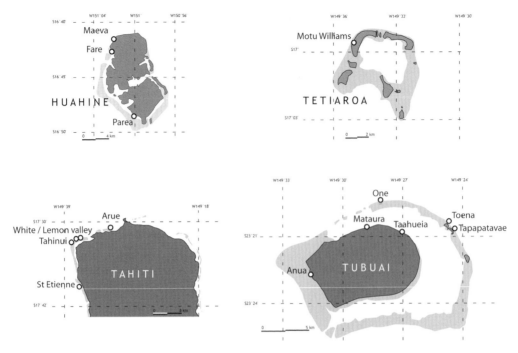

**Fig. 3.** Field survey locations on Tahiti, Huahine, Tetiaroa and the Tubuai Islands.

**Fig. 4.** Beachrock pavement imprint on Maeva beach, Huahine Islands. Letters *A*, *B* and *C* denote the three axis of the presumed boulder transported inland by the waves.

**Table 2.** *Depth limits of coral colonies destruction on the outer-reef slopes of Tubuai and Tahiti after the passage of Tropical Cyclone Oli*

| Coral colonies destruction (%) | Motu Tapapatavae (Tub.) | Mormon Pass (Tub.) | Motu One Pass (Tub.) | St Etienne Fault (Tah.) | Tahinui (Tah.) | White Valley (Tah.) | Lemon Valley (Tah.) | Arue (Tah.) |
|---|---|---|---|---|---|---|---|---|
| 100 | − 16 m | − 12 m | n.obs. | n.obs. | − 8 m | n.obs. | − 8 m | − 8 m |
| 80–90 | − 20 m | − 15 m | n.obs. | n.obs. | − 12 m | − 7 m | − 10 m | − 10 m |
| 70–80 | − 25 m | − 20 m | n.obs. | n.obs. | − 14 m | − 10 m | − 14 m | n.obs. |
| 40–60 | − 37 m | − 25 m | n.obs. | − 6 m | – | | – | n.obs. |
| 25–35 | − 38 m | – | n.obs. | − 8 m | − 21 m | | − 18 m | n.obs. |
| 10–20 | − 39 m | – | − 12 m | − 12 m | − 25 m | | | − 25 m |
| 0–10 | − 42 m | − 35 m | − 14 m | | − 28 m | | | − 30 m |
| Reef front slope | Gentle | Gentle | Steep | Steep | Gentle | Gentle | Gentle | Steep |

n.obs., percentage of destruction not observed.

boulders that have recently been displaced, toppled or overturned were measured (diameter for circular colony, *A–B–C*-axis for quadrangular boulders) and their depth recorded using a Suunto D6 diving computer (precision: 0.1 m), following the methodology of Massel & Done (1993). These measurements are helpful in estimating the minimum flow velocity required to transport boulders following the Nott and NPT equations (see Etienne *et al.* 2011). Boulder measurements were made between 8 and 24 m deep (no boulders were encountered between 0 and 8 m bsl, and no decisive evidence of transport or dislodgement was observed deeper than 24 m bsl); calculations also give the variation in flow velocity with depth. Estimation of the flow velocity is indicative of the hydrodynamical pressure exerted on coral colonies, the potential destruction power of the cyclonic waves (Massel & Done 1993) and the transport competence of the flow (Goff *et al.* 2010).

On Tubuai Island, areas surveyed in February 2010 were studied again in October 2010, 8 months after the passage of TC Oli. A topographical survey of sand cays, motus and beach levels allow the evaluation of post-event recovery (geomorphic resilience): natural recovery in the case of cays and motus lying on the reef margin, and natural, semi-natural or anthropogenic in the case of beaches of the main inhabited island. These GPS field surveys were compared with pre-cyclone high-resolution satellite images from 2008 (Table 3). Image treatment was performed using QuantumGIS 1.0.2 software.

## Results

Geomorphological impacts were widespread on high islands (landslides on steep weathered slopes due to intense rain) but more concentrated on the coastline. Wind effects include tree fall and vegetation burned by sea spray. From the fore-reef to the coastline, four categories of impacts were observed: coral reef erosion (debris production), sandy island migration beyond the reef crest, beach erosion at the shoreline and washover accumulations inland.

*Reef damages.* Submarine geomorphic impacts vary mainly with fore-reef slope angle and reef orientation compared to the cyclone track. Two situations can be distinguished: reefs facing the cyclone track (i.e. where the most powerful winds blow perpendicularly to the reef); and reefs lying almost parallel to the dominant cyclonic winds. In the first case, coral destruction and sediment transport is widespread, but with great variations over short distance.

**Table 3.** *Surface dimensions of Motu One cay, Tubuai Island, before and after Tropical Cyclone Oli*

| Site | Date | Area (m$^2$) | Net erosion (m$^2$) | Max. length (m) | Max. width (m) | Source |
|---|---|---|---|---|---|---|
| Motu One | 4 June 2008 | 11 660 | | 238 | 61 | Quickbird image |
| | 13 August 2008 | 11 738 | +78 | 268 | 79 | Quickbird image |
| | 18 February 2010 | 9295 | −2443 | 206 | 56 | GPS field survey |
| | 21 October 2010 | 9967 | +672 | 238 | 87 | GPS field survey |

Major destruction of living coral colonies is restricted to the upper part of the fore-reef slope. Branching coral damages included breakage of the secondary or primary branches, cutting at the stem level or total destruction of the colony with the hold-fast remaining attached on the bedrock. Damage was most significant between depths of 0 and 16 m along the western side of Tahiti and Moorea, with 80–100% of colonies partially or totally destroyed (Fig. 5a, b), and along the north side of Tubuai (Table 2). The net result was the flattening of the complex coral topography in the upper part of the external reef (Fig. 6). The lower limit of visible destruction ranged between 20 and 25 m bsl in Tahiti and Moorea (Fig. 5d), whereas it reached 42 m bsl on Tubuai. On the western coast of Tubuai, the physical destruction of living corals was very limited; the most noticeable effects were sand accumulations that were transferred from the grooves towards the reef. At a depth of 15 m bsl, sand lowering during the TC Oli event was 110 cm: the lowering can be identified by the colour change on the reef wall, darker when previously exposed in the water column, clearer when previously buried by the sand. Imbricated coral boulders ($A$-axis > 1 m) have been observed in several places between 16 and 20 m bsl at Lemon Valley, Tahiti (Fig. 5c). Boulders and, to a lesser degree, coral rubbles tend to be concentrated in the grooves, whereas spurs were cleaned from coral boulders and partially covered with coral fragments. It is also noticeable that small coral rubble deposits are nearly absent on the upper part of the fore-reef and that the rocky surface has a scraped appearance.

*Submarine boulder transport.* No boulders were encountered between 0 and 8 m bsl, and there were no signs of boulder transport below a depth of 24 m. An estimated flow velocity ($v$) profile shows a decrease with depth, with a value of less than $1$ m s$^{-1}$ below 24 m bsl, and the highest

**Fig. 5.** Geomorphic impacts of TC Oli on the fore-reef slope of Tahiti Island at different depths. On the upper 10 m, coral colonies have been totally erased and sediment sheets have disappeared (**a**). Branching and platy corals have been strongly affected by the cyclonic waves down to nearly 30 m bsl on Tahiti (**d**). Massive coral boulders are not literally destroyed but numerous colonies have been overturned, toppled (**c**) and sometimes imbricated, leading to a partial death of the coral colony. Between 10 and 20 m bsl, coral debris accumulations are important on gentle slopes (**b**).

**Fig. 6.** Destruction of branching and platy coral colonies during the TC Oli event, Tapapatavae fore-reef, Tubuai Island. Images extracted from video recordings (courtesy of L. Juan de Mendoza). (**a**) and (**b**) 17 November 2009; (**c**) and (**d**) 10 February 2010.

value ($v > 3$ m s$^{-1}$) encountered at 8 m bsl (Fig. 7). Lifting values (i.e. forces applied in a vertical direction) can be interpreted as the minimum values required for coral colony detachment from the reef framework. Highest values ($v > 7$ m s$^{-1}$) were encountered on the northern part of the Tubuai reef (Motu Tapapatavae) where coral destruction is also the most severe (Table 2).

*Terrestrial boulder transport.* Minimum flow velocity estimates required to initiate boulder transport are given in Table 4. As rip-rap boulders are not joint-bounded, these values have been excluded, and the subaerial equation is preferred. On Mataura (Tubuai), boulder sizes result in flow velocity estimates at the coast of greater than 2 m s$^{-1}$ and may have reached up to 5 m s$^{-1}$ (Fig. 8). For beachrock dislodgement, it is considered that the joint-bounded scenario is the most probable based on field evidence (Fig. 4). On Huahine, current velocities estimated from beachrock fragments range between 5.15 and 9.29 m s$^{-1}$ (Nott's joint-bounded equation) or between 3.05 and 5.29 m s$^{-1}$ (NPT's joint-bounded equation).

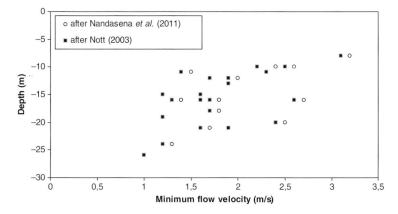

**Fig. 7.** Minimum flow velocity deduced from transported submarine boulders on Tahiti and the Tubuai Islands.

**Table 4.** *Minimum flow velocities required to initiate boulder transport*

| Boulder ID | Lithology | a (cm) | b (cm) | c (cm) | ρ (kg m⁻³) | Nott SB (m s⁻¹) | Nott SA (m s⁻¹) | Nott JB (m s⁻¹) | NPT SB (m s⁻¹) | NPT SA (m s⁻¹) | NPT JB (m s⁻¹) | Sliding (m s⁻¹) | Rolling (m s⁻¹) | Lifting SS (m s⁻¹) | Lifting JB (m s⁻¹) |
|---|---|---|---|---|---|---|---|---|---|---|---|---|---|---|---|
| **Huahine** | | | | | | | | | | | | | | | |
| 1 | Beachrock | 143 | 103 | 21 | 1800 | 5.42 | 5.41 | **7.76** | 3.52 | 3.52 | **4.43** | 2.28 | 3.52 | 4.18 | 4.43 |
| 2 | Beachrock | 175 | 150 | 30 | 1800 | 6.44 | 6.43 | **8.59** | 4.23 | 4.23 | **5.29** | 2.75 | 4.23 | 4.99 | 5.29 |
| 3 | Beachrock | 205 | 74 | 22 | 1800 | 4.15 | 4.14 | **9.29** | 3.12 | 3.12 | **4.53** | 2.01 | 3.12 | 4.27 | 4.53 |
| 4 | Beachrock | 160 | 120 | 30 | 1800 | 5.38 | 5.37 | **8.21** | 3.93 | 3.93 | **5.29** | 2.52 | 3.93 | 4.99 | 5.29 |
| 5 | Beachrock | 110 | 98 | 20 | 1800 | 5.14 | 5.13 | **6.81** | 3.44 | 3.44 | **4.32** | 2.23 | 3.44 | 4.07 | 4.32 |
| 6 | Beachrock | 74 | 57 | 17 | 1800 | 3.45 | 3.43 | **5.58** | 2.74 | 2.74 | **3.98** | 1.77 | 2.74 | 3.76 | 3.98 |
| 7 | Beachrock | 153 | 94 | 19 | 1800 | 5.29 | 5.28 | **8.03** | 3.36 | 3.36 | **4.21** | 2.18 | 3.36 | 3.97 | 4.21 |
| 8 | Beachrock | 120 | 70 | 17 | 1800 | 4.26 | 4.25 | **7.11** | 2.99 | 2.99 | **3.98** | 1.92 | 2.99 | 3.76 | 3.98 |
| 9 | Beachrock | 85 | 70 | 17 | 1800 | 4.12 | 4.1 | **5.99** | 2.99 | 2.99 | **3.98** | 1.92 | 2.99 | 3.76 | 3.98 |
| 10 | Beachrock | 81 | 78 | 25 | 1800 | 3.83 | 3.82 | **5.84** | 3.21 | 3.21 | **4.83** | 2.08 | 3.21 | 4.56 | 4.83 |
| 11 | Beachrock | 105 | 26 | 14 | 1800 | 1.89 | 1.87 | **6.65** | 1.75 | 1.75 | **3.61** | 1.24 | 1.75 | 3.41 | 3.61 |
| 12 | Beachrock | 76 | 60 | 10 | 1800 | 4.4 | 4.38 | **5.66** | 2.56 | 2.56 | **3.05** | 1.7 | 2.56 | 2.88 | 3.05 |
| 13 | Beachrock | 99 | 64 | 12 | 1800 | 4.47 | 4.45 | **6.46** | 2.73 | 2.73 | **3.35** | 1.78 | 2.73 | 3.16 | 3.35 |
| 14 | Beachrock | 63 | 60 | 19 | 1800 | 3.38 | 3.37 | **5.15** | 2.82 | 2.82 | **4.21** | 1.82 | 2.82 | 3.97 | 4.21 |
| 15 | Beachrock | 200 | 135 | 15 | 1800 | 7.75 | 7.74 | **9.18** | 3.34 | 3.34 | **3.74** | 2.39 | 3.34 | 3.53 | 3.74 |
| 16 | Beachrock | 133 | 77 | 27 | 1800 | 3.83 | 3.82 | **7.49** | 3.18 | 3.18 | **5.02** | 2.08 | 3.18 | 4.73 | 5.02 |
| Mean | | | | | | 4.58 | 4.56 | **7.11** | 3.12 | 3.12 | **4.24** | 2.04 | 3.12 | 4.00 | 4.24 |
| **Tubuai** | | | | | | | | | | | | | | | |
| 1 | Basalt rip-rap | 40 | 37 | 24 | 2600 | 2.8 | **2.79** | 5.84 | 2.83 | **2.83** | – | 2.13 | 2.83 | 6.35 | – |
| 2 | Basalt rip-rap | 55 | 36 | 29 | 2600 | 2.55 | **2.54** | 6.85 | 2.62 | **2.62** | – | 2.12 | 2.62 | 6.98 | – |
| 3 | Basalt rip-rap | 55 | 36 | 28 | 2600 | 2.59 | **2.58** | 6.85 | 2.65 | **2.65** | – | 2.12 | 2.65 | 6.86 | – |
| 4 | Basalt rip-rap | 40 | 33 | 18 | 2600 | 2.88 | **2.87** | 5.84 | 2.79 | **2.79** | – | 1.99 | 2.79 | 5.5 | – |
| 5 | Basalt rip-rap | 32 | 26 | 15 | 2600 | 2.49 | **2.48** | 5.23 | 2.45 | **2.45** | – | 1.77 | 2.45 | 5.02 | – |
| 6 | Massive coral | 40 | 30 | 17 | 1400 | 1.33 | – | 2.87 | 1.29 | – | 2.78 | 0.93 | 1.29 | 2.62 | 2.78 |
| 7 | Massive coral | 31 | 23 | 14 | 1400 | 1.13 | – | 2.52 | 1.11 | – | 2.52 | 0.82 | 1.11 | 2.38 | 2.52 |
| 8 | Massive coral | 32 | 24 | 14 | 1400 | 1.17 | – | 2.56 | 1.15 | – | 2.52 | 0.84 | 1.15 | 2.38 | 2.52 |
| 9 | Basalt rip-rap | 120 | 95 | 60 | 2600 | 4.59 | **4.58** | – | 4.57 | **4.57** | – | 3.41 | 4.57 | 10.04 | – |
| 10 | Basalt rip-rap | 210 | 110 | 60 | 2600 | 5.38 | **5.37** | – | 5.1 | **5.1** | – | 3.64 | 5.1 | 10.04 | – |
| 11 | Basalt rip-rap | 74 | 40 | 38 | 2600 | 2.5 | **2.49** | – | 2.62 | **2.62** | – | 2.25 | 2.62 | 7.99 | – |
| 12 | Basalt rip-rap | 100 | 55 | 53 | 2600 | 2.91 | **2.9** | – | 3.05 | **3.05** | – | 2.63 | 3.05 | 9.44 | – |

| # | Material | a | b | c | ρ | | | | | | | | | | | | |
|---|----------|----|----|----|------|------|------|------|------|------|------|------|------|------|------|------|------|
| 13 | Basalt rip-rap | 50 | 46 | 45 | 2600 | 2.6 | **2.59** | — | **2.78** | 2.78 | — | 2.78 | 2.78 | 2.41 | 2.78 | 8.7 | — |
| 14 | Basalt rip-rap | 66 | 60 | 46 | 2600 | 3.32 | **3.31** | — | **3.44** | 3.44 | — | 3.44 | 3.44 | 2.73 | 3.44 | 8.79 | — |
| 15 | Basalt rip-rap | 70 | 60 | 55 | 2600 | 3.07 | **3.06** | — | **3.24** | 3.24 | — | 3.24 | 3.24 | 2.75 | 3.24 | 9.62 | — |
| 16 | Basalt rip-rap | 74 | 34 | 26 | 2600 | 2.56 | **2.55** | — | **2.59** | 2.59 | — | 2.59 | 2.59 | 2.05 | 2.59 | 6.61 | — |
| 17 | Basalt rip-rap | 74 | 45 | 25 | 2600 | 3.39 | **3.38** | — | **3.25** | 3.25 | — | 3.25 | 3.25 | 2.33 | 3.25 | 6.48 | — |
| 18 | Basalt rip-rap | 89 | 42 | 19 | 2600 | 3.63 | **3.62** | — | **3.26** | 3.26 | — | 3.26 | 3.26 | 2.22 | 3.26 | 5.65 | — |
| 19 | Basalt rip-rap | 49 | 32 | 27 | 2600 | 2.35 | **2.34** | — | **2.43** | 2.43 | — | 2.43 | 2.43 | 2 | 2.43 | 6.74 | — |
| 20 | Basalt rip-rap | 43 | 41 | 25 | 2600 | 3.03 | **3.02** | — | **3.03** | 3.03 | — | 3.03 | 3.03 | 2.23 | 3.03 | 6.48 | — |
| 21 | Basalt rip-rap | 30 | 29 | 12 | 2600 | 3 | **2.99** | — | **2.74** | 2.74 | — | 2.74 | 2.74 | 1.84 | 2.74 | 4.49 | — |
| 22 | Basalt rip-rap | 38 | 28 | 27 | 2600 | 2.04 | **2.03** | — | **2.18** | 2.18 | — | 2.18 | 2.18 | 1.88 | 2.18 | 6.74 | — |
| 23 | Basalt rip-rap | 46 | 36 | 34 | 2600 | 2.33 | **2.32** | — | **2.49** | 2.49 | — | 2.49 | 2.49 | 2.13 | 2.49 | 7.56 | — |
| 24 | Basalt rip-rap | 30 | 37 | 26 | 2600 | 2.73 | **2.72** | — | **2.77** | 2.77 | — | 2.77 | 2.77 | 2.14 | 2.77 | 6.61 | — |
| 25 | Basalt rip-rap | 45 | 30 | 25 | 2600 | 2.25 | **2.24** | — | **2.37** | 2.37 | — | 2.37 | 2.37 | 1.94 | 2.37 | 6.48 | — |
| 26 | Basalt rip-rap | 77 | 28 | 26 | 2600 | 2.1 | **2.09** | — | **2.21** | 2.21 | — | 2.21 | 2.21 | 1.88 | 2.21 | 6.61 | — |
| 27 | Basalt rip-rap | 49 | 42 | 20 | 2600 | 3.53 | **3.52** | — | **3.23** | 3.23 | — | 3.23 | 3.23 | 2.23 | 3.23 | 5.8 | — |
| 28 | Basalt rip-rap | 310 | 40 | 29 | 2600 | 2.79 | **2.78** | — | **2.85** | 2.85 | — | 2.85 | 2.85 | 2.22 | 2.85 | 6.98 | — |
| 29 | Massive coral | | 180 | 50 | 1400 | 4.52 | — | 7.98 | 3.39 | 3.39 | 4.77 | 3.39 | 3.39 | 2.18 | 3.39 | 4.5 | 4.77 |
| **Mean** | | | | | | 2.81 | 2.93 | 5.17 | 2.78 | 2.96 | 3.15 | 2.78 | 2.78 | 2.13 | 2.78 | 6.57 | 3.15 |
| **Tetiaroa** | | | | | | | | | | | | | | | | | |
| 1 | Massive coral | 190 | 160 | 48 | 1300 | 3.42 | — | 5.36 | — | 2.75 | 4.01 | 2.75 | 2.75 | 1.77 | 2.75 | 3.78 | 4.01 |
| 2 | Massive coral | 230 | 170 | 65 | 1300 | 3.23 | — | 5.9 | — | 2.82 | 4.66 | 2.82 | 2.82 | 1.86 | 2.82 | 4.4 | 4.66 |
| 3 | Massive coral | 280 | 226 | 70 | 1300 | 4.03 | — | 6.51 | — | 3.28 | 4.84 | 3.28 | 3.28 | 2.11 | 3.28 | 4.57 | 4.84 |
| 4 | Beachrock | 200 | 100 | 22 | 1800 | 5.38 | 5.37 | **9.18** | 3.52 | 3.52 | **4.53** | 3.52 | 3.52 | 2.27 | 3.52 | 4.27 | 4.53 |
| 5 | Beachrock | 90 | 65 | 9 | 1800 | 4.95 | 4.93 | **6.16** | 2.51 | **2.9** | 2.9 | 2.51 | 2.51 | 1.72 | 2.51 | 2.73 | 2.9 |
| 6 | Beachrock | 114 | 100 | 14 | 1800 | 5.91 | 5.9 | **6.93** | 3.13 | **3.61** | 3.61 | 3.13 | 3.13 | 2.14 | 3.13 | 3.41 | 3.61 |
| 7 | Beachrock | 150 | 81 | 20 | 1800 | 4.59 | 4.57 | **7.95** | 3.22 | **4.32** | 4.32 | 3.22 | 3.22 | 2.07 | 3.22 | 4.07 | 4.32 |
| 8 | Beachrock | 90 | 60 | 22 | 1800 | 3.29 | 3.27 | **6.16** | 2.8 | **4.53** | 4.53 | 2.8 | 2.8 | 1.84 | 2.8 | 4.27 | 4.53 |
| 9 | Massive coral | 84 | 60 | 42 | 1300 | 1.47 | — | 3.56 | — | 3.75 | 3.75 | — | 1.49 | 1.14 | 1.49 | 3.54 | 3.75 |
| **Mean** | | | | | | 4.03 | 4.81 | 6.41 | 3.04 | 3.04 | 4.13 | 2.84 | 2.84 | 1.88 | 2.84 | 3.89 | 4.13 |

a, b, c, axis dimensions; ρ, density of rock.

Pre-transport environment (SB, submerged; SA, subaerial; JB, joint-bounded; SS, subaerial or submerged). Bold values indicate the most probable pre-transport environment setting, considering field evidence.

NPT, Nandasena, Paris (Tanaka 2011).

– indicates non-pertinent value (e.g. subaerial pre-transport environment for fresh massive coral).

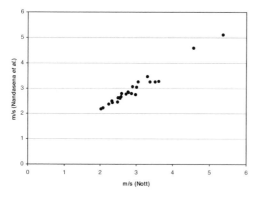

**Fig. 8.** Minimum flow velocity at the shoreline on Tubuai deduced from rip-rap boulders.

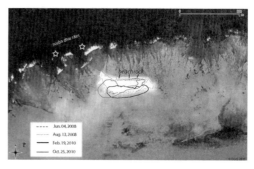

**Fig. 9.** Area variation of Motu One cay, Tubuai Island.

*Sandy island migration.* On Tubuai, the top reef margin was strongly affected by the cyclone, especially unvegetated sandy islands (cays) where sand transfer towards land was very important. The surface area of Motu One, for example, has diminished by 20% since August 2008, but the proper impact of TC Oli is more difficult to assess accurately in the absence of a vertical image dating from earlier in 2010 (Fig. 9, Table 3). The shrinking effect of the cyclone is drastic both in length (23%) and width (29%). Unfortunately, it is also not possible to estimate with vertical images the lowering of the cay (i.e. volume change), but local people testified that the most conspicuous change noticed after TC Oli event was the apparent disappearance of the cay when observed from Mataura village. It is also noticeable that the sandy bank migrated 40–45 m towards the south, revealing a beachrock settled on the reef flat.

*Beach erosion and washover deposits.* On Huahine, mean horizontal retreat varies between 7.52

(Maeva, north of Fare) and 1.53 m (Parea). Mean vertical lowering is less than 50 cm in Fare, but over 60 cm in Parea (Table 5). Erosion variability is high in Maeva (Fig. 10), with a maximal retreat value of 13.9 m and minimal value of 2.3 m (SD = 3.72 m). It also appears that when horizontal retreat is high, vertical retreat is low and vice versa (Fig. 11). So, considering eroded sand volume, values are more grouped with north–south decreasing mean values (3.17 cubic-metres per linear metre ($m^3\ m^{-1}$) in Maeva to 0.99 $m^3\ m^{-1}$ in Parea). Washover deposits were extensive and their extension inland correlated with ground occupation: the landward limit of the deposit was greater when the coastal plain had little vegetation cover compared with urbanized or woody areas (Fig. 12). Owing to the reworking of washover deposits soon after the event, it was not possible to take any reliable measurements.

On Tubuai, mean horizontal retreat varies between 9.75 (East and Centre Mataura) and 2.06 m (West Mataura), but a great variability can be observed too, with a SD of over 6 m (Fig. 13). Mean vertical lowering ranges between 27 and 40 cm (Table 5), and eroded sand volume ranges

**Table 5.** *Quantification of post- Tropical Cyclone Oli beach erosion in Huahine and Tubuai*

| Island | Site | N | Mean retreat (cm) | SD (cm) | Max. retreat (cm) | Min. retreat (cm) | Max. lowering (cm) | Min. lowering (cm) | Mean lowering (cm) | SD (cm) | Volume ($m^3\ m^{-1}$) |
|--------|------|---|------|------|------|------|------|------|------|------|------|
| Huahine | Maeva | 22 | 752 | 372 | 1390 | 230 | 100 | 15 | 46 | 20.5 | 3.17 |
| | Fare Centre | 4 | 311 | n.s. | 395 | 250 | 60 | 53 | 47 | n.s. | 1.52 |
| | Parea | 3 | 153 | n.s. | 210 | 100 | 83 | 47 | 61 | n.s. | 0.99 |
| Tubuai | Mataura centre and east | 35 | 975 | 643 | 1653 | 64 | 80 | 6 | 39 | 17 | 2.93 |
| | Mataura west | 7 | 206 | n.s. | 348 | 64 | 43 | 11 | 27 | n.s. | 0.52 |
| | Taahueia | 16 | 681 | 712 | 1920 | 94 | 37 | 9 | 25 | 8.5 | 2.32 |
| | Anua | 7 | 435 | n.s. | 700 | 60 | 62 | 26 | 40 | n.s. | 1.91 |

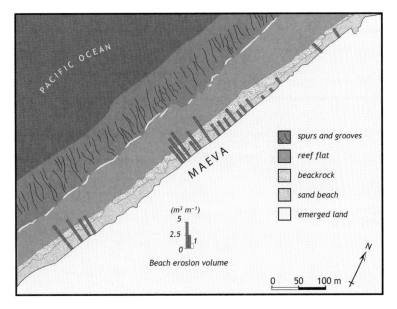

**Fig. 10.** Beach erosion volume north of Fare, Huahine Island.

between 0.5 (West Mataura) and nearly 3 m³ m⁻¹ (East and Centre Mataura). Beach sand was removed and deposited inland by overwash processes during the cyclone. Thick accumulations (30–50 cm) were observed on the coastal road of Tubuai. Washover deposit extension is more limited (at a maximum 70 m from the coastline) when dense bushes of *Crinum asiaticum* were present along the road or private properties. The deposit becomes thinner inland (Table 6). When there is no vegetation or built obstacles to the wave propagation (e.g. playing field or road perpendicular to the coastline) the overwash deposits extend further inland (maximum of 150 m near Mataura) and are thicker *ceteris paribus*.

## Discussion

### *Geomorphic impacts on the coral reef*

The outer-reef slope angle and orientation appear as major controlling influences on the severity of wave destruction: steep reefs (nearly vertical) show extensive damage at the top only (reef crest) when facing directly into the direction of approach of the cyclone waves (Arue site, Tahiti), whereas they

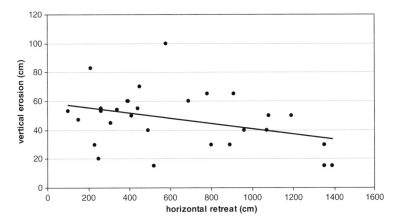

**Fig. 11.** Vertical erosion v. horizontal retreat of beaches on Huahine Island.

**Fig. 12.** Variation of inland extension of washover deposits on Huahine Island.

show a few impacts when they are parallel or tangential to the wave direction (Motu One, Tubuai). A similar response of coral reefs was observed by Bries *et al.* (2004) in the Caribbean after the strike of Hurricane Lenny in 1999. Gently sloping reefs, however, were more seriously impacted by the cyclone, with branching coral colony damage reaching 100% down to a depth of 16 m on the most exposed sites of Tubuai. In Tahiti, this high percentage of damage is restricted to the first 8 m in the most exposed areas. This observation is contrary to previous observations made in the Tuamotu Archipelago (Laboute 1985; Harmelin-Vivien & Laboute 1986) where coral debris avalanche played a major role in the destruction of deep colonies along steep outer slopes. This can be explained by the recurrence interval of the high-energy events impacting the coral colonies in Tahiti, Moorea and Tubuai compared to Takapoto and Tikehau: 12–27 years in Tahiti and Moorea, 10 years in Tubuai, and 76 years in Tikehau and Takapoto. Younger colonies are less developed and less sensitive to destructive wave action, and thus deliver less debris than more mature reefs (Spencer & Viles 2002). Branching and platy colonies appear more susceptible to breakage and removal than massive

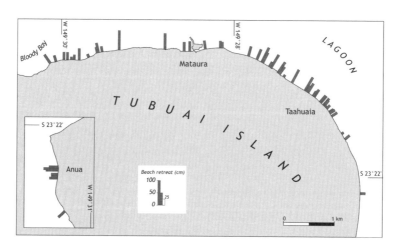

**Fig. 13.** Horizontal retreat of beaches on Tubuai Island.

**Table 6.** *Relationship between overwash deposit thickness and vegetation buffers on Tubuai Island*

| Coastal buffers | Distance from the coastline (m) | Thickness (cm) | Position (UTM) |
|---|---|---|---|
| Dense bush of | 6 | 28 | 244457 7415495 |
| *Crinum asiaticum* | 23 | 14 | 244443 7415472 |
| | 30 | 13 | 244450 7415471 |
| | 43 | 7 | 244452 7415453 |
| | 55 | 5 | 244460 7415445 |
| | 69 | 2 | 244468 7415433 |
| Espaced trees | 31 | 29 | 244980 7415643 |
| *Casuarina equisitifolia* | 33 | 23 | 248154 7416356 |
| | 53 | 35 | 248161 7416337 |

forms, a fact already observed elsewhere (e.g. Scoffin 1993). But, regarding the skeleton strength, branch removal is unlikely to be caused by water motion alone (Madin 2005), and it is more likely to be the result of localized impacts of waterborne projectiles. As cyclone waves are known to exfoliate reefs, chunk by chunk, over the period of local wind-generated waves, especially on the upper part of the reef (Done 1992), the absence of coral rubble on the upper part of the fore-reef can be explained by the over-the-reef transport process that is intensified during storm events owing to the seaward shift of the wave breaker point (Roberts & Suhayda 1983). When comparing reef impacts with flow velocities estimated from submerged and subaerial boulders, it appears that the upper part of the coral reef (between 0 and 10 m) encountered high-energy conditions with flow velocities of over $3 \text{ m s}^{-1}$. This is also consistent with estimated flow velocities on the reef flat deduced from beachrock fragments: following NPT's equations they range from 3 to $5 \text{ m s}^{-1}$ in Huahine, and from 2.9 to $4.5 \text{ m s}^{-1}$ in Tetiaroa. Current velocities estimated using Nott's equation for the joint-bounded scenario appear to overestimate the velocities ($6-9 \text{ m s}^{-1}$). Such values confer a strong destructive power in shallow water with a high competence for sediment transport. In the Caribbean, numerical simulation of hurricane flow velocities gives values of up to $6.5 \text{ m s}^{-1}$ at the reef crest (Buckley *et al.* 2011).

On the reef flat margin, sandy banks (cays) have suffered from a lowering of their summit surface as a consequence of overwash processes during the cyclonic event. The mean position of the cay also migrated around 40–45 m towards the south. The formation of coral–gravel storm ridges has been noted from a number of tropical settings but they are not produced on a regular basis during extreme storm events (Richmond & Morton 2007), and no storm ridges were observed in French Polynesia after the TC Oli event.

### Geomorphic impacts on the sandy coast

Horizontal beach retreat and vertical lowering are two of the major effects of large storm waves. The volume of eroded sand along the coast varies directly with exposure to the waves. For example, in Huahine, the highest erosion values are found where the reef flat is narrow and borders the coast; whereas, on Tubuai, the highest erosion values are found on Mataura in front of a large pass. Wave-energy dissipation is usually due to wave breaking and bottom friction at the reef (Massel & Gourlay 2000). The presence of a pass might allow wave propagation into the lagoon with less energy loss before reaching the coastline. It is noticeable that higher erosion rates are not necessarily found in places that were close to the cyclone track: similar values in Huahine (250 km from the cyclone eye) and Tubuai (0 km from the cyclone eye) reveal the importance of the physiographical situation (i.e. reef width, bathymetry, coastline orientation) on erosion potential. On Tubuai, the barrier reef has acted as a natural buffer that has protected sandy beaches along the coastline; whereas, in the northern part of Huahine, the narrowness of the fringing reef did not perform this role. A similar trend in beach erosion variation was observed in Funafuti atoll after the strike of TC Bebe in October 1972 (Baines & Beveridge 1974), which was explained by variations in bathymetry or the size of the sediment reservoir.

Landward extension of overwash deposits is dependent, first, on the sand stock available prior to the cyclone (i.e. presence or absence of a beach, sediment bodies in the lagoon) and, secondly, on the topography and the coastal 'roughness' (presence of trees, bushes, buildings, etc.). On Huahine, sand accumulations were observed in the backbeach forest and it is probable that these deposits are lost from the beach sediment budget. On Tubuai, the sand deposited on the coast road was used afterwards for reconstruction work and was not used to refill eroded beaches.

## Geomorphic resilience of Tubuai Island

Motu resilience is strongly dependent on sediment-size: sandy cays (e.g. Motu One) showed a strong variability in shape and area between February and October 2010, whereas coral rubble motus (e.g. Motu Tapapatavae and Motu Toena) retained their post-cyclone shape and profile, except in their sand spits. In the fair-weather conditions prevailing after TC Oli, Motu One has started to migrate towards the north, with its tails already reconnected to the beachrock (Fig. 9). Its surface has increased and recovered around 27% of the surface lost during TC Oli, its horizontal dimensions are close to its pre-cyclone ones (Table 3).

On Anua, 8 months after the cyclone, sand scarps have disappeared and beaches present a similar pre-event profile (Fig. 14a, b). This area faces the dominant southerly swells, and lagoon currents are parallel to the coastline (Fig. 15). Thus, beach nourishment by lagoon sediment is favoured by

longshore drift. On Mataura, however, the beach level has lowered by about 50 cm; the beach-lowering total thus reaches approximately 90 cm (Fig. 14c, d). Near the harbour, this lowering can be explained by sand mining for reconstruction as we observed regular sand excavation on the eastern part of the beach in October 2010, but in other places it is possible that a (still undetermined) beach stability threshold has been exceeded. It is possible that extensive sediment transfer inland during the cyclone has not been yet compensated by subsequent lagoon sediment production. Between Anua and Mataura, several places show little change since February 2010, suggesting that there is neither resilience nor aggravation of the beach erosion.

## Conclusion

Tropical cyclones represent a major hazard for coastal populations in the South Pacific, but progress made in meteorology allows a cyclone track forecast to be sufficiently accurate to mitigate the risk. Tropical Cyclone Oli struck French Polynesia

**Fig. 14.** Beach resilience on Tubuai, Island. (**a**) Anua, 17 February 2010; (**b**) Anua, 18 October 2010; (**c**) Mataura, 17 February 2010; (**d**) 19 October 2010.

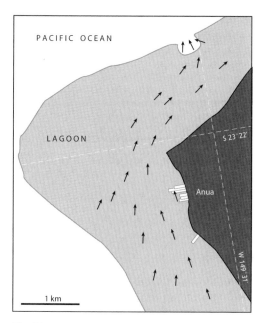

**Fig. 15.** Beach resilience and lagoonal drift currents in Anua area, Tubuai Island. White bars indicate the amount of sand accumulated since the TC Oli event. Arrows indicate the drift current based on sedimentary structures in the lagoon (sandspits).

in February 2010 but prior meteorological forecasts provided 3 days earlier and last-minute evacuation prevented casualties occurring from cyclonic waves. Considering geomorphic impacts, cyclones represent a high-magnitude low-frequency event necessary for the long-term replenishment of sediment on shorelines, but in the short term such storms will seem to have mainly destructive effects (Bayliss-Smith 1988). Observed reef damage is widespread but unevenly distributed: submarine geomorphic impacts include, in the most exposed areas, uprooting of massive (diameter >1 m) coral colonies down to 25 m bsl, and the total destruction of branching corals down to 8 (Tahiti) or 16 m (Tubuai). Reefs not affected directly by cyclonic waves show little damage below a depth of 10 m, but sediment (sand, gravel) transfer appears important there, with clear evidence of sediment lowering in grooves and landward transport. The outer-reef slope angle appears as a major control factor for coral destruction, with vertical submarine cliffs relatively shielded compared to gentle slopes. Submarine boulder measurements provide valuable estimates of flow velocity profile with depth. Beachrock slab measurements also provide estimates of flow velocities at the reef–beach junction. Combining these different geomorphic markers might be a

way to comprehend flow velocity variations when cyclone waves cross coral reefs. Compared with tsunami impacts on reefs, a fundamental distinction seems to be the great variation in cyclonic destruction over short (hundreds of metres) distances. Another difference is coarse sediment (boulder) transport, which appears more limited on the reef flat and on the reef slope. Geomorphic resilience of lagoonal beaches appears highest in the southern part of Tubuai; more information is needed to evaluate the respective influences of lagoonal sediment transfer or anthropogenic interferences on the coastline (urbanization).

## Appendix I

Nott's (2003) equations for estimating the minimum wave heights required to initiate the transport of:

subaerial boulders:

$$H_s \geq \frac{(\rho_s - \rho_w/\rho_w)[(2a - 4C_m(a/b)(\ddot{u}/g))]}{C_d(ac/b^2) + C_1}$$

submerged boulders:

$$H_s \geq \frac{(\rho_s - \rho_w/\rho_w)2a}{C_d(ac/b^2) + C_1}$$

joint-bounded blocks:

$$H_s = \frac{(\rho_s - \rho_w/\rho_w)a}{C_1}$$

where $H_s$ is the height of the storm wave at the breaking point; $a$, $b$ and $c$ are main axes of the boulder; $\rho_s$ is the density of the boulder (km m$^{-3}$ or g cm$^{-3}$); $\rho_w$ is the water density (typically 1.025 g ml$^{-1}$ for sea water); $C_d$ is the drag coefficient ($C_d = 2$ for submerged boulders); $C_m$ is the coefficient of mass ($C_m = 2$); and $C_1$ is the lift coefficient ($C_1 = 0.178$).

## Appendix II

Boulder hydrodynamic transport equations (Nandasena *et al.* 2011).

| Initial transport mode | Boulder/block | | |
|---|---|---|---|
| | Submerged | Subaerial | Joint bounded |
| Sliding | $u^2 \geq \dfrac{2(\rho_s/\rho_w - 1) \times gc(\mu\cos\theta + \sin\theta)}{C_d(c/b) + \mu_s C_1}$ | | – |
| Rolling/over turning | $u^2 \geq \dfrac{2(\rho_s/\rho_w - 1) \times gc(\cos\theta + (c/b)\sin\theta)}{C_d(c^2/b^2) + C_1}$ | | – |
| Saltation/lifting | $u^2 \geq \dfrac{2(\rho_s/\rho_w - 1)gc\cos\theta}{C_1}$ | | $u^2 \geq \dfrac{2(\rho_s/\rho_w - 1) \times gc(\cos\theta + \mu_s\sin\theta)}{C_1}$ |

where $u$ is the flow velocity; $a$, $b$ and $c$ is the main axes of the boulder; $\rho_s$ is the density of the boulder; $\rho_w$ is the density of water; $C_d$ is the coefficient of drag; $C_l$ is the coefficient of lift; $\theta$ is the angle of the bed slope at the pre-transport location in degrees; $\mu_s$ is the coefficient of static friction; and $g$ is the acceleration of gravity.

This study was self-funded by the author. I would like to thank R. Paris for his help on boulder data treatment. W. Doom and L. Juan de Mendoza have provided logistic help during fieldwork on the Tubuai reef. French Air Force co-pilot P.-Y. Boute provided personal aerial oblique pictures from Tubuai 3 days after the event. M. Augeyre provided security and measurement assistance during dives in Tahiti. The N.G.O. *Te Mana o Te Moana* provided access and logistic assistance to the private atoll of Tetiaroa. Comments by referees were very constructive and are greatly appreciated.

# References

APCEDI 2005. *Alert 07F #15, 2005: News from Cook Islands and French Polynesia*. Australian-Pacific Centre for Emergency and Disaster Information. World Wide Web Address: http://www.afap.org/apcedi/2005/02/apcedi-alert-07f-15-2005-news-from.html.

BAINES, G. B. K. & BEVERIDGE, P. J. 1974. Storms and island building at Funafuti atoll, Ellice Islands. *Proceedings of the Second International Coral Reef Symposium*, **2**, 485–496.

BAYLISS-SMITH, T. P. 1988. The role of hurricanes in the development of reef islands, Ontong Jave atoll, Solomon Islands. *The Geographical Journal*, **154**, 377–391.

BONNEVILLE, A., LE SUAVÉ, R. ET AL. 2002. Arago seamount: the missing hotspot found in the Austral Islands. *Geology*, **30**, 1023–1026.

BRIES, J. M., DEBROT, A. O. & MEYER, D. L. 2004. Damage to the leeward reefs of Curaçao and Bonaire, Netherlands Antilles from a rare storm event: Hurricane Lenny, November 1999. *Coral Reefs*, **23**, 297–307.

BUCKLEY, M., WEI, Y., JAFFE, B. & WATT, S. 2011. Inverse modeling of velocities and inferred cause of overwash that emplaced inland fields of boulders at Anegada, British Virgin Islands. *Natural Hazards*, doi: 10.1007/s11069-011-9725-8.

BURKETT, V. R., ZILKOSKI, D. B. & HART, D. A. 2003. Sea-level rise and subsidence: implications for flooding in New Orleans, Louisiana. *In*: PRINCE, K. R. & GALLOWAY, D. L. (eds) *Subsidence Observations Based on Traditional Geodetic Techniques, and Numerical Models*. USGS Open File Report, **03-308**, 63–70.

CABIOCH, G., MONTAGGIONI, L. ET AL. 2008. Successive reef depositional events along the Marquesas foreslopes (French Polynesia) since 25 ka. *Marine Geology*, **254**, 18–34.

DONE, T. J. 1992. Effects of tropical cyclones waves on ecological and geomorphological structures on the Great Barrier Reef. *Continental Shelf Research*, **12**, 859–872.

DUPON, J.-F. 1987. Les atolls et le risque cyclonique: le cas des Tuamotu. *Cahiers des Sciences Humaines*, **23**, 567–599.

ETIENNE, S., BUCKLEY, M. ET AL. 2011. The use of boulders for characterising past tsunamis: Lessons from the 2004 Indian Ocean and 2009 South Pacific tsunamis. *Earth-Science Reviews*, **107**, 76–90, doi: 10.1016/j.earscirev.2010.12.006.

FER, Y. 2000. Coopérative, familles et développement en Polynésie française. La coopérative de pêcheurs Piareare, Ruruti, Archipel des Australes. *Revue Juridique Polynésienne*, **6**, 527–536.

GABRIE, C. & SALVAT, B. 1985. Généralités sur les îles de la Polynésie française et leurs récifs coralliens. *In: Proceedings of the Fifth International Coral Reefs Congress, 27 May–1 June, Tahiti*, Volume 1. Antenne Museum-EPHE, Moorea, 1–16.

GOFF, J., WEISS, R., COURTNEY, C. & DOMINEY-HOWES, D. 2010. Testing the hypothesis for tsunami boulder deposition from suspension. *Marine Geology*, **277**, 73–77.

HARMELIN-VIVIEN, M. L. & LABOUTE, P. 1986. Catastrophic impact of hurricanes on atoll outer reef slopes in the Tuamotu (French Polynesia). *Coral Reefs*, **5**, 55–62.

HCR 2010. *Communiqué no.10 – Alerte Rouge – Cyclone tropical Oli*. Haut-Commissariat de la République. World Wide Web Address: http://www.polynesie-francaise.pref.gouv.fr/sections/actualites/les_communiques/communique_n10_-_al/downloadFile/attachedFile/Communique_n_10_-_01h30.pdf.

HOUCK, O. A. 1985. Rising water: the National Flood Insurance program and Louisiana. *Tulane Law Review*, **60**, 61–164.

ISPF 2010. *La Polynésie en bref*. Institut Statistique de la Polynésie Française, Papeete.

LABOUTE, P. 1985. Evaluation of damage done by the cyclones of 1982–1983 to the outer slopes of the Tikehau and Takapoto atolls (Tuamotu Archipelago). *In: Proceedings of the Fifth International Coral Reefs Congress, 27 May–1 June, Tahiti*, Volume 3. Antenne Museum-EPHE, Moorea, 320–328.

LARRUE, S. & CHIRON, T. 2010. Les îles de Polynésie française face à l'aléa cyclonique. *VertigO*, **10**, 3. http://vertigo.revues.org/10558.

MADIN, J. S. 2005. Mechanical limitations of reef corals during hydrodynamic disturbances. *Coral Reefs*, **24**, 630–635.

MASSEL, S. R. & DONE, T. J. 1993. Effects of cyclone waves on massive coral assemblages on the Great Barrier Reef: meteorology, hydrodynamics and demography. *Coral Reef*, **12**, 153–166.

MASSEL, S. R. & GOURLAY, M. R. 2000. On the modelling of wave breaking and set-up on coral reefs. *Coastal Engineering*, **39**, 1–27.

MINISTÈRE DU DÉVELOPPEMENT DURABLE 2006. *Plan de prévention des risques. Note méthodologique de réalisation des cartes*. BRGM, Papeete.

MEUR-FÉREC, C., DEBOUDT, P. & MOREL, V. 2008. Coastal risks in France: an integrated method for evaluating vulnerability. *Journal of Coastal Research*, **24**, 178–189.

MIRZA, M. Q. 2002. Global warming and changes in the probability of occurrence of floods in Bangladesh and implications. *Global Environmental Change*, **12**, 127–138.

MOTTAY, G. 1976. *Contribution à l'étude géologique de la Polynésie française (Archipel des Australes et Mehetia)*. Unpublished PhD thesis, Paris, Orsay.

NANDASENA, N. A. K., PARIS, R. & TANAKA, N. 2011. Reassessment of hydrodynamic equations: Minimum flow velocity to initiate boulder transport by high energy events (storms, tsunamis). *Marine Geology*, **281**, 70–84.

NOTT, J. 2003. Waves, coastal boulder deposits and the importance of the pre-transport setting. *Earth Planetary Science Letters*, **210**, 269–276.

NOTT, J. 2006. *Extreme Events. A Physical Reconstruction and a Risk Assessment*. Cambridge University Press, Cambridge.

PTWC 2011. *Tsunami bulletin n° 026*. Pacific Tsunami Warning Center. World Wide Web Address: http://ptwc.weather.gov/ptwc/text.php?id=pacific.2011.03.12.054000.

RICHMOND, B. R. & MORTON, R. A. 2007. Coral–gravel storm ridges: examples from the tropical Pacific and Carribean. *In*: KRAUS, N. C. & ROSATI, J. D. (eds) *Coastal Sediments '07 – Proceedings of the 6th International Symposium on Coastal Engineering and Science of Coastal Sediment Processes, held May 13–17, 2007 in New Orleans, Louisiana*. American Society of Civil Engineers, Reston, VA, 572–583.

ROBERTS, H. H. & SUHAYDA, J. N. 1983. Wave-current interactions on a shallow reef (Nicaragua, Central America). *Coral Reefs*, **1**, 209–214.

SCHINDELÉ, F., HÉBERT, H., REYMOND, D. & SLADEN, A. 2006. L'aléa tsunami en Polynésie française : synthèse des observations et des mesures. *Comptes Rendus Géoscience*, **338**, 1133–1140.

SCOFFIN, T. P. 1993. The geological effects of hurricanes on coral reefs and the interpretation of storm deposits. *Coral Reefs*, **12**, 203–221.

SPENCER, T. & VILES, H. 2002. Bioconstruction, bioerosion and disturbance on tropical coasts: coral reefs and rocky limestone shores. *Geomorphology*, **48**, 23–50.

TERRY, J. P. 2007. *Tropical Cyclones. Climatology and Impacts in the South Pacific*. Springer, New York.

TERRY, J. P. & ETIENNE, S. 2010. Tempestuous times in the South Pacific islands. *Science*, **328**, 5977, 428–429.

YAMANO, H., KAYANNE, H., YAMAGUCHI, T., KUWAHARA, Y., YOKOKI, H., SHIMAZAKI, H. & CHIKAMORI, M. 2007. Atoll island vulnerability to flooding and inundation revealed by historical reconstruction: Fongafale Islet, Funafuti Atoll, Tuvalu. *Global and Planetary Change*, **57**, 407–416.

# Records of submarine natural hazards off SW Taiwan

CHIH-CHIEH SU[1]*, JING-YI TSENG[1], HO-HAN HSU[1], CHENG-SHING CHIANG[2], HO-SHING YU[1], SAULWOOD LIN[1] & JAMES T. LIU[3]

[1]*Institute of Oceanography, National Taiwan University, Taipei, Taiwan*

[2]*General Education Centre, Hsiuping Institute of Technology, Taichung, Taiwan*

[3]*Institute of Marine Geology and Chemistry, National Sun Ya-sen University, Kaohsiung, Taiwan*

*\*Corresponding author (e-mail: donccsu@ntu.edu.tw)*

**Abstract:** In the past few years, large earthquakes and torrential rain hit southern Taiwan and induced severe submarine hazards off the SW coast. Marine sediments (turbidites) provide valuable records with which to study and understand the formation of these submarine geo-hazards. The Pingtung Earthquake (two major events ($M_L = 7.0$) plus many aftershocks), on 26 December 2006, triggered turbidity currents that severed submarine cables in the Fangliao and Gaoping submarine canyons. This caused significant economic loss. In addition to earthquake activity, typhoons and torrential rains that induced flooding are also important mechanisms responsible for the formation of turbidites. On 8–9 August 2009 Typhoon Morakot brought heavy rains to southern Taiwan, causing serious landslides and flooding on land. The typhoon also caused submarine cable breaks in the Gaoping Canyon. All such events are likely to be recorded in the marine sediments of the canyon system, and by analysing these records we may be able to reconstruct the history of past earthquakes and floods in the region. Chirp sonar profiles, in conjunction with core analysis, including X-ray radiographs, grain size and $^{210}$Pb analysis, are used to identify the sources, transport and deposition of the turbidites (or hyperpycnite) and to reconstruct the history of earthquakes and flooding in the study area. Results indicate that these submarine hazards are not only related to earthquake and floods but that the unique geological and hydrological setting also plays an important role in the initiation of these submarine geo-hazards.

Taiwan is located on the collision zone between the Philippine Sea and the Eurasian plates that converge at the rate of 80 mm year$^{-1}$ (Yu *et al.* 1997, 1999). It has an uplift rate of 5.7 mm year$^{-1}$ (Peng *et al.* 1977; Liew *et al.* 1993). The tectonic setting of the island connects the Ryukyu arc–trench and the Luzon arc–Manila trench systems, and forms an extremely active region (Teng 1990; Liu *et al.* 1997). As a result, Taiwan has a high frequency of earthquakes. Besides the tectonic setting, Taiwan is also located in the East Asian monsoon region. This geographical setting means that Taiwan faces torrential-rain-induced flooding in the plume rain (May–June) and typhoon (July–October) seasons. According to statistics from the Central Weather Bureau (http://www.cwb.gov.tw), in the last 50 years (1958–2009) the numbers of tropical storms and typhoons formed in the western North Pacific Ocean was 26.6 per year, three or four of which affected Taiwan. These typhoons not only bring disasters but also precipitation to Taiwan, which is an important water supply for the island. Since 2006, southern Taiwan has experienced a series of earthquakes and typhoons that induced severe natural hazards on land, and caused huge

loss of life and economic damage. At the same time, the earthquakes and typhoons also induced turbidity currents or underwater debris flows that caused submarine cable breakages.

Since the 1929 Grand Banks Earthquake, it has been well documented that earthquakes trigger turbidity currents and damaged submarine cables from the shelf to the abyss over hundreds of kilometres (Heezen & Ewing 1952; Piper *et al.* 1999). Although the cable faults generated by natural hazards only represent less than 10% of all breakages, this percentage increases to 30% as the water gets deeper (Carter *et al.* 2009). The break of submarine cables not only records the time of the breakages but also reveals the velocities of sediment-laden flows that broke them. Their deposits also left clues of the origins and flow path, and provided a way of understanding the development and transport of the sediment-laden flows.

Submarine landslide-generated sediment gravity flows may be classified into turbidity currents and debris flows (Piper *et al.* 1999; Talling *et al.* 2007). Turbidity currents are a dense, sediment-laden current in which the turbulence is the principal sediment-support mechanism (Sanders 1965;

*From*: TERRY, J. P. & GOFF, J. (eds) 2012. *Natural Hazards in the Asia–Pacific Region: Recent Advances and Emerging Concepts.* Geological Society, London, Special Publications, **361**, 41–60, http://dx.doi.org/10.1144/SP361.5

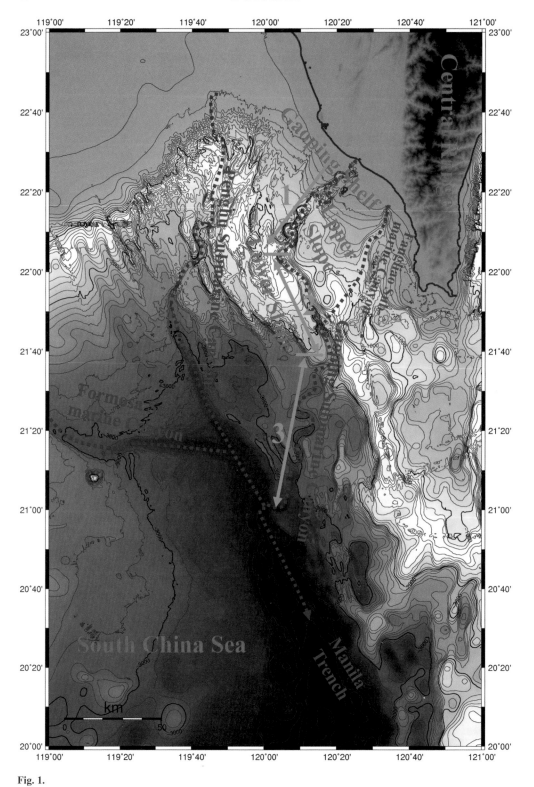

Fig. 1.

Shanmugan 2002), and can be triggered by earthquakes, storms and river floods. It also plays an important role in delivering terrestrial sediments to the deep abyssal plain through submarine canyons and channels. As the sediment concentrations increase, the turbulence is suppressed into sediment gravity flows (Bagnold 1954, 1956; Shanmugam 2002) and the flow rheology is shifted from Newtonian to plastic behaviour (Lowe 1979, 1982; Nardin *et al.* 1979). Based on sediment-support mechanisms, the debris flow is classified into one of the sediment-gravity flows in which sediment is supported by matrix strength (Middleton & Hampton 1973). Both the turbidity currents and the debris flows can be generated by submarine landslides, and deliver or redistribute sediments into the deep sea.

Natural hazards induced by submarine landslides vary by the scale of the landslide, location, type and process (Masson *et al.* 2006). The development of gravity-driven sediment flows from landslide to debris flow to turbidity current is thought to be governed by the volume of water entrained in the flows; however, the whole process is still poorly understood (Mulder & Cochonat 1996; Talling *et al.* 2002; Ilstad *et al.* 2004; Bryn *et al.* 2005; Masson *et al.* 2006).

Based on chirp sonar images accompanied by core analysis (including X-ray radiographs, grain size and $^{210}$Pb) results, we try to answer the following questions. (1) How were the submarine cables severed by submarine gravity processes? (2) Where were the potential sources and pathways of these submarine gravity processes? (3) Why do they occur in these localities?

## Study area and background

The offshore area of SW Taiwan is mainly composed of a narrow Gaoping shelf and broad Gaoping slope, with water depths ranging from 80 to 3400 m (Yu *et al.* 2009). Two major submarine canyons, the Gaoping Submarine Canyon (GPSC) and the Fangliao Submarine Canyon (FLSC), extend into deep waters and subsequently merge into the northern terminus of the Manila Trench (Fig. 1). The GPSC originating from the mouth of the Gaoping River can be divided into three segments (Fig. 1). The upper reach is located on the Gaoping shelf and the upper Gaoping slope that extends southwestwards and turns SE abruptly, at which point the middle reach begins. The middle reach extends southeastwards

and makes a sharp turn to the south connecting with the lower reach, which meanders sinuously over the Gaoping Deep-sea Fan and finally ends in the northern Manila Trench (Yu *et al.* 2009).

The morphology of the GPSC is strongly controlled by mud diapiric intrusions and a thrust faulting system (Chiang & Yu 2006; Yu *et al.* 2009). The GPSC is a two-way conduit of landward sediment transport dominated by the tide; which is offset by energetic events of seaward transport related to hyperpycnal turbidity currents and sediment gravity processes related to failures triggered by earthquakes, slumping and slides (Liu & Lin 2004, Huh *et al.* 2009, Liu *et al.* 2009). In the GPSC the normal mode of transport of suspended sediment associated with tidal propagation from offshore are up-canyon, but episodic modes of sediment transport associated with gravity-driven events are down-canyon (Liu *et al.* 2006, 2010).

The FLSC is a relatively small (about 10 km wide and 60 km long) and young (<3 Ma) submarine canyon that starts on the upper Gaoping slope and extends southwards to the base of the slope (Yu & Lu 1995). The canyon can be divided into two morphologically contrasting parts. The upper canyon begins at the shelf edge and has no direct connections to rivers on land. The length of the upper canyon is approximately 40 km between the 100 and 600 m-isobaths. In the upper canyon, truncation of horizontal parallel strata and sliding/slumping features on the canyon walls are indicative of downcutting and lateral widening of the canyon (Yu & Lu 1995). In the lower canyon, a rising linear ridge, which was formed by shale diapirs, separates the canyon into two segments. The lower one extends downslope to about the 1000 m-isobath, where it connects to the lower reaches of the GPSC.

## Submarine cable break events

Submarine cables can be damaged by fishing activities, ship anchors, the abrasion of cables and natural hazards. Although natural hazards might not be the major cause for cable breaks, they can involve multiple cable breaks in one incident. Many natural hazards can induce submarine cable-break incidents, such as earthquakes, tsunamis, storm surges, hurricanes (typhoons) and volcanic activity. Among all the possibilities, earthquakes and typhoons are probably the most important agents of submarine cable breaks on the sea floor adjacent to

**Fig. 1.** Map showing the location of geomorphic units and the submarine canyons off SW Taiwan. Two major submarine canyons, Gaoping Submarine Canyon (GPSC) and Fangliao Submarine Canyon (FLSC), developed on the Gaoping shelf and slope and merge into the north termination of the Manila Trench. The GPSC, which extends from the Gaoping River, can be divided into three segments: upper reach (1); middle reach (2); and lower reach (3). The blue dotted lines represent the thalweg of these canyons.

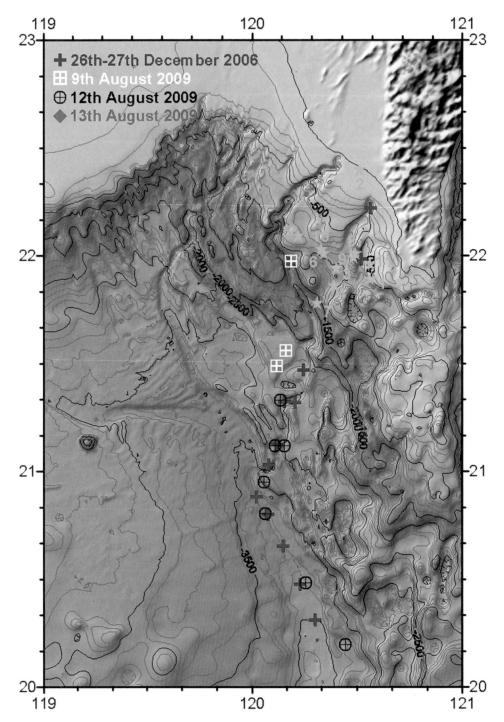

**Fig. 2.** The epicentres of two major 2006 Pingtung Earthquakes ($M_L$ 7.0), which occurred on 26 December 2006 (☆1 and ☆2) and a series of aftershocks with magnitudes larger than 5.0 that occurred in the following days (☆3–☆11). After the earthquake, a series of submarine cable breaks occurred on those cables lying downslope of the FLSC and the GPSC, and extending southwards into the Manila Trench. On 9–13 August 2009, the Morakot typhoon also induced submarine cable breaks following the same path as those in 2006.

Taiwan. In the past, submarine cable breaks were often associated with large earthquakes or severe stormy weathers. For example, the Hualien Earthquake, which occurred in 1986, induced submarine landslides in the waters north of Gueishan Island, and broke the cables connecting Ryukyu and Guam. Huh *et al.* (2004) also pointed out that large earthquakes with a magnitude of greater than 6.8 triggered submarine turbidity currents and formed turbidite layers in the south Okinawa Trough.

The Pingtung Earthquakes occurred on 26 December 2006 at 20:26 (21.9°N, 120.6°E; $M_L$ 7.0) and 20:34 (21.97°N, 120.42°E; $M_L$ 7.0) offshore of Fangliao Township, and a succession of aftershocks with magnitudes larger than 5.0 occurred for several days afterwards (Fig. 2). While the Pingtung Earthquakes occurred off SW Taiwan, three submarine cables broke at the FLSC (SMW3-S1.8: 21°59.101′N, 120°31.161′E and CH-US CN-W2-1: 22°13.287′N, 120°33.722′E) and the GPSC (CH-US CN-W2-2: 22°0.895′N, 120°7.005′E). In the meanwhile, local fishermen reported disturbed waters at the FLSC head. According to the submarine cable breakage timeline, Hsu *et al.* (2008) estimated that at least five submarine landslides took place after the earthquakes. According to the submarine cable-breakage records, in the middle reach of the GPSC only two cable breaks occurred at depths of 1511 and 1570 m, and one non-ruptured cable located at a depth of around 2000 m (Hsu *et al.* 2008). In this case, the earthquakes probably triggered submarine landslides that caused downslope cables along and across the FLSC and the GPSC to break, causing significant economic lost (Fig. 2). In total, 14 cables broke in this event and the repair work involved 11 ships and took 49 days (Hsu *et al.* 2008).

On 6 August 2009, the Central Weather Bureau (CWB) of Taiwan issued warnings for a medium-strength typhoon (Morakot), and the rains enveloped Taiwan from 7 to 9 August. According to previous experiences, the category 2 Typhoon Morakot should not have caused extensive disasters in Taiwan. But it did. Accompanied by strong southwesterly atmospheric circulations, Typhoon Morakot caused more than the annual rainfall figures in many places (Hong *et al.* 2010). The torrential rains were concentrated in the mountainous area of southern Taiwan. The highest rainfall was at CWB's Ali-shan station, which reached 3059.5 mm in 5 days (6–10 August). These torrential rains induced deluges that were far beyond the design standards of being able to withstand 100 year or 200 year floods. Over 41 bridges collapsed during the typhoon period. In addition to the damage to bridges, torrential rains also caused severe landslides, debris and mud flows at more

than 1690 locations. The confirmed death toll was 620, with 80 people still missing. The economic loss was estimated at 16.5 billion NTD (New Taiwan dollars) (Hsu *et al.* 2010). In addition to the loss of lives and property, Morakot-induced deluges also brought large amounts of gravels and sediments into offshore waters, and produced turbidity currents and hyperpycnal flows in the GPSC and onto the shelf and slope off SW Taiwan. The direct effect was over 13 submarine cable breakages off southern (on the 9, 12 and 13 of August: Fig. 2) and eastern (on the 9 and 17 of August) Taiwan after the Morakot typhoon (Carter *et al.* 2009; Kao *et al.* 2010).

The Jiashian Earthquake (22.903°N, 120.823°E; $M_L$ 6.4) occurred on 4 March 2010 at 08:18. It was the largest earthquake in the Kaohsiung area for the last 100 years. Although there was no significant damage on land, four international submarine cables broke at six locations between the afternoons of 4 and 5 March.

## Materials and methods

### Sampling

Over 60 box and gravity cores were collected using R/V *Ocean Researcher-I* (OR-1) from 2005 to 2010. The sampling sites are listed in Table 1 and plotted in Figure 3. Some of the locations have been sampled repeatedly to evaluate the evolution of the turbidite layers in the substrate. After returning to the laboratory, the cores were split into working and archive halves, and surface photographs were taken using a high-resolution digital camera (SmartCIS 1600 SE with Canon EOS 40D Digital SLR camera) at the Core Laboratory of the Taiwan Ocean Research Institute (TORI). Transparent acrylic trays (25 × 10 × 1 cm) were used to take sediment slabs for X-ray radiographic measurements. The remaining sediments in the split barrels were sectioned at 1 cm intervals, sealed in centrifuge tubes and then freeze-dried.

### X-ray radiography

The X-ray radiographic method was first used for the interpretation of marine sediment microtextures by Bouma (1964) and thereafter become an indispensable tool for marine sedimentological research (Stow & Shanmugam 1980). The X-ray images of sediment slabs were taken by digitized X-ray machine (AXR Model M160NH Cabinet X-ray System). The operating condition of the X-ray was set as 4 mA and 60 kV. The integration time for the digital scanner was 100–140 ms and the X-ray images were processed using the iX-Pect EZ software that came with the X-ray scanner.

**Table 1.** *Location of sediment cores in this study*

| Cruise | Station | Date | Latitude | Longitude | Water depth (m) | Core type* |
|---|---|---|---|---|---|---|
| OR1-774 | 8 | 21 November 2005: 00:12 | 22°15.48′ | 120°10.62′ | 940 | GC |
| | 9 | 20 November 2005: 16:41 | 22°18.75′ | 120°16.34′ | 513 | GC |
| | 10 | 20 November 2005: 17:30 | 22°18.44′ | 120°15.72′ | 518 | GC |
| | 11 | 20 November 2005: 18:54 | 22°19.78′ | 120°14.77′ | 623 | GC |
| | 12 | 20 November 2005: 20:41 | 22°21.41′ | 120°–12.46′ | 411 | GC |
| | 13 | 20 November 2005: 22:12 | 22°17.00′ | 120°14.11′ | 699 | GC |
| | E | 21 November 2005: 03:18 | 22°11.47′ | 120°14.64′ | 844 | GC |
| OR1-785 | 1 | 12 March 2006: 04:12 | 21°51.00′ | 120°12.66′ | 2291 | BC |
| | 2A | 12 March 2006: 09:40 | 21°54.15′ | 120°11.50′ | 2040 | GC |
| | 2 | 12 March 2006: 11:38 | 21°54.15′ | 120°11.50′ | 2040 | BC |
| | 3 | 12 March 2006: 14:28 | 22°00.87′ | 120°07.43′ | 1839 | BC |
| | 5A | 12 March 2006: 18:48 | 22°04.45′ | 120°04.97′ | 1807 | GC |
| | 7A | 13 March 2006: 00:36 | 22°17.91′ | 120°13.46′ | 683 | GC |
| | 7 | 13 March 2006: 04:40 | 22°17.95′ | 120°13.50′ | 728 | BC |
| | 8 | 13 March 2006: 03:02 | 22°18.74′ | 120°16.32′ | 507 | BC |
| | 9 | 13 March 2006: 06:20 | 22°21.38′ | 120°12.46′ | 410 | BC |
| | 9A | 13 March 2006: 07:10 | 22°21.42′ | 120°12.46′ | 410 | GC |
| OR1-851 | C | 8 December 2007: 03:23 | 21°54.14 | 120–11.54 | 2008 | GC |
| OR1-888 | BC1 | 27 December 2008: 03:20 | 22°13.26′ | 120°33.79′ | 440 | BC |
| | BC2 | 27 December 2008: 04:45 | 22°12.14′ | 120°34.99′ | 244 | BC |
| OR1-893 | A | 30 March 2009: 20:05 | 22°18.33′ | 120°34.02′ | 30 | BC |
| | B | 31 March 2009: 02:30 | 22°12.47′ | 120°28.99′ | 330 | BC |
| | C | 31 March 2009: 05:18 | 22°12.13′ | 120°34.99′ | 244 | BC |
| OR1-915 | K1 | 30 September 2009: 16:10 | 22°27.46′ | 120°24.85′ | 156 | BC |
| | K8 | 30 September 2009: 13:10 | 22°19.95′ | 120°15.26′ | 711 | GC |
| | K8X | 3 October 2009: 08:15 | 22°17.71′ | 120°17.14′ | 749 | BC |
| | K11A | 29 September 2009: 13:10 | 22°15.19′ | 120°10.58′ | 957 | BC |
| | K12 | 28 September 2009: 18:05 | 22°24.33′ | 120°24.51′ | 350 | BC |
| | K15 | 30 September 2009: 04:05 | 22°18.82′ | 120°13.54′ | 976 | BC |
| | K15X | 3 October 2009: 10:44 | 22°17.49′ | 120°12.24′ | 914 | BC |
| | K25B | 28 September 2009: 15:50 | 22°24.02′ | 120°20.62′ | 436 | BC |
| | K29 | 2 October 2009: 03:00 | 22°04.99′ | 120°04.91′ | 1794 | BC |
| | 5 | 29 September 2009: 00:55 | 22°13.68′ | 120°34.17′ | 361 | GC |
| | 8 | 29 September 2009: 06:00 | 22°06.56′ | 120°28.77′ | 825 | BC |
| | 9 | 29 September 2009: 13:50 | 22°04.03′ | 120°27.56′ | 859 | BC |
| | S09 | 29 September 2009: 04:10 | 22°09.85′ | 120°30.63′ | 657 | BC |
| | L9 | 3 October 2009: 04:05 | 22°11.04′ | 120°21.68′ | 495 | BC |
| | L11 | 29 September 2009: 22:50 | 22°13.62′ | 120°15.51′ | 729 | BC |
| | L26 | 1 October 2009: 04:00 | 22°23.71′ | 120°13.05′ | 307 | BC |
| | L28 | 1 October 2009: 06:05 | 22°29.88′ | 120°07.67′ | 375 | BC |
| | L31 | 1 October 2009: 02:10 | 22°21.08′ | 120°10.81′ | 495 | BC |
| | X1 | 3 October 2009: 05:50 | 22°12.98′ | 120°22.78′ | 375 | BC |
| | MV | 29 September 2009: 02:45 | 22°12.58′ | 120°29.17′ | 324 | BC |
| OR1-919 | S1 | 2 March 2010: 16:45 | 22°11.98′ | 120°13.75′ | 824 | BC |
| | S2 | 2 March 2010: 20:15 | 22°10.83′ | 120°12.58′ | 823 | GC |
| | S3 | 2 March 2010: 21:45 | 22°10.78′ | 120°14.98′ | 842 | GC |
| | C1 | 4 March 2010: 10:18 | 22°11.05′ | 120°24.67′ | 408 | GC |
| OR1-923 | K1 | 4 April 2010: 13:25 | 22°27.34′ | 120°24.76′ | 190 | BC |
| | K8X | 5 April 2010: 00:20 | 22°17.74′ | 120°17.17′ | 795 | BC |
| | K11A | 5 April 2010: 12:25 | 22°15.18′ | 120°10.57′ | 958 | BC |
| | K15X | 5 April 2010: 09:30 | 22°17.52′ | 120°12.23′ | 909 | BC |
| | K29 | 6 April 2010: 18:59 | 22°04.96′ | 120°04.96′ | 1795 | GC |
| | K30 | 6 April 2010: 14:20 | 21°57.86′ | 120°10.04′ | 2011 | GC |
| | K31 | 6 April 2010: 10:06 | 21°53.02′ | 120°11.54′ | 2007 | GC |
| | L9 | 4 April 2010: 19:23 | 22°11.01′ | 120°21.65′ | 495 | BC |
| | L11 | 4 April 2010: 21:20 | 22°13.59′ | 120°15.49′ | 733 | BC |
| | L26 | 5 April 2010: 02:33 | 22°23.69′ | 120°13.08′ | 305 | BC |
| | L28 | 5 April 2010: 04:25 | 22°29.86′ | 120°07.67′ | 374 | BC |

*(Continued)*

**Table 1.** *Continued*

| Cruise | Station | Date | Latitude | Longitude | Water depth (m) | Core type* |
|---|---|---|---|---|---|---|
| | L31 | 5 April 2010: 06:40 | 22°21.21′ | 120°10.80′ | 492 | BC |
| | X1 | 4 April 2010: 18:06 | 22°12.96′ | 120°22.80′ | 377 | BC |
| | B1 | 5 April 2010: 15:35 | 22°09.08′ | 120°14.09′ | 857 | GC |
| | B2 | 5 April 2010: 16:55 | 22°07.62′ | 120°14.19′ | 855 | GC |
| | B3 | 5 April 2010: 18:16 | 22°05.98′ | 120°15.44′ | 875 | GC |
| | B4 | 5 April 2010: 22:50 | 22°04.04′ | 120°16.20′ | 863 | GC |
| | B5 | 6 April 2010: 00:38 | 21°59.99′ | 120°17.89′ | 1156 | GC |
| | B6 | 6 April 2010: 02:20 | 21°57.49′ | 120°19.07′ | 1195 | GC |
| | B7 | 5 April 2010: 20:55 | 22°06.10′ | 120°18.56′ | 718 | GC |
| | B8 | 6 April 2010: 05:32 | 21°55.03′ | 120°19.96′ | 1276 | GC |
| | B9 | 4 April 2010: 16:11 | 22°12.13′ | 120°35.00′ | 228 | GC |

*GC, gravity core; BC, box core.

## Grain-size analysis

The laser diffraction particle size analyser (Beckman Coulter LS13 320) was used for grain-size analysis. All sediment samples were pretreated following the USGS procedures (Poppe *et al.* 2000). The cement and carbonates were removed by using 10% hydrochloride (HCl) and carbonate-free samples were treated with 15% hydrogen peroxide ($H_2O_2$) for 1–2 days to remove organic matter. Ultrasonic devices and sodium hexametaphosphate ($Na(PO_3)_6$) were used to deflocculate and disperse sediment grains prior to the grain-size analysis.

## Lead-210 analysis

$^{210}$Pb activity was determined by $\alpha$-spectrometer, via the granddaughter nuclide $^{210}$Po. The polonium-209 standard obtained from the ORNL (Oak Ridge National Laboratory) was added as a yield determinant prior to the total digestion of the samples. The $^{209}$Po spike was calibrated v. NIST-certified $^{208}$Po (SRM-4327). Polonium isotopes were plated onto a silver disc from the sample solution (in 1.5 M HCl, in the presence of ascorbic acid) at 80–90 °C for approximately 1–2 h. The counting results were corrected for the decay of $^{210}$Po (from the time of plating to counting) and $^{210}$Pb (from sample collection to Po plating). Supported $^{210}$Pb activity was estimated from the mean of the lowermost samples that showed a near-constant value in the core, and was subtracted from the total $^{210}$Pb activity when calculating the excess $^{210}$Pb activity.

## Sub-bottom echo profiling (Chirp sonar)

Seven cruises were used for collecting chirp sonar profiles (Fig. 4). On four of these cruises (OR3-

1253, OR3-1262, OR3-1434 and OR1-942), a high-resolution EdgeTech 0512i sub-bottom profiling system (set at the frequency range 0.5–12 kHz and towed 5–10 m below the sea surface) was used. Another three cruises (OR1-783, OR1-825 and OR1-851) conducted a hull-mounted chirp sonar survey by using the ODEC Bathy 2000p system, which was set at the frequency range 3–11 kHz.

## Results and discussion

### 2006 Pingtung Earthquake deposits

Before the Pingtung Earthquake, a box core (OR1-785-BC2) in conjunction with a gravity core (OR1-785-GC2A) was collected from the middle reaches of the GPSC. The $^{210}$Pb profile shows a subsurface maximum in the gravity core indicating that there was a quick deposit event at the core top. The low $^{210}$Pb activities may extend to the box core, which has coarser median grain size (c. 5$\phi$–6$\phi$) and sorting values (c. 1.9) than the gravity core (5.5$\phi$–6.5$\phi$ and c. 1.5) (Fig. 5a). Combing the box and gravity cores, the thickness of the quick deposit layer was at least 40 cm and might represent deposits disturbed by flooding-induced rapid input events in 2005. One year after the Pingtung Earthquake, on 8 December 2007, we revisited the same coring site and took a 1.4 m gravity core (OR1-851-GCC). Comparing the $^{210}$Pb profiles of OR1-785-BC2 with OR OR1-851-GCC, there was increased $^{210}$Pb activity at the core top indicating that the topmost layer was formed after 12 March 2006, which was the date that OR785-BC2 was taken (Fig. 5b). Clearly, there was no earthquake-induced turbidite layer in this core. This suggests that the Pingtung-Earthquake-induced submarine landslides in the upper and middle reaches did not pass beyond the mid-middle reach (Hsu *et al.* 2008).

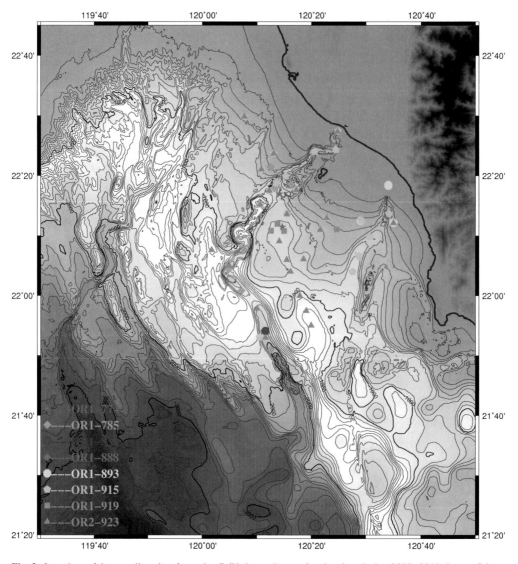

**Fig. 3.** Locations of the sampling sites from nine R/V *Ocean Researcher-1* cruises during 2005–2010. Some of the locations have been sampled repeatedly in order to evaluate the evolution of the turbidite layers in the sediments. The sampling date and co-ordinates of the core sites are listed in Table 1.

In the FLSC there were two submarine cable breakages after the Pingtung Earthquake. On the OR3-1262 cruise, we found a chaotic deposit located near the submarine cable break at the head of the FLSC (Fig. 6). From the chirp sonar profile, the chaotic deposit was around 1 km wide and over 5 m thick. A box core (OR1-888-BCC2, 27 December 2008) and a gravity core (OR1-893-GCC, 31 March 2009) were taken after the Pingtung Earthquake. Comparing the down-core values of total $^{210}$Pb activity, water content

and loss of ignition (at 550 °C) (Fig. 7a), the top 10 cm of the OR OR1-893-GCC was deposited after 27 December 2008 and the chaotic deposit sediments were buried below 22 cm, showing a clear erosional surface in the X-ray radiograph image (Fig. 7b). The grain-size profile in the OR OR1-893-GCC core at the depth of 55–80 cm reveals a turbidite layer that is characterized by the inverse graded bedding at the bottom (69–80 cm) overlain by a graded bedding at 55–69 cm. This sequence implies that the chaotic deposit

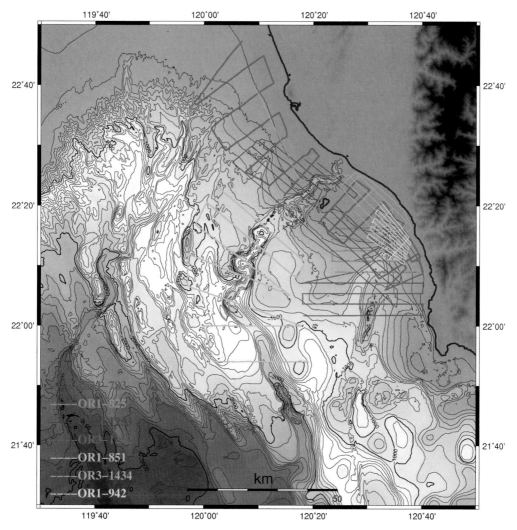

**Fig. 4.** Map showing the track lines of the chirp sonar survey works. Over 1500 km of chirp sonar profiles have been collected from seven cruises. Two types of chirp sonar profiler, EdgeTech 0512i sub-bottom profiling system and ODEC Bathy 2000p chirp sonar system, were used on *Ocean Researcher-I* and *Ocean Researcher-III*.

should be classified as a debris-flow event (Lastras *et al* 2004). It probably occurred at the same time as the Pingtung Earthquake and struck the submarine cable at the head of the Fangliao Canyon.

## 2006 Morakot typhoon deposit

After Typhoon Morakot severely impacted southern Taiwan on 7–9 August 2009, the FATES-HYPERS (Fate of Terrestrial/Nonterrestrial Sediments in High Yield Particle-Export River–sea Systems) research program initiated two cruises (OR1-915 and OR1-923), from 28 September to 3 October 2009 and from 6 to 9 April 2010, for identifying

and documenting the influence of Typhoon Morakot on the sea floor off SW Taiwan. As opposed to the submarine cable-break incidents induced by the 2006 Pingtung Earthquake, the onset of the Morakot cable-break incidents were not all synchronized with the peak discharge of the Gaoping River during the typhoon period. In cruise OR1-915, coarse sands, gravels and branches of tree were seen in the upper reaches of the GPSC (Fig. 8). At the OR1-915-K29 core site located at the bend between the upper and middle reaches of the GPSC, box coring brought large rocks and mud balls to the deck from the underlying sea floor. One thing worth mentioning is that near the

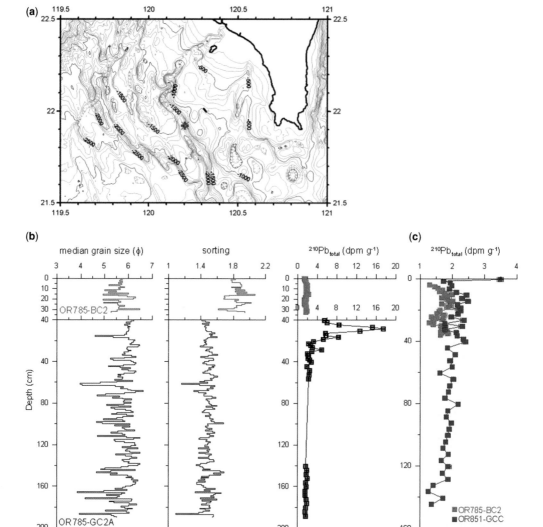

**Fig. 5.** (a) The index map for OR1-785-BC2, OR1-785-GC2A (+) and OR1-851-GCC (×) cores. The co-ordinates of the cores are listed in Table 1. (b) Profiles of median grain size, sorting and total $^{210}$Pb activity in OR785-BC2 and OR785-GC2A. Note a subsurface maximum of total $^{210}$Pb activity appears in the gravity core, and the box core has coarser median grain size and poorer sorting than the gravity core. (c) A comparison of total $^{210}$Pb activity in cores (OR1-785-BC2 and OR1-851-GCC) collected on different dates. An increase in total $^{210}$Pb activity at the top of OR1-851-GCC represents the newest deposits at the sampling site.

OR1-915-K29 site, the submarine cables were broken on 9 and 13 August. Two submarine cables were also destroyed in adjacent waters after the Pingtung Earthquake. The gravel on the sea floor may be related to the cable-break events on 9 and 13 August. We suggest that the 9 August submarine cable-break events might have resulted from the flow of the Gaoping River hyperpycnal plume, but the 13 August event was induced by the slumping of canyon walls or the occurrence of mud diapirs.

At the mid- to lower-middle reaches of the GPSC, there was no further destruction of submarine cables, and in core OR1-915-K31 no coarse sediment or large gravel was found. It seems that the turbidity current (sediment gravity processes) that induced the submarine cable breaks at the joint of the upper and middle reaches did not pass though the middle reach. The question therefore remains as to what caused the cable breakages further down the canyon.

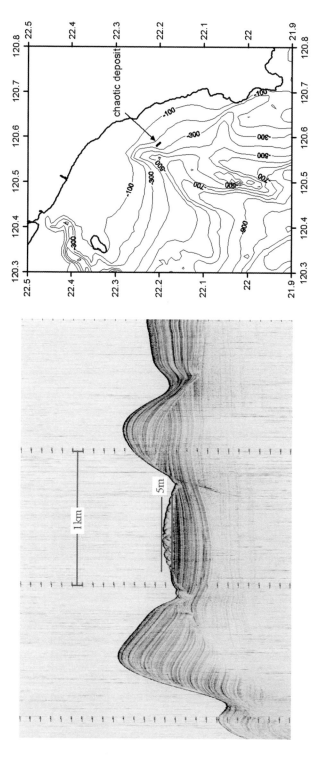

**Fig. 6.** The chaotic deposit near the submarine cable-break location at the head of the FLSC. The dimension of the deposit is around 1 km wide and over 5 m thick.

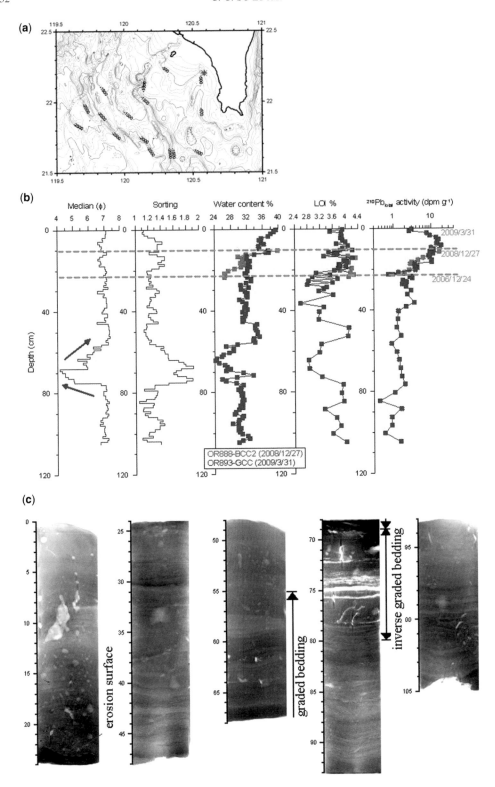

Fig. 7.

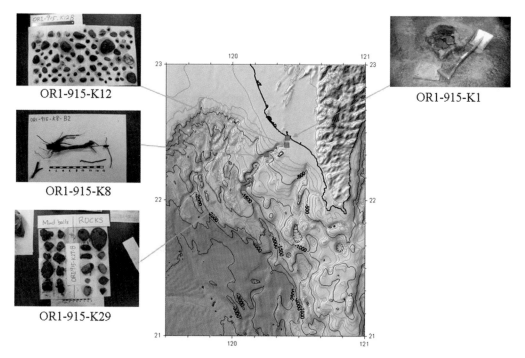

**Fig. 8.** On cruise OR915, coarse sands, gravels and branches of tree were collected at the upper reach of the Gaoping Submarine Canyon (OR1-915-K1, K12, K8, K27). The co-ordinates of the cores are listed in Table 1.

A series of submarine cables broke at the lower reaches of the GPSC and followed the path of the PHSC into the Manila Trench on 9 and 12 August (Fig. 2 also shows the breaking locations). According to the observations of the T–S (temperature–salinity) data on 14–15 August, the cable-break events on 12 August are probably related to hyperpycnal flows from the river or nearshore area (Kao et al. 2010). To understand the cable-breaking events in the deep sea, a series of cores were collected on the slopes off SW Taiwan to investigate the possibility of the slope source for the sediment gravity processes. A gravity core, OR1-923-B8, taken from the Gaoping slope at the depth of 1276 m has shed some light on this issue. According to the composition of lithology and grain size, the sediments in core OR1-923-B8 are different from the hemipelagic sediments on the slope. The core shows that there are at least four layers containing coarse slate fragments (0–2$\phi$) (Fig. 9) and it implies that the sediments could be derived from the southernmost Central Mountain Range of

Taiwan. The coarse slate layers also contained plant fragments and shell debris. All of the evidence suggests that the sediments originated from the mountainous area or the coastal zone that has stored the sediments from the Central Mountain Range. From the locations of submarine cable breaks after the 2006 Pingtung Earthquakes and Typhoon Morakot, the Gaoping shelf and slope near the FLSC are the potential/source areas for submarine landslides that facilitated pathways of debris flow to the deep ocean (Fig. 10).

*Fangliao Canyon as a source region for sediment gravity flows*

To understand the regional geological background, over 1500 km-long chirp sonar profiles were collected (Fig. 4). The geological framework off SW Taiwan was established during the Pliocene–Quaternary (Covey 1984). The fundamental description of the morphology and evolution of the FLSC was described by Yu & Lu (1995). The shallow

**Fig. 7.** (**a**) The index map for OR1-888-BC2 ( + ) and OR1-893-GCC (×) cores. The co-ordinates of the cores are listed in Table 1. (**b**) Profiles of median grain size, sorting, water content, loss of ignition (LOI) and total [210]Pb activity in OR888-BCC2 and OR893-GCC. (**c**) X-ray radiographic images of OR1-893-GCC. Note that there is an erosion surface at 22 cm depth, which has the lowest total [210]Pb activity. A turbidite layer at 55–80 cm is characterized by inverse graded bedding at the bottom of the layer (69–80 cm) and is overlain by graded bedding at 55–69 cm.

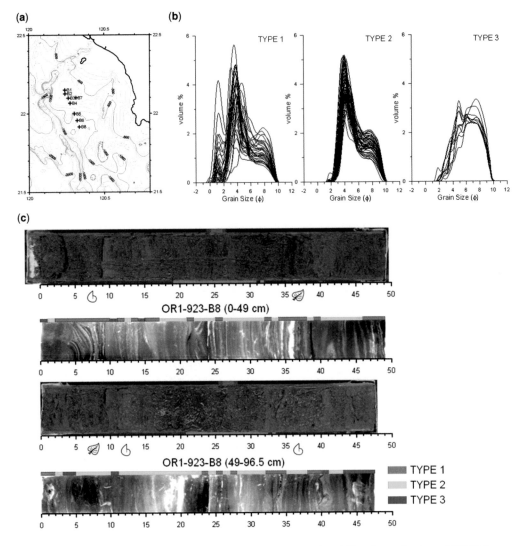

**Fig. 9.** (**a**) The index map of the cores which were collected during the OR1-923 cruise on the slope off SW Taiwan. The co-ordinates of the cores are listed in Table 1. (**b**) Plots show the different types of grain-size distribution patterns in core OR1-923-BC8. For Type 1, the sediments are composed of three components, medium sands $(0–2\phi)$, silt–find sand $(2\phi–6\phi)$ and mud $(4\phi–10\phi)$. In Type 2, the sediments are mainly composed of silt–find sand and mud. Type 3 sediments are composed solely of mud. For Type 1 and Type 2 samples, slates and quartz are the dominant fraction of the sediments. The different types of grain-size distribution pattern are superimposed on the X-ray radiographic images with red (Type 1), yellow (Type 2) and green (Type 3) block diagrams. (**c**) The surface and X-ray radiographic images of core OR1-923-B8. The ⌀ and 🍃 symbols represent shell fragments and plant detritus that were observed during the core description.

structures of the strata on the shelf and slope across the FLSC show a distinct inconsistency in this region (Fig. 11). On the western side of the FLSC (the shelf-slope region between the GPSC and the FLSC), the morphology of the sea floor is smooth and characterized by parallel layered strata. In contrast, the morphology and strata profile of the eastern side of the region between the FLSC and

the shoreline is relatively rugged, with chaotic deposits on the sea floor. In addition to the morphological and compositional variations of the sea floor, the chirp sonar data also indicated a series of faults on the Gaoping shelf close to the head of the FLSC (Fig. 12). Another significant geological process that may be related to the generation of the turbidity currents or debris flows on the sea floor is the

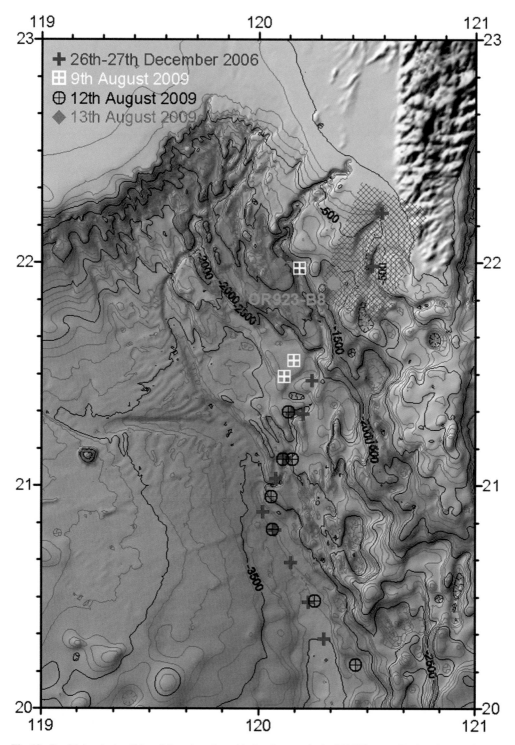

**Fig. 10.** Combining the localities of the submarine cable-break events in the 2006 Pingtung Earthquake and Morakot Typhoon with the analysis results of the core samples, it shows that the Gaoping shelf and slope near the FLSC is a potential area for producing submarine landslides and acts as a pathway for debris flows to the deep ocean.

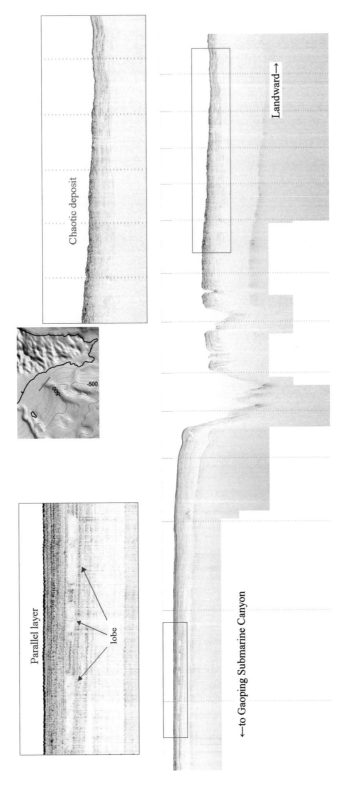

**Fig. 11.** The chirp sonar profile near the head of Fangliao Canyon. The morphology of the sea floor on the left-hand side of Fangliao Canyon (blue frame) is smooth and characterized by parallel layered strata. Below the parallel layers, several lobes can be seen in the strata that represent rapid deposition events. The morphology and strata profile for the right-hand side region (red frame) is relatively rough, with chaotic deposits on the sea floor.

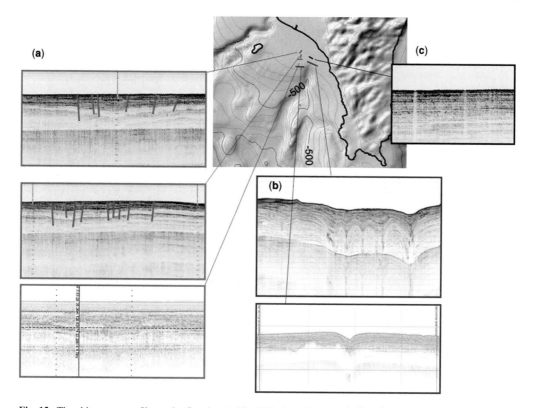

**Fig. 12.** The chirp sonar profiles at the Gaoping shelf, which show that near the Fangliao Submarine Canyon head there are a series of: (**a**) normal faults, (**b**) liquefaction structures and (**c**) pockmarks on the sea floor.

occurrence of liquefaction. After the 2006 Pingtung Earthquake, local fishermen reported turbid waters at the FLSC head. Many researchers conjectured that the disturbance might be caused by the eruption of submarine mud volcanoes that had been widely discovered off SW Taiwan. According to chirp sonar profiles, a series of liquefaction strata exist near the head of the FLSC, which are acoustically transparent sediments with doming structures. They are also observed in the adjacent area (Fig. 12). Integrating all of these data, we may reasonably deduce that the disturbed turbid waters reported by the fishermen were caused by liquefaction of the sea floor. In addition to faulting and liquefaction, we also found pockmarks with acoustic blanking under them on the Gaoping shelf (Fig. 12). On the EK500 sonar profiles, a series of gaseous plumes gushing out from the sea floor in the shallow waters were also found (Fig. 13). All of the evidence indicates that the pore fluid pressures of the surface sediments were high and might have easily triggered the liquefaction process that further contributed to the generation of debris-flow events after the earthquakes.

## Conclusion

The case studies of the 2006 Pingtung Earthquakes and the 2009 Typhoon-Morakot-induced submarine cable breakages on the sea floor reveal the destructive power of submarine failures. All of the evidence from core analysis and geophysical investigations indicate that the geological setting plays an important role in the generation of submarine landslides, slumping or debris flows. Even for the river-flooding event associated with Typhoon Morakot, the plunging of hyperpycnal flows down the canyons may trigger turbidity currents that caused submarine cable breakage. The instability of the sea floor caused by faulting or liquefaction in the strata can also be an important factor for generating submarine hazards. Our findings show that the submarine cable breaks occurring off SW Taiwan can be divided into two types. The first type is located in the upper reach or the upper-middle reach of the GPSC and relates to turbidity (hyperpycnal) currents from GPR or canyon-wall failures. The other type is located in the deep-sea off SW Taiwan. The Gaoping shelf and slope near the FLSC is an

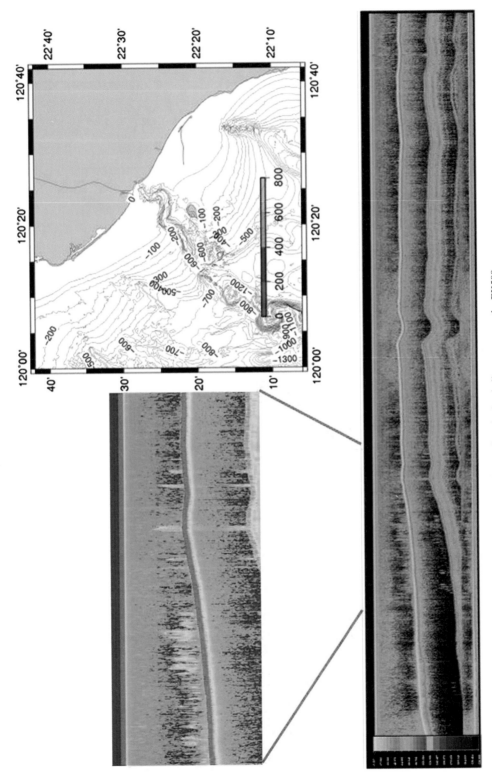

**Fig. 13.** On cruise OR893, a series of gaseous plumes gushed from the sea floor in the shallow waters on the EK500 sonar.

area where submarine landslides might trigger debris flows that cause undersea cable breakages. The high seismic acceleration after great earthquakes or the flux of increased submarine groundwater discharge (SGD) after torrential rains or typhoons all may increase the instability of the sea floor in this region. Furthermore, the instability of the Gaoping shelf and slope is likely to make it a potential area for the generation of tsunami hazards in the future.

The ROC National Science Council provided funding for this research. We thank the captains and crew of R/V *Ocean Researcher-I* and *Ocean Researcher-III* for shipboard assistance, as well as the assistance at sea and/or in the laboratory of S.D. Chiu, Valuable Instruments Centre, College of Science, National Taiwan University; and J.-R. Liao and J.-J. Zhou, Core Laboratory at the Taiwan Ocean Research Institute, National Applied Research Laboratories. Comments and constructive suggestions from Dr J. Milliman and another anonymous reviewer greatly improved the manuscript.

# References

BAGNOLD, R. A. 1954. Experiments on a gravity-free dispersion of large solid spheres in a Newtonian fluid under shear. *Proceedings of the Royal Society of London, Series A: Mathematical and Physical Sciences*, **225**, 49–63.

BAGNOLD, R. A. 1956. The flow of cohesionless grains in fluids. *Philosophical Transactions of the Royal Society of London, Series A: Mathematical and Physical Sciences*, **249**, 235–297.

BOUMA, A. H. 1964. Notes on X-ray interpretation of marine sediments. *Marine Geology*, **2**, 278–309.

BRYN, P., BERG, K., FORSBERG, C. F., SOLHEIM, A. & KVALSTAD, T. J. 2005. Explaining the Storegga slide. *Marine and Petroleum Geology*, **22**, 11–19.

CARTER, L., BURNETT, D., DREW, S., HAGADORN, L., MARLE, G., BARTLETT-MCNEIL, D. & IRVINE, N. 2009. *Submarine Cables and the Oceans – Connecting the World*. UNEP-WCMC Biodiversity Series, **31** (ISBN 978-0-9563387-2-3)

CHIANG, C.-S. & YU, H.-S. 2006. Morphotectonics and incision of the Kaoping submarine canyon, SW Taiwan orogenic wedge. *Geomorphology*, **80**, 199–213.

COVEY, M. 1984. Lithofacies analysis and basin reconstruction, Plio-Pleistocene western Taiwan foredeep. *Petroleum Geology of Taiwan*, **20**, 53–83.

HEEZEN, B. C. & EWING, M. 1952. Turbidity currents and submarine slumps, and the 1929 Grand Banks earthquake. *American Journal of Science*, **250**, 849–873.

HONG, C. C., LEE, M. Y., HSU, H. H. & KUO, J. L. 2010. Role of submonthly disturbance and 40–50 day ISO on the extreme rainfall event associated with Typhoon Morakot (2009) in southern Taiwan. *Geophysical Research Letters*, **37**, L08805, doi: 10.1029/2010GL042761.

HSU, H.-H., KUO, H. C., JOU, J.-D., WANG CHEN, T.-C., LIN, P.-H., YEH, T.-C. & WU, C. C. 2010. *The*

*Scientific Report of Morakot Typhoon*. National Science Council. Scientific Subcommittee of Morakot Typhoon, Taiwan (in Chinese).

HSU, S.-K., KUO, J., LO, C.-L., TSAI, C.-H., DOO, W.-B., KU, C.-Y. & SIBUET, J.-C. 2008. Turbidity currents, submarine landslides and the 2006 Pingtung Earthquake off SW Taiwan. *Terrestrial Atmospheric and Oceanic Sciences*, **19**, 767–772.

HUH, C.-A., LIU, J. T., LIN, H.-L. & XU, J. P. 2009. Tidal and flood signatures of settling particles in the Gaoping submarine canyon (SW Taiwan) revealed from radionuclide and flow measurements. *Marine Geology*, **267**, 8–17.

HUH, C.-A., SU, C.-C., LIANG, W.-T. & LIN, C.-Y. 2004. Linkages between turbidites in the southern Okinawa Trough and submarine earthquakes. *Geophysical Research Letters*, **31**, L12304, doi: 10.1029/2004GL019731.

ILSTAD, T., ELVERHØI, A., ISSLER, D. & MARR, J. G. 2004. Subaqueous debris flow behaviour and its dependence on the sand/clay ratio: a laboratory study using particle tracking. *Marine Geology*, **213**, 415–418.

KAO, S. J., DAI, M. *ET AL.* 2010. Cyclone-driven deep sea injection of freshwater and heat by hyperpycnal flow in the Subtropics. *Geophysical Research Letters*, **37**, L21702, doi: 10.1029/2010GL044893.

LASTRAS, L. G., CANALS, M., URGELES, R., DE BATIST, M., CALAFAT, A. M. & CASAMOR, J. L. 2004. Characterisation of the recent BIG'95 debris flow deposit on the Ebro margin, Western Mediterranean Sea, after a variety of seismic reflection data. *Marine Geology*, **213**, 235–255.

LIEW, P. M., PIRAZZOLI, P. A., HSIEH, M. L., ARNOLD, M., BARUSSEAU, J. P., FONTUGNE, M. & GIRESSE, P. 1993. Holocene tectonic uplift deduced from elevated shorelines, eastern coastal range of Taiwan. *Tectonophysics*, **222**, 55–68.

LIU, C.-S., HUANG, I. L. & TENG, L. S. 1997. Structural features off southwestern Taiwan. *Marine Geology*, **137**, 305–319.

LIU, J. T. & LIN, H.-L. 2004. Sediment dynamics in a submarine canyon: a case of river–sea interaction. *Marine Geology*, **207**, 55–81.

LIU, J. T., HUNG, J.-J. *ET AL.* 2009. From suspended Particles to strata: the fate of Terrestrial Substances in the Gaoping (Kaoping) submarine canyon. *Journal of Marine Systems*, **76**, 417–432.

LIU, J. T., LIN, H.-L. & HUNG, J.-J. 2006. A submarine canyon conduit under typhoon conditions off Southern Taiwan. *Deep Sea Research I*, **53**, 223–240.

LIU, J. T., WANG, Y.-H., LEE, I.-H. & HSU, T. R. 2010. Quantifying tidal signatures of the benthic nepheloid layer in Gaoping Submarine Canyon in southern Taiwan. *Marine Geology*, **271**, 119–130.

LOWE, D. R. 1979. Sediment gravity flows: their classification and some problems of application to natural flows and deposits. *In*: DOYLE, L. J. & PIKEY, O. H. (eds) *Geology of Continental Slopes*. SEPM, Special Publications, **27**, 75–82.

LOWE, D. R. 1982. Sediment gravity flows: II. Depositional models with special reference to the deposits of high-density turbidity currents. *Journal of Sedimentary Petrology*, **52**, 279–297.

MASSON, D. G., HARBITZ, C. B., WYNN, R. B., PEDERSEN, G. & LOVHOLT, F. 2006. Submarine landslides: processes, triggers and hazard prediction. *Philosophical Transactions of the Royal Society A: Mathematical, Physical & Engineering Sciences*, **364**, 2009–2039.

MIDDLETON, G. V. & HAMPTON, M. A. 1973. Sediment gravity flows: mechanics of flow and deposition. *In*: MIDDLETON, G. V. & BOUMA, A. H. (eds) *Turbidites and Deep-water Sedimentation*. SEPM Pacific Section, Short Course Notes, 1–38.

MULDER, T. & COCHONAT, P. 1996. Classification of offshore mass movements. *Journal of Sedimentary Research*, **66**, 43–57.

NARDIN, T. R., HEIN, F. J., GORSLINE, D. S. & EDWARDS, B. D. 1979. A review of mass movement processes, sediment and acoustic characteristics, and contrasts in slope and base-of-slope systems versus canyon-fan-basin floor systems. *In*: DOYLE, L. J. & PIKEY, O. H. (eds) *Geology of Continental Slopes*. SEPM, Special Publications, **27**, 61–73.

PENG, T.-H., LI, Y.-H. & WU, F. T. 1977. Tectonic uplift rates of the Taiwan Island since the early Holocene. *Memoir of the Geological Society of China*, **2**, 57–69.

PIPER, D. J. W., COCHONAT, P. & MORRISON, M. L. 1999. The sequence of events around the epicentre of the 1929 Grand Banks earthquake: initiation of the debris flows and turbidity current inferred from side scan sonar. *Sedimentology*, **46**, 79–97.

POPPE, L. J., ELIASON, A. H., FREDERICKS, J. J., RENDIGS, R. R., BLACKWOOD, D. & POLLONI, C. F. 2000. Grain size analysis of marine sediments: methodology and data processing. *In*: POPPE, L. J. & POLLONI, C. F. (eds) *USGS East-coast Sediment Analysis: Procedures, Database, and Georeferenced Displays*. US Geological Survey Open-File Report, **00-358** (CD-ROM).

SANDERS, J. E. 1965. Primary sedimentary structures formed by turbidity currents and related resedimentation mechanisms. *In*: MIDDLETON, G. V. (ed.) *Primary Sedimentary Structures and Their Hydrodynamic Interpretation*. SEPM, Special Publications, **12**, 192–219.

SHANMUGAM, G. 2002. Ten turbidite myths. *Earth-Science Reviews*, **58**, 311–341.

STOW, D. A. V. & SHANMUGAN, G. 1980. Sequence of structures in fine-grained turbidites: comparison of recent deep-sea and ancient flysch sediment. *Sedimentary Geology*, **25**, 23–42.

TALLING, P. J., PEAKALL, J. *ET AL.* 2002. Experimental constraints on shear mixing rates and processes: implications for the dilution of submarine debris flows. *In*: DOWDESWELL, J. A. & Ó COFAIGH, C. S. (eds) *Glacier-influenced Sedimentation on High-latitude Continental Margins*. Geological Society, London, Special Publications, **203**, 89–103.

TALLING, P. J., WYNN, R. B. *ET AL.* 2007. Onset of submarine debris flow deposition far from original giant landslide. *Nature*, **450**, 22, doi: 10.1038/nature 06313.

TENG, L. S. 1990. Geotectonic evolution of late Cenozoic arc-continent collision in Taiwan. *Tecionophysics*, **183**, 57–76.

YU, H.-S. & LU, J. C. 1995. Development of the shale diapir-controlled Fangliao Canyon on the continental slope off southwestern Taiwan. *Journal of Southeast Asian Earth Sciences*, **11**, 265–276.

YU, H.-S., CHIANG, C.-S. & SHEN, S.-M. 2009. Tectonically active sediment dispersal system in SW Taiwan margin with emphasis on the Gaoping (Kaoping) Submarine Canyon. *Journal of Marine Systems*, **76**, 369–382.

YU, S.-B., CHEN, H.-Y. & KUO, L.-C. 1997. Velocity field of GPS stations in the Taiwan area. *Tectonophysics*, **274**, 41–59.

YU, S.-B., KUO, L.-C., PUNONGBAY, R. S. & RAMOS, E. G. 1999. GPS observation of crustal deformation in the Taiwan-Luzon region. *Geophysical Research Letters*, **26**, 923–926.

# Bedding structures in Indian tsunami deposits that provide clues to the dynamics of tsunami inundation

ADAM D. SWITZER[1]*, S. SRINIVASALU[2], N. THANGADURAI[2] & V. RAM MOHAN[3]

[1]*Earth Observatory of Singapore, Nanyang Technological University, 639798 Singapore*

[2]*Department of Geology, Anna University, Chennai 600025, India*

[3]*Department of Geology, University of Madras, Chennai 600025, India*

*\*Corresponding author (e-mail: aswitzer@ntu.edu.sg)*

**Abstract:** The 2004 Indian Ocean tsunami deposited an extensive sandsheet on the coastal plain of SE India. At particular sites, the sedimentary bedding in the sandsheet provides evidence of variable energy conditions and flow during inundation of the coast. Trenching of the deposits at sites where only unidirectional flow was observed allowed the investigation of changes in hydrodynamics recorded in bedding structures without the added complexity of return flows and reworking. A high-velocity initial surge is recorded as upper flow regime (UFR) plane bedding. Following the initial high flow a period of falling flow velocity and quiescence occurs where sediments settle out of suspension, often resulting in a reverse graded bed that transitions to a graded (fining-up) bed. As water levels begin to decline after maximum inundation sheet flow caused the formation of inversely graded (coarsening-up) beds or a return to UFR conditions. At one site the final stages of tsunami inundation is recorded as small channels that have an erosional base and are filled with graded sediments that exhibit complex patterns of sedimentation. Pits excavated in areas of unidirectional flow allow the development of a sedimentary model for tsunami sediment dynamics across flat topography under unidirectional flow conditions.

Despite recent advances, the hydrodynamics of tsunami inundation and the inherent relationship between inundation hydrodynamics and sedimentary bedding in tsunami deposits remain poorly understood. Much can be learnt from the careful study and interpretation of modern tsunami deposits as they provide a valuable and powerful analogue to palaeostudies, and provide insights into the dynamics of erosion and deposition during tsunami inundation and back flow (e.g. Le Roux & Vargas 2005; Dawson & Stewart 2007; Hawkes *et al.* 2007; Jaffe & Gelfenbaum 2007; Morton *et al.* 2007; Paris *et al.* 2007, 2008; Srinivisalu *et al.* 2007; Choowong *et al.* 2008*a, b*; Komatsubara *et al.* 2008; Naruse *et al.* 2010). Owing to the relative rarity and geographical distribution of tsunami, few descriptions are available of the sedimentary structures and facies of onshore tsunami deposits (e.g. Gelfenbaum & Jaffe 2003; Nanayama & Shigeno 2006; Bahlburg & Weiss 2007; Hawkes *et al.* 2007; Hori *et al.* 2007; Morton *et al.* 2007; Paris *et al.* 2007; Umitsu *et al.* 2007; Choowong *et al.* 2008*a, b*; Naruse *et al.* 2010). Investigations of sedimentary processes associated with modern tsunami are extremely important in the interpretation of tsunami deposits in the geological record as many identified tsunami signatures or features can be equally attributed to storm surge or other

depositional processes (Witter *et al.* 2001; Switzer *et al.* 2005; Dawson & Stewart 2007; Jaffe & Gelfenbaum 2007; Kortekaas & Dawson 2007; Morton *et al.* 2007; Switzer & Jones 2008*a, b*; Switzer & Burston 2010). Recent studies on tsunami-deposited sandsheets, such as those deposited by tsunami events in 1983 at Nihonkai-chubu (Minoura & Nakaya 1991), the 1992 Flores (Shi *et al.* 1995; Minoura *et al.* 1997), 1993 at Hokkaido–Nansei-oki (Nishimura & Miyaji 1995; Sato *et al.* 1995; Nanayama *et al.* 2000), 1994 in Java (Dawson *et al.* 1996), 1998 in Papua New Guinea (e.g. Gelfenbaum & Jaffe 2003) and the recent 2004 Indian Ocean tsunami (e.g. Szczucinski *et al.* 2005, 2007; Bahlburg & Weiss 2007; Hawkes *et al.* 2007; Hori *et al.* 2007; Morton *et al.* 2007; Paris *et al.* 2007; Srinivasalu *et al.* 2007; Umitsu *et al.* 2007; Choowong *et al.* 2008*a, b*; Naruse *et al.* 2010), are of considerable importance in understanding the dynamics of tsunami inundation in different coastal settings.

The tsunami run-up process is very complex, and it is pertinent to any study of onshore tsunami deposits that analysis of the likely pre-event morphology, sedimentary environments and sediment dynamics of the seabed, nearshore and onshore systems be considered. One of the most widely recognized sedimentary signatures for tsunami inundation is landwards-tapering wedges

*From*: TERRY, J. P. & GOFF, J. (eds) 2012. *Natural Hazards in the Asia–Pacific Region: Recent Advances and Emerging Concepts*. Geological Society, London, Special Publications, **361**, 61–77, http://dx.doi.org/10.1144/SP361.6

of marine material, often in the form of extensive sheets of marine sand (e.g. Minoura & Nakaya 1991; Dawson *et al.* 1996; Minoura *et al.* 1997; Jaffe & Gelfenbaum 2007; Morton *et al.* 2007; Matsumoto *et al.* 2008). Often these sandsheets contain sequences of normal (fining-up) or inversely (coarsening-up) graded beds (Dawson *et al.* 1991; Nishimura & Miyaji 1995; Benson *et al.* 1997; Gelfenbaum & Jaffe 2003; Morton *et al.* 2007), non-graded (massive) or multiple graded sandsheets (Benson *et al.* 1997; Gelfenbaum & Jaffe 2003; Moore *et al.* 2006; Paris *et al.* 2007), and sharp erosional bases (Nanayama *et al.* 2000; Switzer *et al.* 2006; Switzer & Jones 2008*b*). Some deposits contain 'bioclasts' or rip-up clasts of muddy soil and, in some locations, mud caps or rafted debris (Dawson *et al.* 1996; Goff *et al.* 2001, 2004*a*, *b*; Gelfenbaum & Jaffe 2003; Dawson & Stewart 2007; Naruse *et al.* 2010). Current ripples and dunes in onshore tsunami deposits, formed by tsunami inflows and outflows, have also been reported by Sato *et al.* (1995), Nanayama *et al.* (2000) and Nanayama & Shigeno (2006).

A large earthquake on Sunday 26 December 2004 occurred 160 km west of Sumatra, Indonesia at a depth of approximately 25–30 km (Fig. 1a). The earthquake generated a tsunami that caused over 280 000 fatalities across the entire Indian Ocean Basin (Lay *et al.* 2005; Stein & Okal 2005; Grilli *et al.* 2007). On the Indian coast the tsunami consisted of three large waves, with the first making landfall 3 h after the initial earthquake, followed by two more waves approximately 5 min apart that flowed over the low-lying coast before the first wave completely receded (Srinivasalu *et al.* 2007). Tsunami run-up levels ranged from 0.7 to 6.5 m above sea level, and inundation distance varied from 30 to more than 850 m from the swash zone (Chadha *et al.* 2005; Jayakumar *et al.* 2005; Ramanamurthy *et al.* 2005). The average landwards inundation distance was approximately 250 m. The tsunami waves extensively transformed the morphology of the Tamil Nadu coast as they inundated estuaries, overtopped dunes and resulted in considerable alteration to the coastal morphology (Narayana *et al.* 2007; Mascarenhas & Jayakumar 2008; Pari *et al.* 2008). In many places waves ripped large trees out of the ground, and moved both traditional wooden and modern brick and mortar structures off of their pilings or foundations tens to hundreds of metres away from the coast (Srinivasalu *et al.* 2007; Mascarenhas & Jayakumar 2008).

This paper looks at the sedimentary bedding characteristics of tsunami overwash deposits from four specific pits excavated on the SE coast of India. Trenching and coring elsewhere on this coast has allowed mapping of the extent of the 2004 tsunami deposits, and investigation of the affects on coastal topography and indicators of sediment sources (Thangadurai *et al.* 2006; Srinivasalu *et al.* 2007). This work focuses on two sites where unidirectional flow occurred, and investigates the relationship between sedimentary bedding, flow regime, bedform morphology and flow velocity. The four pits (of 12) were chosen to minimize the added complication of reworking during back flow (Nanayama & Shigeno 2006; Hori *et al.* 2007; Choowong *et al.* 2008*a*, *b*; Naruse *et al.* 2010). Sedimentary beds identified here are representative of different stages of flow change during unidirectional tsunami overwash across relatively flat topography (relief less than 1 m change over more than 150 m) at 2–3 m above present mean sea level.

## Study sites

The study area consists of approximately 160 km of coastal tract from Vedarranniyam in the south to Cuddalore in the north (Fig. 1). The landforms of the northern part of the study area are characterized by low-angle (<3°) siliclastic beaches with an average width of about 50–100 m that are backed by a coastal dune system usually of less than 5 m elevation (Anbarasu 1994; Pari *et al.* 2008). In the northern study area, two prominent sets of well-developed beach ridges that are almost parallel to the shore lie landwards of the modern dune system (Fig. 1). The southern part of the study area shows more complex delta morphology, and is dominated by silty floodplain sediments and strandlines and a coastal morphology of beach ridges and tidal flats that overlie the prograded deltaic system of the Kaveri (Cauvery) River. These ridges are dissected by the numerous small rivers and estuaries along with the two large rivers, the Pallar River and the Kaveri River (Fig. 1). Two main sites are presented here: Silver Beach near Cuddalore (Fig. 1b) and Kallar near Nagipattinum (Fig. 1c).

## Methods

The study focuses on the bedding structures, bioturbation and sediment particle-size variation observed in tsunami-deposited sediments in two areas affected by unidirectional flow. Unidirectional flow was confirmed by eyewitness accounts and geomorphic indicators, such as grassy debris wrapped around scattered trees or the presence of erosional scour marks behind trees. The study sites were also located on local topographical highs (50–80 cm higher than surrounds) seawards of a slope that ran into the creeks at the back of the sites. Flow depths at Silver Beach and Kallar were estimated to be around 2–3 and 3–4 m,

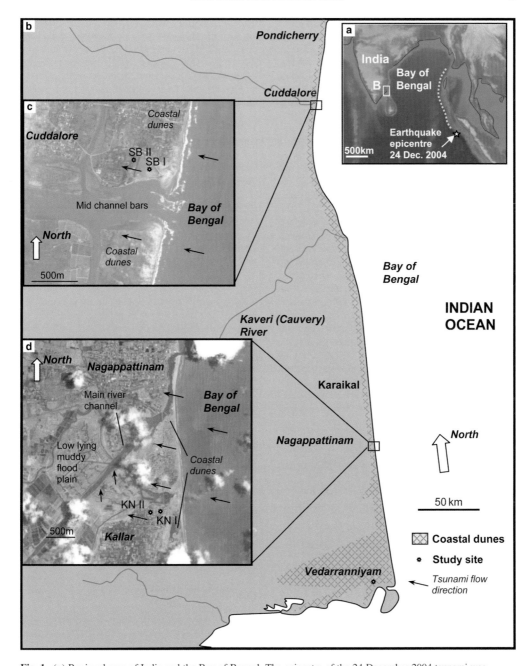

**Fig. 1.** (**a**) Regional map of India and the Bay of Bengal. The epicentre of the 24 December 2004 tsunami was situated offshore of Banda Aceh in northern Sumatra, Indonesia. The yellow dotted line is the 1500 km + rupture. The tsunami wave generated struck the Indian coast approximately 3 h after generation. (**b**) Map of the SE coast of India. Maximum inundation was up to 2 km at Verdarranniyam. (**c**) The study site at Silver Beach near Cuddalore. Here the tsunami waves washed into a small estuary. Two pits were excavated, SB-I and SB-II. Pit SBI shows a clear tsunami deposit of marine sand. Eyewitness accounts suggest that tsunami waves passed over the site of pit SB-II, no tsunami deposit was identified. (**d**) The study site at Kallar near Nagappattinam. Two pits were excavated here to investigate the unidirectional washover dynamics where eyewitness accounts stated that the waves washed across the dunefield and into the low-lying floodplain below before draining out through Nagappattinam Port.

respectively, based on eyewitness accounts of levels on walls and estimations based on debris in trees. Inflow velocities in the area are believed to have been in excess of $3\,\mathrm{m\,s^{-1}}$ based on eyewitness accounts and videos from sites nearby. These velocities are consistent with those derived from videos in studies of inundation in Banda Aceh (Sakakiyama *et al.* 2005; Fritz *et al.* 2006).

Although many pits have been excavated and described for this coast (Srinivasalu *et al.* 2007), the four study sites chosen here were selected because they show clear bedding structures that are the result of variation in unidirectional flow or evidence of significant bioturbation, which was deemed to be the most important aspects of this study. For this purpose, several pits of approximately $40 \times 40\,\mathrm{cm}$ were excavated in October 2005. Excavations extended through the tsunami deposit and into the underlying soil at sites where no evidence of bidirectional flow was found. Samples were collected at 2 cm intervals, with extra samples taken across stratigraphic contacts and in areas of key interest. Sedimentary bedding features along with sediment grain-size characteristics were used to define facies within the tsunami deposit and the underlying units with the aim of developing a model that relates grain-size patterns, sedimentary bedding and tsunami flow dynamics. Grain-size parameters, including the percentage of sand, silt and clay along with graphic mean,

inclusive graphic standard deviation, inclusive graphic skewness and graphic kurtosis (after Folk & Ward 1957), were obtained using a Malvern Mastersizer 2000 (laser diffraction particle-size analysis) and a method modified from Chivas *et al.* (2001) and Switzer *et al.* (2005).

## Results

### Silver Beach

At Silver Beach the tsunami waves inundated the coastal plain at depths estimated to be around 2 m and flowed up the estuary towards the town of Cuddalore. Two pits (SB-I and SB-II) were excavated on the northern bank of the estuary behind a small car park that lies on the heavily modified (anthropogenically flattened) beach ridge (Fig. 2). Small pits were excavated along a transect from the dune and car park to a grassy berm with a small wall 1.6 m high that was partially destroyed in the tsunami. The distance from the shore to the wall was approximately 600 m. Local residents outlined the extent of the tsunami deposit and it was identified as a thin sandsheet that started approximately 50 m from the shore. The deposit thickness increased landwards to a maximum thickness of about 32 cm approximately 200 m from the coast before thinning and becoming patchy at about 350 m from shore.

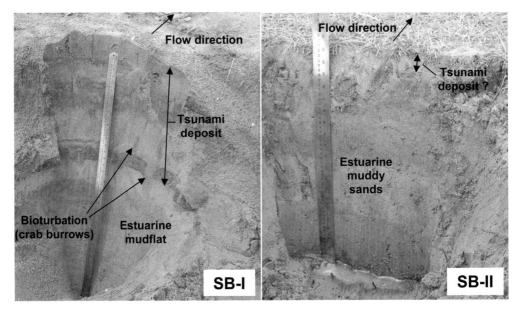

**Fig. 2.** Photographs of excavated pits SB-I and SB-II near the town of Cuddalore on the SE coast of India. In pit SB-I, the tsunami deposit is identified as a thin layer of fine- to medium-grained sand 32 cm thick. In pit SB-II, the facies are predominantly estuarine mud and sand. The upper 12 cm may be a tsunami deposit but it has been heavily reworked by aeolian activity and affected by soil development.

## Pit SB-I

Pit SB-I was excavated close to the area of maximum thickness (*c.* 200 m from shore) where the sedimentary record of the tsunami is identified as a thin deposit of fine- to medium-grained sand 32 cm thick, which exhibits several layers and complex bedding patterns (Figs 2a & 3). At this site the deposit sharply overlies the muddy fine sand (*c.* 2.06$\phi$–2.10$\phi$) of the coastal plain. The base of the tsunami deposit found in pit SB-I exhibits complex bedding with low-angled cross-bedding occurring in a basal layer of fine sand (*c.* 2.17$\phi$–2.21$\phi$) that is approximately 5 cm thick. The basal layer is composed of a facies that contains abundant heavy minerals. This layer is sharply overlain by a lighter coloured (tan) relatively massive fine- to medium-grained sand (*c.* 2.08$\phi$–1.95$\phi$) layer with noticeable bioturbation (burrows). This facies exhibits little variation in

grain size, showing only a slight coarsening-up trend (reverse grading), and becomes slightly coarser (1.79$\phi$) and more poorly sorted (0.71$\phi$) towards the top of the light coloured layer. The light coloured layer is sharply overlain by a layer of sediments that has a higher proportion of heavy minerals (>10%) (including abundant zircons, ilmenite and rutile) and undetermined lithic clasts (indicated by a dark colour). The top layer is composed of fine- to medium-grained sand (*c.* 1.95$\phi$–1.79$\phi$), and exhibits complex bedding that is recorded as small cross-bedded channels and micro-bars outlined by dark coloured beds composed almost entirely of heavy minerals. The deposit then grades to a muddy sand (*c.* 2.05$\phi$–2.35$\phi$) that is topped by a sandy soil (*c.* 1.88$\phi$). The top of the tsunami deposit is poorly defined, although grain-size data of the overlying layer shows considerable contrast with the underlying (tsunami) layers (much coarser) and are dissimilar to that of

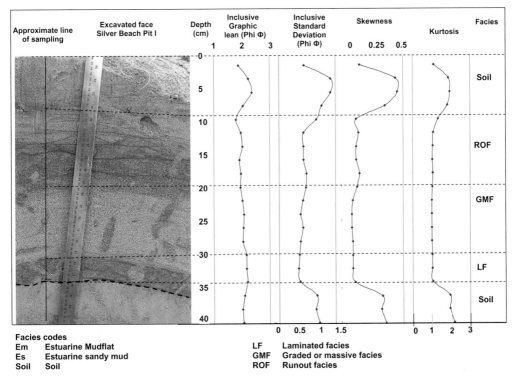

Facies codes
Em   Estuarine Mudflat
Es   Estuarine sandy mud
Soil   Soil

LF   Laminated facies
GMF   Graded or massive facies
ROF   Runout facies

**Fig. 3.** Photograph of face and grain-size data from pit SB-I. The base of the tsunami deposit contains a laminated facies (LF) that exhibits complex bedding that is approximately 5 cm thick and contains abundant heavy minerals. Laminated facies is sharply overlain by fine- to medium-grained sand facies (GMF) with noticeable bioturbation. This bed exhibits little variation in grain size, showing only a slight coarsening-up trend and with only a slight increase in sorting towards the top of the bed. This bed is sharply overlain by a bed that has a higher proportion of heavy minerals (ROF), where complex bedding includes small cross-bedded channels and micro-bars outlined by dark coloured beds. The uppermost unit (Soil) is a muddy sand that is topped by a sandy soil. The top of the tsunami deposit is poorly defined, although the overlying bed shows considerable contrast with the underlying (tsunami) beds, and is similar to that of the underlying muddy soil of the coastal plain.

the underlying muddy soil of the coastal plain. This may represent post-depositional aeolian reworking of the sediments deposited by the tsunami.

## Pit SB-II

Pit SB-II (Figs 2b & 4) was excavated near the reported landward extent of the deposit. Here the only deposit considered as a 'suspect tsunami' deposit is a poorly defined thin muddy sand (*c.* 3.01$\phi$–3.34$\phi$) unit approximately 12 cm thick that overlies an interbedded series of muddy sand and silts. The 'suspect tsunami' deposit appears to have been considerably modified by soil development. All units show considerable variation in grain size but they are all muddy-sand units that are considerably finer and more poorly sorted than the tsunami sediments identified in face SB-I. If the top unit in the sequence is, indeed, the deposit of the tsunami event, then it provides some evidence of landwards fining within the deposit. If not, then it may suggest that, even if tsunami deposits are identified by eyewitnesses, the preservation and differentiation from confining facies can remain problematic.

## Kallar

At Kallar, south of Nagapattinam town, the tsunami waves inundated the coastal plain at depths of 3–

4 m. Unidirectional inundation at the study site was across two poorly defined, low-relief (<2 m), well-vegetated beach ridges before flowing into the Uppanar River flood plain and out through the heavily modified entrance of Nagapattinam Port (Fig. 1b). No evidence of return flow was observed at this site and, although vegetation is likely to have affected flow characteristics to an extent (Dahdouh-Guebas *et al.* 2005), the sediments deposited here are likely to have been emplaced under flow directions that were close to unidirectional (Fig. 2c). Two pits, Kallar-I and Kallar-II (Fig. 5), were excavated in a fenced area that had been sealed off by the local community and the environment had been well preserved since the tsunami some 5 months earlier. Pits Kallar-I (Figs 5a & 6) and Kallar-II (Figs 5b & 7) were excavated along a transect perpendicular to the shore at distances of approximately 420 and 580 m from the shore, respectively (Fig. 2c). Local residents described the tsunami deposit as a thin sandsheet that started approximately 120 m from the shore and ran into the low-lying floodplain (Fig. 2c).

## Kallar-I

The pit Kallar-I was excavated at a site away from surrounding vegetation where the tsunami deposit

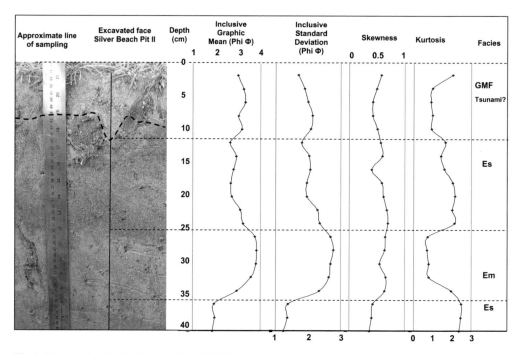

**Fig. 4.** Photograph and grain-size data from pit SB-II where the only bed considered as a 'candidate tsunami' deposit is a poorly defined thin muddy sand unit approximately 12 cm thick that overlies an interbedded series of estuarine muddy sand and silts. The unit appears to have been modified by soil development.

**Fig. 5.** Pits Kallar-I and Kallar-II were excavated south of Nagapattinam town where tsunami waves 2 and 3 inundated the coastal plain across two poorly defined low-relief (<2 m), well-vegetated beach ridges before flowing into the Uppanar River flood plain and out through the entrance of Nagapattinam Port. No evidence of return flow was observed at this site, although vegetation is likely to have affected flow characteristics to some extent. The sediments deposited here are likely to have been emplaced under flow directions that were close to unidirectional, and the two pits Kallar-I and Kallar-II were excavated at distances of approximately 420 and 580 m from the shore, respectively, along a transect perpendicular to the shore (Fig. 1d).

was thought to be thickest. Here the sedimentary record of the tsunami was identified as a thin deposit of fine- to medium-grained sand, which consists of four sedimentary layers that exhibit considerable horizontal lamination and complex bedding patterns, and sharply overlie the muddy sand of the coastal plain (Fig. 5a). The base of the tsunami deposit shows a 15–20 cm-thick layer that exhibits prominent thin, laterally continuous, laminations between 0.5 and 2 cm thick, which are well defined by heavy mineral horizons. The grain-size characteristics of the basal layer show considerable variation in the lowest parts (Fig. 6) before

exhibiting a well-defined trend of increased sorting (c. $1\phi$–$0.6\phi$) and fining-up (c. $2.6\phi$–$2.2\phi$). The basal layer is sharply overlain by a massive layer of fine- to medium-grained sand with very few sedimentary features, and is 14–22 cm thick. This unit exhibits subtle variation in mean grain size and it becomes slightly coarser from its base value of approximately $2.3\phi$ to a maximum mean grain size of $1.9\phi$ (reverse grading) before fining up to about $2.1\phi$. The relatively massive unit is sharply overlain by a laterally discontinuous layer of laminated fine- to medium-grained sand similar to the basal layer that varies between 0 and 4 cm thickness.

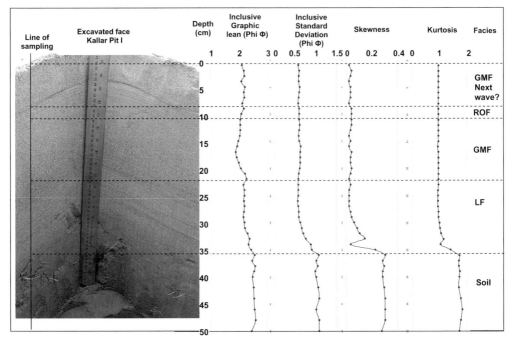

**Fig. 6.** Photograph and grain-size data from a sampling transect in pit Kallar-I. The base of the tsunami deposit shows a unit 15–20 cm thick that exhibits prominent, thin, laterally continuous laminations between 0.5 and 2 cm thick that are well defined by heavy mineral layers (LF). The basal unit is sharply overlain by a massive bed of fine- to medium-grained sand that exhibits few sedimentary features (GMF). The massive unit is overlain by a laterally discontinuous bed of laminated fine- to medium-grained sand similar to the basal unit, and has been incised and reworked at its upper boundary. The base of the overlying bed rests unconformably on the underlying bed and exhibits complex bedding. This complex unit is overlain by a massive fine- to medium-grained sand that exhibits little variation in grain size.

At times, this layer has been incised and reworked at its upper boundary. Overlying the relatively massive unit is a thin prominent layer with a higher proportion of heavy minerals resting unconformably on the erosional boundary (Fig. 5a). Complex bedding is recorded above this boundary with poorly defined cross-bedding and evidence of small infilled channels that, at times, exhibit a slight coarsening-up in mean grain size. This complex layer is overlain by a massive fine- to medium-grained sand layer that exhibits little variation in grain size. The combined thickness of this unit varies between 4 and 11 cm.

## Kallar-II

The pit Kallar-II was excavated approximately 160 m further inland than the site of the Kallar-I pit. The tsunami imprint was identified as a thin deposit of fine- to medium-grained sand that sharply overlies the muddy sand of the coastal plain (Fig. 5b). The deposit here consists of four layers and shows a similar vertical variation as the

Kallar-I pit. The basal layer of the tsunami deposit in Kallar-II is an 8–13 cm-thick sand layer that exhibits prominent, thin, laterally continuous laminations between 0.5 and 2 cm thick that are well defined by heavy mineral horizons. The grain-size characteristics of the basal unit show considerable variation in the lowest parts (Fig. 7). A small depression has been infilled with laminated sediment and exhibits a rapid coarsening near the bottom (reverse grading) before showing a well-defined trend of increased sorting (c. $1.2\phi$–$0.2\phi$) and fining-up (c. $2.6\phi$–$2.4\phi$). Like the sequence in Kallar-I, the basal layer is sharply overlain by a 12–24 cm-thick massive bed of fine- to medium-grained sand with very few sedimentary structures. This unit exhibits subtle variation in mean grain size and, in contrast to the same unit in Kallar-I, it becomes slightly finer from its base value of around $2.35\phi$ fining up to approximately $2.1\phi$. The massive sands of this layer are sharply overlain by a laterally discontinuous unit of fine- to medium-grained sand that varies between 0 and 4 cm in thickness and has numerous thin well-defined

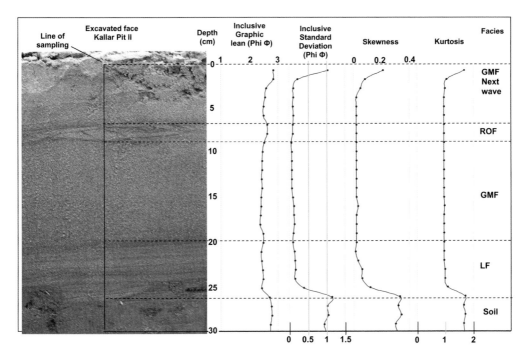

**Fig. 7.** The deposit identified in the pit at Kallar-II consists of four units and shows a similar vertical variation as the Kallar-I pit. The deposit overlies a muddy soil and the base of the tsunami deposit contains a thin, laterally continuous laminated sand that is well defined by heavy mineral layers (LF). A small depression has been infilled with laminated sediment and exhibits a rapid coarsening at the base. The basal unit is sharply overlain by a massive bed of fine- to medium-grained sand (GMF) with very few sedimentary features. This unit exhibits very little variation in mean grain size and, in contrast to the same unit in Kallar-I, it fines-up slightly. The massive unit is sharply overlain by a laterally discontinuous unit of fine- to medium-grained sand that is similar to the basal unit. A series of small incised channels unconformably overlie this unit and contain complex bedding with occasional low-angle cross-beds. This complex channel unit is overlain by a thin prominent bed that has a higher proportion of heavy minerals.

laminations similar to those found in the basal layer. A series of small incised channels unconformably overlie this unit and contain complex bedding with occasional low-angle cross-beds. This complex channel unit is overlain by a thin prominent bed that has a higher proportion of heavy minerals (Fig. 5a). The unit exhibits poorly defined lamination and grades into a massive fine- to medium-grained sand that exhibits little variation grain size. The combined thickness of this unit varies between 8 and 14 cm (Fig. 7), and it fines up to a muddy soil similar in sediment characteristics to the underlying pre-tsunami soil profile.

*Other sites with laminated (plane-bedded) facies*

At many places along the SE coast of India post-tsunami surveys identified tsunami deposits (Fig. 8) with laminated or plane bedding (Thangadurai *et al.* 2006; Srinivasalu *et al.* 2007). In places (Fig. 8a, b), the tsunami deposit is entirely composed of thin, 1–4 cm-thick, lamina sets of fine- to medium-grained sand. The laminated or partially laminated deposits are primarily found closest to the coast in the seaward one-third of the tsunami deposit. Figure 8a shows a photograph of a deposit from Velankanni, where the deposit was identified as a strongly laminated sequence of heavy-mineral-rich sands. Here a prominent rounded boulder, approximately 15 cm in diameter, was also found in the base of the deposit.

## Discussion

Understanding the key transport mechanisms and depositional processes of tsunami deposits is a basic requirement for explaining and predicting the dispersal of sediment in coastal settings during tsunami inundation (Moore *et al.* 2007; Paris *et al.* 2007; Szczucinski *et al.* 2007; Choowong *et al* 2008a, b; Naruse *et al.* 2010). Although geological investigations of former tsunami are a relatively new research area, many papers on the topic have

**Fig. 8.** The laminated facies identified at Silver Beach and Kallar are not local anomalies. Similar deposits with laminated or plane bedding are found at many places along the SE coast of India. In places, the tsunami deposit is entirely composed of thin 1–4 cm-thick lamina sets of fine- to medium-grained sand. The laminated or partially laminated deposits are usually found in the seaward one-third of the tsunami deposit. (**a**) and (**b**) show the tsunami deposit from Velankanni near Nagapattinam where the deposit was identified as a strongly laminated sequence of heavy-mineral-rich sands. In (a), a prominent rounded boulder approximately 15 cm in diameter was also found in the base of the deposit. (**c**) shows a partially laminated sequence near Karaikal and (**d**) shows a sequence from the dunes at Vedarranniyam, the southern most part of the area.

been published over the last 20 years. From these studies, a wide range of sedimentary evidence from different locations has been attributed to a series of former tsunami (see reviews by Dawson & Shi 2000; Goff *et al.* 2001; Scheffers & Kelletat 2003; Dawson & Stewart 2007; Kortekaas & Dawson 2007; Morton *et al.* 2007; Bryant 2008; Switzer & Jones 2008*b*). Many authors have argued that tsunami are frequently associated with the deposition of continuous and discontinuous sediment sheets across large areas of the coastal zone, provided that there is an adequate sediment supply. More recent research has demonstrated that the bedding relationships found in tsunami deposits are more complex than that first described. Such research has only recently yielded significant insights on the understanding of tsunami dynamics during inundation (e.g. Choowong *et al* 2008*a*, *b*; Naruse *et al*. 2010). The distinction of depositional units within tsunami deposits formed by different stages and flow characteristics will assist in extending our understanding of the relationship between tsunami inflow, sediment deposition and bed preservation.

Deposit characteristics depend on a number of factors, including: tsunami height and period; local bathymetry and topography; sediment source; and vegetation and other roughness elements (Bourgeois 1993; Morton *et al*. 2007; Moore *et al*. 2007; Choowong *et al* 2008*a*, *b*). All tsunami deposits are inherently different, some deposits exhibit evidence of multiple waves (Dawson *et al*. 1991), but others do not, even where eyewitnesses described more than one significant wave (Bourgeois 1993). Early descriptions of tsunami deposits suggested that the vertical profile of most tsunami deposits consisted of a series of fining-up units often attributed to individual tsunami waves (e.g. Dawson *et al*. 1991; Shi *et al*. 1995; Dawson 1999). These simple descriptions have evolved through time, and over the last decade the internal sedimentary structures of tsunami deposits have been used extensively to infer flow directions and changes in hydraulic behaviour during inundation (e.g. Fujiwara *et al*. 2003; Panegina *et al*. 2003; Nelson *et al*. 2004; Cisternas *et al*. 2005; Williams *et al*. 2005; Moore *et al*. 2006, 2007; Nanayama & Shigeno 2006; Jaffe & Gelfenbaum 2007; Choowong *et al* 2008*a*, *b*; Paris *et al*. 2008). Prior to 2004, sharp contacts between layers of normal grading deposits were considered good criteria to separate inflow and outflow units (e.g. Nanayama *et al*. 2000); however, recent work (e.g. Paris *et al*. 2007; Choowong *et al* 2008*a*, *b*; Naruse *et al*. 2010) has demonstrated the complexity of the bedding relationships found in tsunami deposits. Tsunami deposits are a product of the source environment, and grain size and sorting will commonly reflect the source material available (Bourgeois 1993; Switzer & Jones 2008*b*). Where unconsolidated sediment is available, tsunamis can erode significant amounts of sediment from the coastal zone and offshore; such material will also consist of coastal sediments but will also often include large amounts of displaced and reworked coastal vegetation and fauna. Several authors have identified large volumes of sediment sourced from the continental shelf incorporated into the tsunami deposit. For example, Gelfenbaum & Jaffe (2003) noted that, in several locations, the 1998 Papua New Guinea tsunami deposit was composed of more than 65% offshore sediment. Similar findings were presented by Babu *et al*. (2007) and Paris *et al*. (2008) in reference to the 2004 Indian Ocean tsunami. In these cases, both studies identified that more than 75% of the sediments came from offshore. The tsunami deposits of the SE Indian coast directly relate to their source, and all contain abundant fine- to medium-grained sand (Fig. 8) with minor heavy minerals and relatively low carbonate content.

## Flow characteristics and sedimentary facies

Three main facies are identified in the Indian tsunami deposits (Figs 3–8) and are thought to reflect different stages of inundation, energy dissipation and changes in flow regime for the specific sites investigated. The majority of deposits are associated with the much larger second wave that struck the coast at approximately 9.35 a.m. local time (Srinivasalu *et al*. 2007). The dominant facies is a massive sand (GMF) that exhibits subtle evidence of reverse grading (coarsening-up), followed by normal grading (fining-up) that is usually the thickest of the units and is often found in the middle section of the deposits. The second prominent facies is a plane-bedded or laminated facies (LF) composed of numerous lamina sets that dominate the most seaward areas of the deposits and are also often found in the lower parts of the middle section of most transects. The final facies is termed the runout facies (ROF) and consist of complex bedding with laminated sediments and evidence of channelized flow including complex low-angle cross-bedding. In some places, including the Kallar sites, deposits from a later, possibly third, wave are found overlying the sequence deposited from the initial inundation.

*Deposition of plane-parallel laminated facies (LF).* Laminated sediments segregated into multiple discrete lamina sets are often found in sandy storm deposits and rarely in tsunami deposits (Morton *et al*. 2007; Choowong *et al* 2008*a*, *b*). Most storm deposits exhibit at least some subhorizontal planar stratification and may have inverse or normal grading (Leatherman & Williams 1977; Morton 1979; Schwartz 1982; Tuttle *et al*. 2004; Switzer & Jones 2008*a*). The number of layers or lamina sets inherently depends on the thickness of the deposit and there is often no clear correlation between the number of layers within a bed and the number of waves either for tsunami or storm deposits (Morton *et al*. 2007).

The presence of plane-parallel lamination or plane bedding in deposits gives clues to the dynamics of sedimentation. The presence of parallel or flat bedding in sandy sediments is often presented as evidence of deposition by a strong unidirectional, turbulent, high velocity flow (Bridge & Best 1988; Cheel 1990; Tucker 2001; Fielding 2006). At many localities along the southeast coast of India, sandy tsunami deposits exhibit planar-parallel lamination occasionally throughout the entire deposit, but more often in the lower and upper parts of the deposit where the plane bedded units often confine beds of massive or graded fine- to medium-grained sand. The presence of these beds is thought to be indicative of upper flow regime (UFR) plane bedding during period of high velocity, turbulent flow. The grain size range of the planar-parallel laminated deposits studied here indicate that the mean grain size is generally between 1.5 and 2.8 $\phi$ (Figs 5, 7 & 8). UFR plane bedding is often the result of unidirectional high velocity flows. Although plane bedding is a common sedimentary feature in modern depositional environments, the physical conditions and hydraulic process that form plane beds under UFR conditions remains poorly understood (Fielding 2006). Some suggest that the dominant controlling factor is shallow flow depth (Smith 1971). In contrast, Paola *et al.* (1989) cited turbidites and deep fluvial channels as examples where UFR plane beds occur but flow depth is not a factor. In coastal settings plane or laminated bedding is found in storm deposits (Leatherman & Williams 1977; Sedgwick & Davis 2003; Switzer & Jones 2008*a*) where it is attributed to repeated inundation by storm waves and not due to UFR high velocity turbulent flows. The presence of these laminated beds is peculiar within tsunami deposits and is most likely associated with UFR plane bedding at high velocities during the initial stages of shallow heavily sediment-laden flow.

*Deposition of the massive or graded facies (GMF).* In a recent review Morton *et al.* (2007, p. 202) stated that 'most modern tsunami deposits consist of one layer or only a few layers or lamina sets' and usually contain a sequence of less than five normally graded beds, citing references to studies by Nishimura & Miyaji (1995), Nanayama *et al.* (2000), Gelfenbaum & Jaffe (2003), Jaffe *et al.* (2003) and Tuttle *et al.* (2004). Morton *et al.* (2007) also suggested that extremely rapid deposition occurs when flow decelerates between the up-rush and back-wash phases of inundation, often resulting in single-layer, homogeneous and structureless tsunami deposits where inverse grading is rare. In contrast, Choowong *et al.* (2008*a*, *b*) suggested that the reverse grading found in tsunami deposits could be attributed to high grain

concentration and mutual collisions among grains within a traction carpet or grain flow, as described by Hand (1997). Choowong *et al.* (2008*a*, *b*) suggested that reverse grading in tsunami deposits indicates a very high grain concentration within the tsunami flow. They theorized that this was possibly formed at the initial stages of inundation at a shallow water depth. This is consistent with the findings of this study, where a slight coarsening-up pattern is found in the lowermost parts of the GMF facies. Although the tsunami deposits do contain a structureless fine- to medium-grained sand unit, the presence of confining plane-bedded or laminated sediments or sediments exhibiting complex bedding or small channels suggest that tsunami sedimentation is significantly more complex than reverse grading followed by normal grading.

The massive (Figs 5–7) or slightly graded facies identified at Kallar is most probably due to settling from suspension during the final stages of inundation. In tsunami deposits, fining-up units have been recorded in many instances, and are attributed to deposition during periods when flow wanes and sediments drop out of suspension, often depositing fining-up units (Dawson *et al.* 1991; Dawson & Shi 2000; Gelfenbaum & Jaffe 2003; Dawson & Stewart 2007; Morton *et al.* 2007). In pits Kallar I and Kallar II, the GMF facies shows initial fining-up but then coarsens towards the top of the unit. This may reflect a slight increase in flow strength and shear stress as the runout sequence begins.

*Deposition of runout facies (ROF).* The final facies identified in the tsunami deposits of the SE Indian coast is the runout facies. This facies is thought to be deposited during the final stages of tsunami inundation and is identified as two sandy facies. The first exhibits complex bedding that often has small channels that have incised and reworked the upper boundary of the underlying unit. The lower contact of this unit rests unconformably on the erosional boundary and is defined by a thin prominent bed that has a higher proportion of heavy minerals (Fig. 5a). Complex bedding is recorded above this boundary with poorly defined cross-bedding, and is attributed to channelization of the flow during the final stages. The second subfacies, is a planar laminated unit that occurs at the base of the unit in Kallar I. This subfacies is attributed to a return to UFR plane bedding as the area drains by sheet flow. It is likely that, where preserved, the UFR plane bedded subfacies of the runout facies will be incised by the channelized flow subfacies during the final stages of flow.

*Bioturbation.* Considerable evidence was found in several areas along the SE Indian coast for

## Pre tsunami system

Back barrier sandy soils and estuarine mudflats

Beach ridges and accumulations of fine-grained aeolian dune sand

Medium- to coarse-grained dune and beach sand

Sandy near shore sediments with abundant heavy minerals

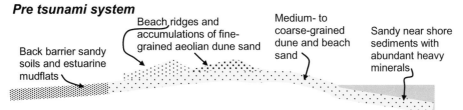

## Initial inundation

High energy overwash erodes and transports a large amount of material from the dune, beach face and nearshore zone. The sediments are deposited as upper flow regime plane beds (laminated facies (LF)) due to the very high velocity (see Figures 5, 6, 7 and 8).

## Maximum inundation

Water depth reaches a maximum and landward velocity slows to 0. Sediments are deposited from suspension as flow wanes. Graded beds reflect areas where flow reduction is greatest (massive or graded facies (GMF)). Initial back flow of sediments near the sea, often carrying large amounts of sediment to the nearshore and offshore zone

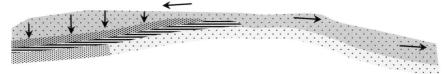

## Initial stages of outflow

Flow increases as water drains toward topographic lows. Complex sedimentation occurs during this stage (Run out facies – ROF). Inversely graded beds can occur due to increasing flows and sediment carrying competence and upper flow regime plane bedding may reflect high velocity during sheet flow (see Figure 6).

High velocity sheetflow

## Final stages of outflow

Sheet flow becomes channelized and channels often erode into underlying layers. Bedding includes small scale cross bedding and graded beds. Channel infill in the final stages can yields upward fining beds as flow wanes before coarsening rapidly at the top due to relative swallowing and increased shear stress in the final run outflow phase.

Channelized flow

**Fig. 9.** Schematic model for the sedimentary processes, facies and bedform associations observed at sites of unidirectional flow under tsunami conditions on the SE coast of India.

bioturbation of the deposits from the 2004 tsunami. At Silver Beach, the excavated face SB-I (Fig. 3) shows significant bioturbation in the form of crab burrows up to 4 cm in diameter that are observed to mix sediments of the differing sedimentary layers. The crab burrows destroy bedding and are present as elongate structures in vertical profile, which shows obvious evidence of sediment mixing. Some bioturbation is also present in the faces of Kallar-II (Fig. 5), where bedding has also been destroyed and sediments appear to show considerable mixing. The identification of significant bioturbation features indicates that the preservation of these deposits may be problematic, reinforcing the point of Nichol & Kench (2008) who indicated that bioturbation is a significant issue when considering older deposits of unknown origin. When studying prehistoric tsunami deposits, bioturbation by animals and plants and other post-depositional modification due to extraneous factors such as groundwater movement must all be considered (Switzer & Jones 2008*b*; Nichol *et al.* 2010). It is possible that much of the bedding described in this paper will be destroyed over the next few years due to burrowing organisms and the re-establishment of vegetation.

*Depositional model.* The tsunami-deposited sediments at Kallar reveal a series of unique characteristics that allow the development of a modified depositional model for unidirectional tsunami washover on low-lying siliclastic coasts (Fig. 9). As tsunami strike the shoreline they experience very large growth in wave amplitude and very high velocity at the shoreface. Tsunami waves then inundate the coast causing rapid short-duration inundation and high shear stress and erosion. Sediments are mobilized from a variety of onshore and offshore environments during the high-energy passage of tsunami waves, and they can easily breach small coastal dune systems and carry sediment into the coastal plain. It follows that the internal sedimentology of any washover sediments deposited on the coastal plain will, at least in part, reflect the conditions of the source area immediately preceding the depositional event. The offshore sediments in the study area are predominantly siliclastic fine- to medium-grained sands with a relatively high (5–15%) component of heavy minerals, and the deposits of the 2004 tsunami share similar composition (Stephen-Pichaimani *et al.* 2008).

Complex bedding in tsunami deposits has been reported previously by Nanayama *et al.* (2000) and Nanayama & Shigeno (2006) but that was associated with back flow. The sites studied here allow the study of unidirectional flow, and provide clues to the changes in hydrodynamics as the tsunami inundates the landscape and runs towards topographical lows. Although initial tsunami inundation is known to be characterized by high velocity and unidirectional flow at the shoreline, surprisingly, UFR plane bedding has rarely been reported for tsunami deposits. It is also likely that sheet flow during the initial stages of tsunami runout may also deposit sediments under UFRs resulting in plane-laminated bedding. The final stages of tsunami runout will often involve the development of channelized flow. Such channels will often range from several centimetres to several metres in width and exhibit distinctive complex sedimentation patterns including the formation of small bars.

## Conclusions

The facies and bedding features identified in the tsunami deposits of SE India indicate several key features about the dynamics of tsunami inundation on this coast. Analysis of the sediment composition indicates a dominance of marine sand, which suggests that a considerable proportion of sediments were carried from offshore during the tsunami. The presence of different bedding features allowed the study of flow regime and grading pattern variation in sites that experienced unidirectional flow. At these sites, the presence of laminated beds attributed to UFR plane bedding that confine graded or massive beds is of note. The laminated sequence shows that tsunami deposits can and do contain horizontally laminated beds, a feature of vital importance to palaeo-overwash studies. The laminated appearance is most probably related to periods of high shear stress during high-velocity flow that results in UFR plane bedding. Further analysis of other deposits may yield valuable information on the dynamics of tsunami inundation and the preservation of features that indicate changes in flow regime and flow conditions.

We thank the Department of Science and Technology, Ministry of Science and Technology, Government of India for the financial support. This work was carried out as a part of Tsunami research programme. The authors are grateful to Prof. S.P. Mohan, Head, Department of Geology, University of Madras for providing laboratory facilities and The Director, CPEES, Anna University for providing the transportation and support for the fieldwork. For fieldwork A.D. Switzer obtained financial assistance from the Department of Earth Sciences at Hong Kong University to participate in this study. Reviews of early drafts by C.H. Chim, C. Gouramanis and C. Sloss helped greatly in developing the ideas in this paper. This paper is Earth Observatory of Singapore contribution number 23. It is also a contribution to IGCP Project 588 'Preparing for coastal change: A detailed process-response framework for coastal change at different timescales' and the INQUA working group on ''Coastal and Marine

Processes'' through project INQUA 1001: 'Quaternary Coastal Change and Records of Extreme Marine Inundation on Coastal Environments'.

# References

ANBARASU, K. 1994. *Geomorphological configuration of Tamil Nadu Coast from Coleroon to Pulicat.* PhD thesis, Bharathidasan University, Tiruchirapalli.

BABU, N., SURESH BABU, D. S. & MOHAN DAS, P. N. 2007. Impact of tsunami on texture and mineralogy of a major placer deposit in southwest coast of India. *Environmental Geology,* **52,** 71–80.

BAHLBURG, H. & WEISS, R. 2007. Sedimentology of the December 26, 2004 Sumatra tsunami deposits in eastern India (Tamil Nadu) and Kenya. *International Journal of Earth Sciences India,* **96,** 1195–1209.

BENSON, B. E., GRIMM, K. A. & CLAGUE, J. J. 1997. Tsunami deposits beneath tidal marshes on northwestern Vancouver Island British Columbia. *Quaternary Research,* **48,** 192–204.

BOURGEOIS, J. M. 1993. Tsunami deposits: geological warnings of future inundation. *International Tsunami Information Centre Newsletter,* **XXV,** 44–45.

BRIDGE, J. S. & BEST, J. L. 1988. Flow, sediment transport and bedform dynamics over the transition from dunes to upper-stage plane beds: implications for the formation of planar laminae. *Sedimentology,* **35,** 753–763.

BRYANT, E. A. 2008. *Tsunami: The Underrated Hazard,* 2nd edn. Cambridge University Press, New York.

CHADHA, R. K., LATHA, G., YEH, H., PETERSON, C. & KATADA, T. 2005. The tsunami of the great Sumatra earthquake of M 9.0 on 26 December 2004 – impact on the east coast of India. *Current Science,* **88,** 1297–1301.

CHEEL, R. J. 1990. Horizontal lamination and the sequence of bed phases and stratification under upper-flow-regime conditions. *Sedimentology,* **37,** 517–529.

CHIVAS, A. R., GARCÍA, A. *ET AL.* 2001. Sea-level and environmental changes since the last interglacial in the Gulf of Carpentaria, Australia: an overview. *Quaternary International,* p83–85, 19–46.

CHOOWONG, M., MURAKOSHI, N. *ET AL.* 2008a. Flow conditions of the 2004 Indian Ocean tsunami in Thailand, inferred from capping bedforms and sedimentary structures. *Terra Nova,* **20,** 141–149.

CHOOWONG, M., MURAKOSHI, N. *ET AL.* 2008b. 2004 Indian Ocean tsunami inflow and outflow at Phuket, Thailand. *Marine Geology,* **248,** 179–192.

CISTERNAS, M., ATWATER, B. F. *ET AL.* 2005. Predecessors of the giant 1960 Chile earthquake. *Nature,* **437,** 404–407.

DAHDOUH-GUEBAS, F., JAYATISSA, L.P., DI NITTO, D., BOSIRE, J.O., LO SEEN, D. & KOEDAM, N. 2005. How effective were mangroves as a defence against the recent tsunami? *Current Biology,* **15,** 443–447.

DAWSON, A. G. 1999. Linking tsunami deposits, submarine slides and offshore earthquakes. *Quaternary International,* **60,** 119–126.

DAWSON, A. G. & SHI, S. Z. 2000. Tsunami deposits. *Pure and Applied Geophysics,* **157,** 875–897.

DAWSON, A. G. & STEWART, I. 2007. Tsunami deposits in the geological record. *Sedimentary Geology,* **200,** 166–183.

DAWSON, A. G., FOSTER, I. D. L., SHI, S., SMITH, D. E. & LONG, D. 1991. The identification of tsunami deposits in coastal sediment sequences. *Science of Tsunami Hazards,* **9,** 73–82.

DAWSON, A. G., SHI, S., DAWSON, S., TAKAHASHI, T. & SHUTO, N. 1996. Coastal sedimentation associated with the June 2nd and 3rd, 1994 tsunami in Rajegwesi, Java. *Quaternary Science Reviews,* **15,** 901–912.

FIELDING, C. R. 2006. Upper flow regime sheets, lenses and scour fills: extending the range of architectural elements for fluvial sediment bodies. *Sedimentary Geology,* **190,** 227–240.

FOLK, R. L. & WARD, W. C. 1957. Brazos River bar, a study in the significance of grain size parameters. *Journal of Sedimentary Petrology,* **27,** 3–27.

FRITZ, H. M., BORRERO, J. C., SYNOLAKIS, C. E. & YOO, J. 2006. 2004 Indian Ocean tsunami flow velocity measurements from survivor videos. *Geophysical Research Letters,* **33,** L24604-2, doi: 10.1029/2006GL026784.

FUJIWARA, O., KAMATAKI, T. & TAMURA, T. 2003. Grain-size distribution of tsunami deposits reflecting the tsunami waveform; an example from a Holocene drowned valley on the southern Boso Peninsula, East Japan. *Quaternary Research,* **42,** 68–81.

GELFENBAUM, G. & JAFFE, B. 2003. Erosion and sedimentation from the 17 July, 1998, Papua New Guinea Tsunami. *Pure and Applied Geophysics,* **160,** 1969–1999.

GOFF, J. R., CHAGUE-GOFF, C. & NICHOL, S. 2001. Palaeotsunami deposits: a New Zealand perspective. *Sedimentary Geology,* **143,** 1–6.

GOFF, J. R., MCFADGEN, B. G. & CHAGUE-GOFF, C. 2004a. Sedimentary differences between the 2002 Easter storm and the 15th-century Okoropunga tsunami, southeastern North Island, New Zealand. *Marine Geology,* **204,** 235–250.

GOFF, J. R., WELLS, A., CHAGUÉ-GOFF, C., NICHOL, S. L. & DEVOY, R. J. N. 2004b. The elusive AD 1826 tsunami, South Westland. *New Zealand Geographer,* **60,** 28–39.

GRILLI, S. T., IOUALALEN, M., ASAVANANT, J., SHI, F., KIRBY, J. T. & WATTS, P. 2007. Source constraints and model simulation of the December 26, 2004, Indian Ocean Tsunami. *Journal of Waterway. Port, Coastal, and Ocean. Engineering,* **133,** 414.

HAND, M. B. 1997. Inverse grading resulting from coarse-sediment transport lag. *Journal of Sedimentary Research,* **67,** 124–129.

HAWKES, A. D., BIRD, M. *ET AL.* 2007. Sediments deposited by the 2004 Indian Ocean tsunami along the Malaysia–Thailand Peninsula. *Marine Geology,* **242,** 169–190.

HORI, K., KUZUMOTO, R., HIROUCHI, D., UMITSU, M., JANJIRAWUTTIKUL, N. & PATANAKANOG, B. 2007. Horizontal and vertical variation of 2004 Indian tsunami deposits: an example of two transects along the western coast of Thailand. *Marine Geology,* **239,** 163–172.

JAFFE, B. E. & GELFENBAUM, G. 2007. A simple model for calculating tsunami flow speed from tsunami deposits. *Sedimentary Geology,* **200,** 347–361.

JAFFE, B., GELFENBAUM, G. *ET AL.* 2003. Tsunami deposits – Identification and interpretation of tsunami deposits from the June 23, 2001, Perú tsunami. *In: Proceedings of the International Conference on Coastal Sediments 2003.* World Scientific Publishing Corp and East Meets West Productions, Corpus Christi, TX.

JAYAKUMAR, S., ILANGOVAN, D. *ET AL.* 2005. Run-up and inundation limits along southeast coast of India during the 26 December 2004 Indian Ocean tsunami. *Current Science,* **88**, 1741–1743.

KOMATSUBARA, J., FUJIWARA, O., TAKADA, K., SAWAI, Y., AUNG, T. T. & KAMATAKI, T. 2008. Historical tsunamis and storms recorded in a coastal lowland, Shizuoka Prefecture, along the Pacific Coast of Japan. *Sedimentology,* **55**, 1703–1716.

KORTEKAAS, S. & DAWSON, A. G. 2007. Distinguishing tsunami and storm deposits: an example from Martinhal, SW Portugal. *Sedimentary Geology,* **200**, 208–221.

LAY, T., KANAMORI, H. *ET AL.* 2005. The great Sumatra–Andaman earthquake of 26 December 2004. *Science,* **308**, 1127–1133.

LEATHERMAN, S. P. & WILLIAMS, A. T. 1977. Lateral textural grading in washover sediments. *Earth Surface Process and Landforms,* **2**, 333–341.

LE ROUX, J. P. & VARGAS, G. 2005. Hydraulic behavior of tsunami back flows: insights from their modern and ancient deposits. *Environmental Geology,* **49**, 65–75.

MASCARENHAS, A. & JAYAKUMAR, S. 2008. An environmental perspective of the post-tsunami scenario along the coast of Tamil Nadu, India: role of sand dunes and forests. *Journal of Environmental Management,* **89**, 24–34.

MATSUMOTO, D., NARUSE, H., JARUPONGSAKUL, T., SAKAKURA, N. & MURAYAMA, M. 2008. Truncated flame structures within a deposit of the Indian Ocean Tsunami: evidence of syn-sedimentary deformation. *Sedimentology,* **55**, 1559–1570.

MINOURA, K. & NAKAYA, S. 1991. Traces of tsunami preserved in inter-tidal lacustrine and marsh deposits: some examples from Northeast Japan. *Journal Geology,* **99**, 265–287.

MINOURA, K., IMAMURA, F., TAKAHASHI, T. & SHUTO, N. 1997. Sequence of sedimentation processes caused by the 1992 Flores tsunami: evidence from Babi Island. *Geology,* **25**, 523–526.

MOORE, A., NISHIMURA, Y., GELFENBAUM, G., KAMATAKI, T. & TRIYONO, R. 2006. Sedimentary deposits of the 26 December 2004 tsunami on the northwest coast of Aceh, Indonesia. *Earth Planets Space,* **58**, 253–258.

MOORE, A. L., MCADOO, B. G. & RUFFMAN, A. 2007. Landward fining from multiple sources in a sand sheet deposited by the 1929 Grand Banks tsunami, Newfoundland. *Sedimentary Geology,* **200**, 336–346.

MORTON, R. A. 1979. Subaerial storm deposits formed on barrier flats by wind-driven currents. *Sedimentary Geology,* **24**, 105–122.

MORTON, R. A., GELFENBAUM, G. & JAFFE, B. E. 2007. Physical criteria for distinguishing sandy tsunami and storm deposits using modern examples. *Sedimentary Geology,* **200**, 184–207.

NANAYAMA, F. & SHIGENO, K. 2006. Inflow and outflow facies from the 1993 tsunami in southwest Hokkaido. *Sedimentary Geology,* **187**, 139–158.

NANAYAMA, F., SHIGENO, K., SATAKE, K., SHIMOKAWA, K., KOITABASHI, S., MAYASAKA, S. & ISHII, M. 2000. Sedimentary differences between 1993 Hokkaido-nansei-oki tsunami and 1959 Miyakojima typhoon at Tasai, southwestern Hokkaido, northern Japan. *Sedimentary Geology,* **135**, 255–264.

NARAYANA, A. C., TATAVARTIB, R., SHINUA, N. & SUBEERA, A. 2007. Tsunami of December 26, 2004 on the southwest coast of India: post-tsunami geomorphic and sediment characteristics. *Marine Geology,* **242**, 155–168.

NARUSE, H., FUJINO, S., SUPHAWAJRUKSAKUL, A. & JARUPONGSAKUL, T. 2010. Features and formation processes of multiple deposition layers from the 2004 Indian Ocean Tsunami at Ban Nam Kem, southern Thailand. *Island Arc,* **19**, 399–411.

NELSON, A. R., ASQUITH, A. C. & GRANT, W. C. 2004. Great earthquakes and tsunamis of the past 2000 years at the Salmon River estuary, central Oregon coast, USA. *Bulletin of the Seismological Society of America,* **94**, 1276–1292.

NICHOL, S. L. & KENCH, P. S. 2008. Sedimentology and preservation potential of carbonate sand sheets deposited by the December 2004 Indian Ocean tsunami: South Baa Atoll Maldives. *Sedimentology,* **55**, 1173–1187.

NICHOL, S. L., CHAGUÉ-GOFF, C., GOFF, J. R., HORROCKS, M., MCFADGEN, B. G. & STROTZ, L. C. 2010. Geomorphology and accommodation space as limiting factors on tsunami deposition: Chatham Island, southwest Pacific Ocean. *Sedimentary Geology,* **229**, 41–52.

NISHIMURA, Y. & MIYAJI, N. 1995. Tsunami deposits from the 1993 Southwest Hokkaido earthquake and the 1640 Hokkaido Komagatake eruption, northern Japan. *Pure and Applied Geophysics,* **144**, 719–733.

PANEGINA, T. K., BOURGEOIS, J., BAZANOVA, I. V. & BRAITSEVA, O. A. 2003. A millennial scale record of Holocene tsunamis on the Kronotskiy Bay coast, Kamchatka, Russia. *Quaternary Research,* **59**, 26–47.

PAOLA, C., WIELE, S. M. & REINHART, M. A. 1989. Upper-regime parallel lamination as the result of turbulent sediment transport and low amplitude bedforms. *Sedimentology,* **36**, 47–60.

PARI, Y., RAMANA MURTHY, M. V., JAYA KUMAR, S., SUBRAMANIAN, B. R. & RAMACHANDRAN, S. 2008. Morphological changes at Vellar estuary, India—Impact of the December 2004 tsunami. *Journal of Environmental Management,* **89**, 45–57.

PARIS, R., LAVIGNE, F., WASSMER, P. & SARTOHADI, J. 2007. Coastal sedimentation associated with the December 26, 2004 in Lhok Nga, west Banda Aceh (Sumatra, Indonesia). *Marine Geology,* **238**, 93–106.

PARIS, R., WASSMER, P. *ET AL.* 2009. Tsunamis as geomorphic crises: lessons from the December 26, 2004 tsunami in Lhok Nga, West Banda Aceh (Sumatra, Indonesia). *Geomorphology,* **104**, 59–72.

RAMANAMURTHY, M. V., SUNDARAMOORTHY, S. *ET AL.* 2005. Inundation of seawater in Andaman and Nicobar Islands and parts of Tamil Nadu coast during

2004 Sumatra tsunami. *Current Science*, **88**, 1736–1740.

SAKAKIYAMA, T., MATSUTOMI, H., TSUJI, Y. & MURAKAMI, Y. 2005. *Comparison of Tsunami Inundation Flow Velocities Based on Analysis of Video Pictures and Field Survey.* Tsunami Engineering Technical Report, Tohoku University, **22**, 111–117 (in Japanese).

SATO, H., SHIMAMOTO, T., TSUTSUMI, A. & KAWAMOTO, E. 1995. Onshore tsunami deposits caused by the 1993 southwest Hokkaido and 1983 Japan Sea earthquakes. *Pure and Applied Geophysics*, **144**, 693–717.

SCHEFFERS, A. & KELLETAT, D. 2003. Sedimentologic and geomorphologic tsunami imprints worldwide- a review. *Earth-Science Reviews*, **63**, 83–92.

SCHWARTZ, R. K. 1982. Bedform and stratification characteristics of some modern small-scale washover sand bodies. *Sedimentology*, **29**, 835–849.

SEDGWICK, P. E. & DAVIS, R. A. 2003. Stratigraphy of washover deposits in Florida: implications for recognition in the stratigraphic record. *Marine Geology*, **200**, 31–48.

SHI, S. Z., DAWSON, A. G. & SMITH, D. E. 1995. Coastal sedimentation associated with the December 12th, 1992 tsunami in Flores, Indonesia. *Pure and Applied Geophysics*, **144**, 525–536.

SMITH, N. D. 1971. Pseudo-planar stratification produced by very low amplitude sand waves. *Journal of Sedimentary Petrology*, **41**, 69–73.

SRINIVASALU, S., THANGADURAI, N., SWITZER, A. D., RAM MOHAN, V. & AYYAMPERUMAL, T. 2007. Erosion and sedimentation in Kalpakkam (N Tamil Nadu, India) from the 26th December 2004 tsunami. *Marine Geology*, **240**, 65–75.

STEIN, S. & OKAL, E. 2005. Speed and size of the Sumatra earthquake. *Nature*, **434**, 581–582.

STEPHEN-PICHAIMANI, V., JONATHAN, M. P., SRINIVASALU, S., RAJESHWARA-RAO, N. R. & MOHAN, S. P. 2008. Enrichment of trace metals in surface sediments from northern part of Point Calimere, SE coast of India. *Environmental Geology*, **55**, 1811–1819.

SWITZER, A. D. & JONES, B. G. 2008a. Set-up, deposition and sedimentary characteristics of two storm overwash deposits, Abrahams Bosom Beach, eastern Australia. *Journal of Coastal Research*, **24**, 189–200.

SWITZER, A. D. & JONES, B. G. 2008b. Large-scale washover sedimentation in a freshwater lagoon from the southeast Australian coast: tsunami or exceptionally large storm. *Holocene*, **18**, 787–803.

SWITZER, A. D. & BURSTON, J. M. 2010. Competing mechanisms for boulder deposition on the southeast Australian coast. *Geomorphology*, **114**, 42–54.

SWITZER, A. D., PUCILLO, K., HAREDY, R. A., JONES, B. G. & BRYANT, E. A. 2005. Sea-level, storms or tsunami: enigmatic sand sheet deposits in a sheltered coastal embayment from southeastern Australia. *Journal of Coastal Research*, **21**, 655–663.

SWITZER, A. D., BRISTOW, C. S. & JONES, B. G. 2006. An erosional signature for large-scale washover identified using ground penetrating radar on a small Holocene barrier from the southeast Australian coast. *Sedimentary Geology*, **183**, 145–156.

SZCZUCINSKI, W., NIEDZIELSKI, P., KOZAK, L., FRANKOWSKI, M., ZIOŁA, A. & LORENC, S. 2007. Effects of rainy season on mobilization of contaminants from tsunami deposits left in a coastal zone of Thailand by the 26 December 2004 tsunami. *Environmental Geology*, **53**, 253–264.

SZCZUCINSKI, W., NIEDZIELSKI, P. ET AL. 2005. Contamination of tsunami sediments in a coastal zone inundated by the 26 December 2004 tsunami in Thailand. *Environmental Geology*, **49**, 321–331.

THANGADURAI, N., SRINIVASALU, S., RAM MOHAN, V. & SWITZER, A. D. 2006. Erosion and sedimentation in Kalpakkam (N Tamil Nadu, India) from the 26 December 2004 M9 tsunami. *Geophysical Research Abstracts*, **8**, 00262.

TUCKER, M. E. 2001. *Sedimentary Petrology: An Introduction to the Origin of Sedimentary Rocks.* Blackwell, Oxford.

TUTTLE, M. P., RUFFMAN, A., ANDERSON, T. & JETER, H. 2004. Distinguishing tsunami from storm deposits in eastern North America: the 1929 Grand Banks tsunami versus the 1991 Halloween storm. *Seismological Research Letters*, **75**, 117–131.

UMITSU, M., TANAVUD, C. & PATANAKANOG, B. 2007. Effects of landforms on tsunami flow in the plains of Banda Aceh, Indonesia, and Nam Khem. *Thailand Marine Geology*, **242**, 141–153.

WILLIAMS, H. F., HUTCHINSON, I. & NELSON, A. R. 2005. Multiple sources for late-Holocene tsunamis at Discovery Bay, Washington State, USA. *Holocene*, **15**, 60–73.

WITTER, R. C., KELSEY, H. M. & HEMPHILL-HALEY, E. 2001. Pacific Storms, El Niño and Tsunamis: competing mechanisms for sand deposition in a Coastal Marsh, Euchre Creek, Oregon. *Journal of Coastal Research*, **17**, 563–583.

# Tsunami hazard related to a flank collapse of Anak Krakatau Volcano, Sunda Strait, Indonesia

T. GIACHETTI[1,3]*, R. PARIS[2,4,6], K. KELFOUN[2,4,6] & B. ONTOWIRJO[5]

[1]*Clermont Université, Université Blaise Pascal, Geolab, BP 10448, F-63000 Clermont-Ferrand, France*

[2]*Clermont Université, Université Blaise Pascal, Laboratoire Magmas et Volcans, BP 10448, F-63000 Clermont-Ferrand, France*

[3]*CNRS, UMR 6042, Geolab, F-63057 Clermont-Ferrand, France*

[4]*CNRS, UMR 6524, LMV, F-63038 Clermont-Ferrand, France*

[5]*Coastal Dynamics Research Center, BPDP-BPPT, 11th Floor, Building 2, BPPT, Jl, M. H. Thamrin no 8, Jakarta 10340, Indonesia*

[6]*IRD, R 163, LMV, F-63038 Clermont-Ferrand, France*

*\*Corresponding author (e-mail: giachettithomas@club-internet.fr)*

**Abstract:** Numerical modelling of a rapid, partial destabilization of Anak Krakatau Volcano (Indonesia) was performed in order to investigate the tsunami triggered by this event. Anak Krakatau, which is largely built on the steep NE wall of the 1883 Krakatau eruption caldera, is active on its SW side (towards the 1883 caldera), which makes the edifice quite unstable. A hypothetical 0.280 km³ flank collapse directed southwestwards would trigger an initial wave 43 m in height that would reach the islands of Sertung, Panjang and Rakata in less than 1 min, with amplitudes from 15 to 30 m. These waves would be potentially dangerous for the many small tourist boats circulating in, and around, the Krakatau Archipelago. The waves would then propagate in a radial manner from the impact region and across the Sunda Strait, at an average speed of 80–110 km h⁻¹. The tsunami would reach the cities located on the western coast of Java (e.g. Merak, Anyer and Carita.) 35–45 min after the onset of collapse, with a maximum amplitude from 1.5 (Merak and Panimbang) to 3.4 m (Labuhan). As many industrial and tourist infrastructures are located close to the sea and at altitudes of less than 10 m, these waves present a non-negligible risk. Owing to numerous reflections inside the Krakatau Archipelago, the waves would even affect Bandar Lampung (Sumatra, *c.* 900 000 inhabitants) after more than 1 h, with a maximum amplitude of 0.3 m. The waves produced would be far smaller than those occurring during the 1883 Krakatau eruption (*c.* 15 m) and a rapid detection of the collapse by the volcano observatory, together with an efficient alert system on the coast, would possibly prevent this hypothetical event from being deadly.

Most recorded historical tsunamis have a seismic origin, but such events may also be triggered by phenomena related to huge volcanic eruptions, such as large pyroclastic flows entering the water (e.g. de Lange *et al.* 2001; Maeno & Imamura 2007), submarine explosions (e.g. Mader & Gittings 2006), caldera collapse (e.g. Nomanbhoy & Satake 1995; Maeno *et al.* 2006) or by a large, rapidly sliding mass impacting the water (e.g. Tinti *et al.* 1999, 2000, 2006; Keating & McGuire 2000; Ward 2001; Harbitz *et al.* 2006; Fritz *et al.* 2008; Waythomas *et al.* 2009; Kelfoun *et al.* 2010). The December 2002 $17 \times 10^6$ m³ flank collapse of Stromboli triggered a 8 m-high run-up on the coast of Stromboli, but had little effect on coasts located

more than 200 km from the collapse (Maramai *et al.* 2005). The tsunami generated by the $30 \times 10^6$ m³ Lituya Bay collapse in Alaska in 1958 (Fritz *et al.* 2001) reached 60 m at 6 km laterally from the collapse and 30 m at 12 km. These tsunamis had very few fatalities as they occurred either in isolated locations (Lituya Bay, Alaska) or during a period of no tourist activity (Stromboli). The largest lateral collapse of an island volcano recorded in historical times (*c.* 5 km³) took place during the 1888 eruption of Ritter Island (New Guinea), producing witnessed waves of up to 10–15 m at tens to hundreds of kilometres from the source (Ward & Day 2003). With 15 000 fatalities, the tsunami generated by the 1792 sector collapse of Mount

*From*: TERRY, J. P. & GOFF, J. (eds) 2012. *Natural Hazards in the Asia–Pacific Region: Recent Advances and Emerging Concepts*. Geological Society, London, Special Publications, **361**, 79–90, http://dx.doi.org/10.1144/SP361.7

Mayuyama in Ariake Bay (Kyushu Island, Unzen volcanic complex) was the second worst disaster in Japan, and the second deadliest volcanic tsunami (after that produced by the eruption of Krakatau in 1883). The failure was most probably triggered by a strong earthquake, and its volume was about $340 \times 10^6$ m$^3$ (Michiue *et al.* 1999). Tsunami run-ups ranged from 8 to 24 m on the opposite side of Ariake Bay (Tsuji & Hino 1993).

The 26–28 August 1883 Plinian eruption of Krakatau Volcano, and its subsequent tsunamis, caused more than 35 000 casualties along the coasts of the Sunda Strait in Indonesia (Self & Rampino 1981; Simkin & Fiske 1983; Sigurdsson *et al.* 1991*a*, *b*). This eruption was one of the most powerful and devastating eruptions in recorded history. Many tsunamis were produced during this approximately 2 day eruption, the largest one occurring after 10 a.m. on the 27 August (Warton & Evans 1888; Yokoyama 1981). The leading wave reached the cities of Anyer and Merak on Java after 35–40 min, and after approximately 1 h for the city of Bandar Lampung (Teluk Betung) on Sumatra. A tide gauge located near Jakarta (Batavia Harbour, Java) registered the wave arrival approximately 140 min after its inferred initiation at Krakatau Island. Using the tsunami run-ups determined along the coasts of Java and Sumatra (Verbeek 1885), the tsunami heights before run-up were estimated to be about 15 m at the coastline all around the Sunda Strait (Symons 1888). The generation mechanism of these 1883 tsunamis is still controversial and several processes may have acted successively or together (Self & Rampino 1981; Yokoyama 1981; Camus & Vincent 1983; Francis 1985). Based on low-resolution numerical simulations, Nomanbhoy & Satake (1995) concluded that a series of submarine explosions over a period of 1–5 min was the most probable source for the major tsunami. Nevertheless, pyroclastic flows formed by the gravitational collapse of the eruptive columns are also a possible source for most of the tsunamis observed before and during the paroxysm (Carey *et al.* 1996; de Lange *et al.* 2001).

Nearly 45 years after this 1883 cataclysmal eruption, Anak Krakatau ('Child of Krakatau' in Indonesian) emerged from the sea in the same location as the former Krakatau, and has since grown to its current height of more than 300 m (Hoffmann-Rothe *et al.* 2006). It exhibits frequent activity, still posing a risk to the coastal population of Java and Sumatra, and for the important shipping routes through the Sunda Strait. Following the active phase of Anak Krakatau in 1980, a permanent volcano observatory was established in Pasauran on the western coast of Java, about 50 km east of the Krakatau Archipelago. A short-period seismometer placed on the volcano flank, visual control and daily seismic event statistics are used to determine the current alert level, on the basis of which Indonesian authorities decide about preventive measures, sometimes prohibiting tourism around the archipelago (Hoffmann-Rothe *et al.* 2006).

One possible major hazard emerging from Anak Krakatau would be a tsunami triggered by a collapse of its flank, as the volcano is partly built on a steep wall of the caldera resulting from the 1883 eruption. A small tsunami (*c.* 2 m high) was experienced on Rakata Island in October 1981 during an awakening of Anak Krakatau (Camus *et al.* 1987). In the present study, we numerically simulate a sudden southwestwards destabilization of a large part of the Anak Krakatau Volcano, and the subsequent tsunami formation and propagation. We show results concerning the time of arrival and the amplitude of the waves produced, both in the Sunda Strait and on the coasts of Java and Sumatra. We then discuss the relationships between the morphology of Anak Krakatau, the locations of the surrounding islands, the bathymetry of the strait and the triggered waves.

## Geography, population and infrastructures in the Sunda Strait

The Sunda Strait, in which Anak Krakatau Volcano lies, has a roughly NE–SW orientation, with a minimum width of 24 km at its NE end between Sumatra and Java (Fig. 1). Its western end is deep ($< -1500$ m), but it shallows significantly as it narrows to the east, with a depth of only about 20 m in parts of the eastern end, making it difficult to navigate due to sandbanks and strong tidal flows. The numerous islands in the strait and the nearby surrounding regions of Java and Sumatra were devastated by the 1883 Krakatau eruption. The eruption drastically altered the topography of the strait, with approximately 12 km$^3$ (DRE, dense rock equivalent) of ignimbrite being deposited around the volcano (Carey *et al.* 1996). The small to moderate volcanic explosions of Anak Krakatau, which is partly built on the site of the former Krakatau Island, attract tourist boats that circulate between the islands of the Krakatau Archipelago.

Some areas have never been resettled since the 1883 eruption (e.g. the SW of Java), but much of the coastline is now densely populated, especially in Bandar Lampung (*c.* 900 000 inhabitants) on Sumatra, and on the west coast of the Cilegon District (*c.* 400 000 inhabitants) in Java (Fig. 1). Moreover, many of the roads on western Java and southern Sumatra are located near the sea and at low altitude ($< 10$ m), as well as important economic infrastructures such as power stations (e.g. Labuhan, NE of Merak and SE of Banda

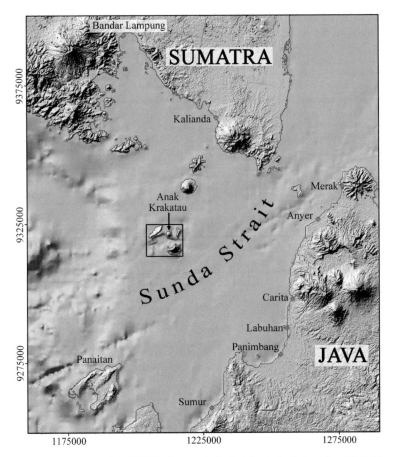

**Fig. 1.** Shaded relief representation of the DEM (100 m resolution) of Sunda Strait, based on ASTER topography, GEBCO bathymetry and a digitization of the bathymetric map of Krakatau from Deplus *et al.* (1995, their fig. 7). This DEM is the calculation grid used to simulate the Anak Krakatau landslide and the subsequent tsunami propagation (calculations were made at a resolution of 200 m). The main coastal cities or important infrastructures around the Sunda Strait are indicated by red diamonds. The black frame around the Krakatau Archipelago corresponds to the limits of Figure 2b, c. Geographical co-ordinates are in metres.

Lampung), industries (e.g. steel industries in Cilegon), major harbours connecting Java and Sumatra (Merak, Bakaheuni), and tourist resorts (e.g. Anyer, Kalianda). There are also several oil platforms in the strait, notably off the Java coast. Such infrastructures would potentially be badly affected by a tsunami of several metres, as was produced during the 1883 eruption.

In October 2007, the Indonesian government planned the construction of a 30 km road and railway connection between the islands of Sumatra and Java (the Selat Sunda Bridge), across the 26 km Sunda Strait, at an altitude of 70 m asl (above sea level). In 2009, the 'pre-feasibility' study for this 10 billion dollar project was completed and the construction is expected to begin in 2012. Owing to the seismic and volcanic activity

in the Sunda region, this project faces many challenges. Krakatau Volcano is located only 40 km away from the future bridge. Some of the bridge's piles may suffer from tsunamis crossing the Sunda Strait, therefore such hazards need to be quantified.

## Anak Krakatau Volcano: evolution and actual morphology

Anak Krakatau first rose up out of the sea in 1928, sited just off the steep NE wall of the basin formed by the collapse of the 1883 Krakatau eruption caldera. This volcano was built where the main vent for the 1883 eruption is supposed to have been located, about midway between the former craters of Danan and Perbuatan (Deplus *et al.* 1995). Between 1928 and 1930, the volcano receded and reappeared three times until it established itself permanently above sea level. In 1959, an uninterrupted 152 m-high hyaloclastic tuff-ring developed (Sudradjat 1982) and a lake formed in the crater. The eruption style was Surtseyan during the 1928–1930 period (Stehn 1929; Camus *et al.* 1987), then Vulcanian until 1960, before shifting to Strombolian explosions that created a cone reaching 200 m asl in 1981 (Oba *et al.* 1983). In 1981, a Vulcanian eruption marked a southwestwards shift of Anak Krakatau activity (Sudrajat 1982) with more differentiated volcanic products (acid andesites, dacites) than previously erupted (mainly basalts and andesites before 1981: Camus *et al.* 1987). At the time of writing, the latest eruption of Anak Krakatau, which started on 25 October 2010, is still ongoing, with dense ash clouds forming plumes 100–1000 m high.

Rapid soundings in 1928 have shown that the western slope of the volcano was considerably steeper ($>28°$) than the eastern, as a consequence of its position on the steep wall of the basin and also of the strong current that is generally running from SW to NE (Stehn 1929). Deplus *et al.* (1995) showed that this slope was still in existence in 1995, and that the successive eruptions had not resulted in an infilling of the caldera. According to these data concerning the steep slopes on which Anak Krakatau is built and the fact that this volcano is growing towards the SW, landslides along its southwestern flank cannot be excluded (Deplus *et al.* 1995). Such a landslide would be directed southwestwards into the 1883 caldera and would trigger waves that would propagate into the Sunda Strait, possibly affecting the Indonesian coasts.

## Methodology

### Digital elevation model used and scenario envisaged

The collapse of the Anak Krakatau Volcano was simulated on a digital elevation model (DEM) obtained by merging the ASTER (*Advanced Spaceborne Thermal Emission and Reflection Radiometer*) topography (*c.* 30 m resolution), bathymetric maps (one from Dishidros Indonesian Navy and a Sunda Strait navigation chart) and the GEBCO (General Bathymetric Chart of the Oceans) bathymetry (*c.* 900 m resolution) of the whole Sunda Strait region (Fig. 1). In addition, the bathymetric map of the Krakatau Archipelago from Deplus *et al.* (1995, their fig. 7) was digitized and added to the DEM in order to obtain a better resolution of the zone where the collapse occurs and where the waves are initially produced (Fig. 2b).

The final DEM produced, which is the calculation grid used for the numerical simulation, is a $1500 \times 1300$ pixel grid with a spatial resolution of 100 m (Fig. 1). In order to maximize on the best spatial resolution available to register the initial waves produced, some of the simulations were performed on a portion of the grid centred on the landslide event. Owing to the long calculation times we down-sampled the grid by a factor of 2 (i.e. $750 \times 650$ pixel calculation grid and a spatial resolution of 200 m) for the simulations of tsunami propagation over the entire Sunda Strait area.

Some level lines of the DEM were modified to build the sliding surface of the hypothetical landslide; that is, to define the hypothetical collapse scar. This was done so that: (1) the upper end of the scar is broadly defined by the limit between the older tuff-ring and the new cone (Fig. 2a, c); (2) the base of the scar lies at the bottom of the 1883 caldera (Fig. 2a); and (3) the scar is horseshoe-shaped (Fig. 2c). The scar is oriented southwestwards, with an average slope of 8.2° (Fig. 2a) and a width of *c.* 1.9 km, defining a collapsing volume of 0.280 km³. This scar probably cuts the NE wall of the 1883 caldera, but this cannot be clearly traced on the DEM as no precise bathymetric data immediately following the 1883 eruption are available. In our simulation, the debris avalanche is released in a single event.

### Numerical model

We used the numerical code *VolcFlow* (Kelfoun *et al.* 2010; Giachetti *et al.* 2011) to simulate both the Anak Krakatau landslide and the tsunami propagations. A full explanation of the code and equations is given in the previously cited papers. This code is based on the two-dimensional (2D) depth-average approach, modified to incorporate 3D interactions with greater accuracy; both the landslide and the sea water being simulated using the general shallow-water equations of mass conservation and momentum balance. In the model, the water interacts with the bathymetry/topography and floods onto the land, but waves breaking and other complex second-order 3D effects are not taken into account, and sediment erosion and transport are also ignored.

We simulated the water propagation using a density of 1000 kg m$^{-3}$ and a viscosity of 0.001 Pa s. As emissions from Anak Krakatau are mainly composed of scoriaceous material with a basaltic (common) to dacitic (rarer) chemical composition (Sudradjat 1982; Camus *et al.* 1987), we used a density of 1500 kg m$^{-3}$ to simulate the landslide. Kelfoun *et al.* (2010) and Giachetti *et al.* (2011) showed that the rheology used to simulate the landslide propagation may be important when dealing with second-order variations of the profile

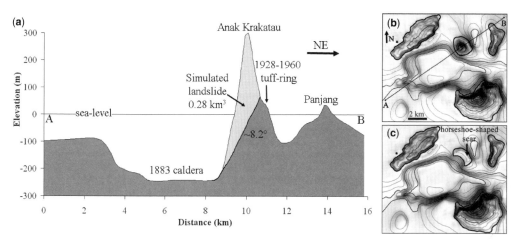

**Fig. 2.** (**a**) Cross-section of Anak Krakatau (inset: Fig. 1) and the 1883 eruption caldera. The landslide scar, defined by modifying some level lines on our initial DEM, is drawn in black. It is orientated southwestwards, with a slope of 8.2°, delimiting a collapsing volume of about 0.28 km³. (**b**) Topography before the simulated landslide, with the location of the cross-section presented in (a). The caldera resulting from the 1883 Krakatau eruption is clearly visible, as well as Anak Krakatau, which is built on the NE flank of this caldera. (**c**) Topography after the simulated landslide, with the horseshoe-shaped scar clearly visible.

and amplitude of the triggered waves. Thus, we tested four sets of rheological parameters to simulate the debris avalanche propagation: a commonly used Mohr–Coulomb frictional law with a basal friction angle of 1° or 2° (hereafter referred to as rheologies 1 and 2, respectively) and a constant retarding stress of 5 or 10 kPa (rheologies 3 and 4, respectively). Although the Mohr–Coulomb frictional law is often used in granular-flow dynamics because it represents the behaviour of deposits at rest and of sand flows in the laboratory, the constant retarding stress appears to be better adapted to the

reproduction of the extent, thickness on all slopes and some morphological features of natural deposits (e.g. Dade & Huppert 1998; Kelfoun & Druitt 2005). Figure 3a shows that the surface area covered by the simulated debris avalanche deposits varies depending on the rheology used (the numerical deposits obtained using rheologies 1–2 and rheologies 3–4 are quasi-identical and are thus drawn together). Figure 3b presents the water surface displacement recorded using a gauge placed approximately 15 km southwestwards from the landslide scar (black diamond in Fig. 3a), in

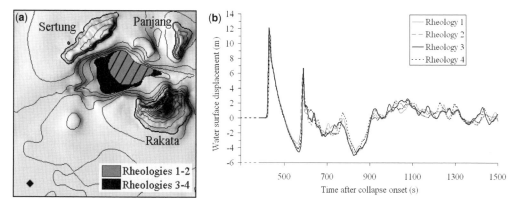

**Fig. 3.** (**a**) Simulated debris avalanche deposits obtained using rheologies 1–2 (grey) and 3–4 (black hatching and black) to simulate the landslide propagation. (**b**) Simulated water surface displacement recorded at the gauge located in Figure 2a (black diamond). This figure shows that the waves produced are very similar, whatever the rheology used to simulate the landslide propagation.

the direction of propagation of the major triggered waves, where the water depth is aproximately 100 m. It shows that the wave profiles and amplitudes created are very similar, whichever of the four rheologies are used. The maximum amplitude recorded at the gauge placed approximately 15 km southwestwards varies between 11 (rheology 2) and 12 m (rheology 3).

We believe that the similarity between the wave profiles presented in Figure 3b is due to the initial geometry of the collapsing volume and the landslide scar. Indeed, as the collapsing volume is initially partly submerged and the landslide scar directs the debris avalanche southwestwards, the initial waves triggered by the landslide–water impact are poorly influenced by the rheology used to simulate landslide propagation. This rheology, however, plays a role in the final run-out of the modelled debris avalanche deposits (Fig. 3a). The morphology of the modelled deposits (not shown here) is very similar whatever the rheology used because of the dominant controlling factor of the structure of the 1883 caldera. The rheology used to simulate the landslide propagation is also responsible for the small second-order discrepancies existing between the wave profiles registered, which are amplified over time (Fig. 3b). However, since in this paper we focus on the tsunami hazards and not on the simulated morphology of the debris avalanche deposits, we arbitrarily chose the constant retarding stress of 10 kPa (rheology 4) to simulate the landslide propagation for the whole calculation grid.

## Results

When interacting with the water, the debris avalanche triggers waves whose maximum initial amplitude is around 45 m, measured approximately 45 s after the collapse onset at 2.5 km southwestwards from the landslide scar. The waves produced then propagate in a radial manner away from the impact region, reaching the islands of Sertung, Panjang and Rakata (Fig. 3a) in less than 1 min, with amplitudes from 15 to 30 m. Owing to the southwestwards propagation of the landslide, the highest waves are produced in this direction. The wave profile obtained about 15 km SW from the landslide scar (Fig. 3b, rheology 4) shows a first wave with an amplitude of 11.3 m and a period of around 162 s (wavelength of *c.* 3.4 km). This is followed by another 5.3 m wave, with a smaller period of approximately 60 s (wavelength of *c.* 1.3 km). This is then followed by several smaller and shorter waves, the sea level regaining its initial position after a few tens of minutes. The travel time of the first wave is shown in Figure 4, and is given more precisely in Table 1 for the main coastal cities and infrastructures located in

Figure 1. The cities situated on the western coast of Java are all touched by the first wave between 36 and 47 min after the onset of the Anak Krakatau collapse. The first wave reaches Kalianda and Bandar Lampung, located on Sumatra, 45 and 68 min after the onset of the collapse, respectively. Note that everywhere in the Sunda Strait the wavelength of the simulated waves is always more than 25 times the water depth. This demonstrates that the use of the general shallow-water equations of mass conservation and momentum balance to simulate the water propagation is appropriate in this case (e.g. Synolakis *et al.* 1997).

Figure 5 presents the maximum wave amplitude registered over 6000 s of simulation. It shows that the highest waves are mainly concentrated around

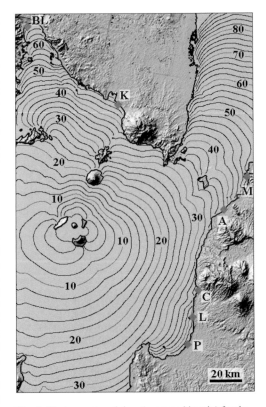

**Fig. 4.** First wave travel time (expressed in min) for the first 90 min of simulation. Black lines are at 2 min intervals. Main coastal cities (names in Fig. 1) are shown by red diamonds. The impact of the sudden increase in water depth westwards from the Krakatau Archipelago is clearly seen (see Fig. 1 for bathymetry), the waves being more rapid than those crossing the shallow strait. BL, Bandar Lampung; K, Kalianda; M, Merak; A, Anyer; C, Carita; L, Labuhan; P, Panimbang. The simulation of the landslide propagation was carried out using a constant retarding stress of 10 kPa.

**Table 1.** *Travel time and maximum wave amplitude recorded at gauges located close (<900 m) to the main coastal cities of the Sunda Strait (see Fig. 1)*

|  | Bandar Lampung (−13 m) | Kalianda (−5 m) | Merak (−12 m) | Anyer (−12 m) | Carita (−12 m) | Labuhan (−4 m) | Panimbang (−2 m) | Sumur (−7 m) |
|---|---|---|---|---|---|---|---|---|
| Travel time (min) | 68 | 44 | 47 | 38 | 37 | 40 | 43 | 36 |
| Maximum wave amplitude (m) | 0.3 | 2.7 | 1.5 | 1.4 | 2.9 | 3.4 | 1.5 | 1.2 |

For each city, the initial water depth at the gauge site is given in brackets.

the Krakatau Archipelago, as it is the location of the triggering event, and their amplitude logically decreases away from Anak Krakatau. Westwards, at about 20 km from the landslide, the wave amplitude is slightly reduced because of the strong increase in water depth, and waves do not exceed 1–2 m when they reach the western edge of the calculation grid. The highest waves produced are directed southwestwards and their amplitude decreases when they reach greater water depths in the SW. However, they still have an amplitude of more than 3–4 m when they arrive near Panaitan and near the southwestern coast of Java (Ujung Kulon National Park). The presence of the islands of Sertung and Rakata (Fig. 3a) – NW and SW of the landslide, respectively – also causes the wave amplitude to be reduced. The maximum amplitude of the waves recorded northwards and northeastwards is not related to the first wave produced. It appears that they come from the reflection of the initial waves off the coasts of Sertung and Rakata (the former consisting of a high cliff orientated NNW). However, owing to the numerous interactions of the waves with the four islands of the Krakatau Archipelago, it is difficult to establish exactly what happens near the impact point. Figure 5 also shows some reflections of the waves, in particular off the western coast of Java.

Figure 6 presents the evolution of the water level over 6500 s of simulation, recorded at gauges placed in the sea a few hundreds of metres (<900 m) off eight of the main coastal cities or infrastructures of the Sunda Strait (located in Fig. 1). The gauges were placed in the sea near the coasts to free the sea-level profiles recorded from the 3D interactions that the program fails to reproduce in an accurate manner. The maximum wave amplitudes measured at these gauges are indicated in Table 1 (the vertical water depth at each gauge is indicated in Table 1). The water-level profiles are different from one city to another, being complicated by numerous reflections of the waves throughout the Krakatau Archipelago, as well as around the Sumatran and Javanese coasts. All of the cities are touched by a first positive wave with amplitude ranging from 0.3 to 2.3 m, but

this first wave is never the highest one. Near Bandar Lampung and Kalianda, the maximum wave amplitude measured is 0.3 and 2.7 m respectively, and the coastal cities of western Java are generally affected by waves with maximums of between 1.2 (Sumur) and 3.4 m (Labuhan).

## Discussion

### Influence of the initial parameters on the wave characteristics

The volume of a debris avalanche and the way it occurs (e.g. in one go, by retrogressive failures) are the parameters that most influence the characteristics of the triggered tsunami (Locat *et al.* 2004; Giachetti *et al.* 2011). In the present case, the hypothetical scar has a slope of 8.2°, for an initial Anak Krakatau average slope of 24.2° (Fig. 3a). These values are lower than those observed for other scars of debris avalanches that triggered tsunamis, like the Palos Verdes debris avalanche (California, scar slope of $10°-17°$: Locat *et al.* 2004) or 29 submarine events identified at Stromboli (average scar slope of *c.* 25°, and pre-failure slope of *c.* 28° for debris avalanches between 5 and 200 m b.s.l.: Casalbore *et al.* 2011). In this study, we decided to base the structural definition of the hypothetical scar on the known structural evolution of Anak Krakatau: the upper end of the scar being defined by the limit between the older tuff-ring and the new cone, and its base by the bottom of the 1883 caldera. Therefore, our numerical model of Anak Krakatau involves a debris avalanche volume of 0.280 km³. The definition of a steeper scar (closer to the values observed by Locat *et al.* 2004 or Casalbore *et al.* 2011) would lead to a more rapid landslide into the water, and thus possibly to higher waves. However, a steeper scar would also result in a smaller collapsing volume (considering the lower end of the scar as fixed) and thus to slightly smaller waves. Since in this study our aim is to quantify the tsunami hazard linked to a realistic partial flank collapse of Anak Krakatau, we decided to maximize the volume involved in the debris avalanche (and

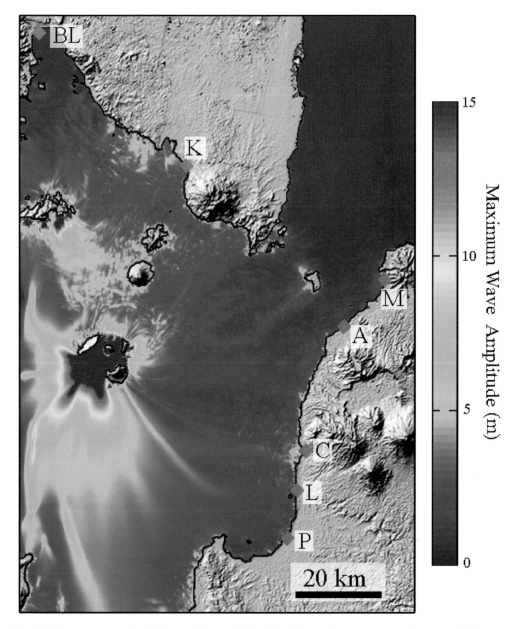

**Fig. 5.** Maximum wave amplitude (m) recorded over 6000 s of simulation, using a constant retarding stress of 10 kPa to simulate the landslide propagation.

thus the waves produced) while remaining consistent with the structure of the volcano.

## Influence of the bathymetry/topography on the tsunami characteristics

To define the initial volume that would hypothetically collapse, we used the available topography data (ASTER data, spatial resolution of 30 m) for Anak Krakatau Island. However, there is no up-to-date high-resolution topography and bathymetry data for this volcano, whose morphology changes rapidly due to its numerous eruptions. For this reason, we think that high-resolution topographical and bathymetric surveys of the Anak Krakatau Volcano should be performed in order to

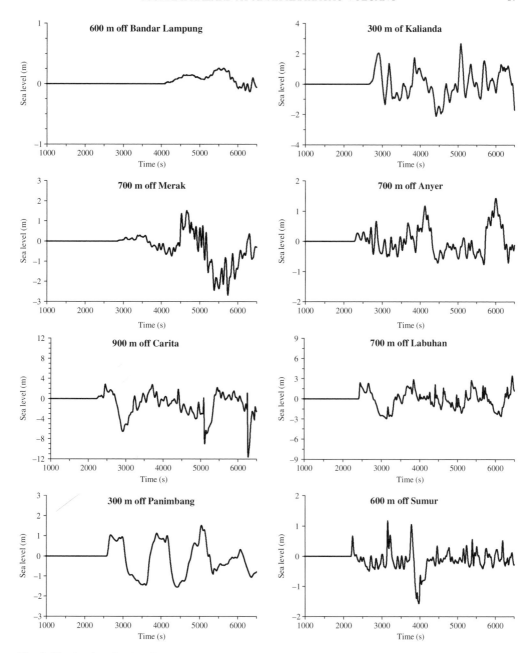

**Fig. 6.** Simulated sea-level profiles (m) registered several hundred metres (indicated on the plots) off eight of the main coastal cities located in Figure 1. The simulation of the landslide propagation was carried out using a constant retarding stress of 10 kPa. Time is expressed in seconds after the collapse onset. The water depth below each gauge is indicated in Table 1.

improve the accuracy when defining the initial conditions of the landslide. Side-scan sonar surveys coupled with INSAR (Interferometric Synthetic Aperture Radar) monitoring may also reveal evidence of slope instability. The travel time map

of the first wave based on the simulations (Fig. 4) is consistent with the refraction diagram of the tsunami caused by the 1883 Krakatau eruption (Yokoyama 1981). However, the wave travel time estimated may suffer from artefacts in the bathymetry used for calculations. The inclusion of bathymetric maps of parts of Sunda Strait in the constructed DEM allowed us to minimize these artefacts, but new bathymetric maps of this region would be useful for a better tsunami hazard assessment.

## Tsunami hazards

Our simulation shows that the first wave produced has a maximum amplitude of about 45 m. This height is reached at approximately 2.5 km SW of the landslide scar (i.e. Anak Krakatau Island), inside the Krakatau Archipelago. Moreover, the waves produced reach the surrounding islands of Sertung, Rakata and Panjang in less than 1 min, with heights of up to 30 m. These waves could be a serious hazard for the many tourist boats that visit these islands every day. Further from the Krakatau Archipelago, the wave amplitude decreases in Sunda Strait and waves are generally smaller than 10 m at a distance of more than 20 km from the landslide scar. However, these waves could still be dangerous for the small boats crossing the strait between the Krakatau Archipelago and the coasts of Java or Sumatra. It should be noted that the islands of the Krakatau Archipelago (Anak Krakatau, Sertung, Panjang and Rakata), as well as those of Sebesi and Sebuku in the NE, those of Legundi and Siuntjal in the NNW, and Panaitan in the SSW are uninhabited, and thus the risk is drastically reduced. Between the two islands of Java and Sumatra, where the planned bridge is to be constructed (see the explanation in the earlier section on 'Geography, population and infrastructures in the Sunda Strait'), the waves do not reach more than 3.8 m, and the construction should be able to absorb the strain developed by such a wave.

Our numerical simulation of the sudden collapse of Anak Krakatau Volcano into the 1883 caldera shows that all the coasts around the Sunda Strait could potentially be affected by waves of more than 1.0 m in less than 1 h after the event. Even the southern coasts of Sumatra, which are located more than 40 km to the north of the landslide, would be touched by the tsunami because of the numerous wave reflections off the islands of the Krakatau Archipelago. All of the main cities or infrastructures of the Sunda Strait would be affected within 1 h of the collapse. The highest waves registered off these coastal cities are those near Labuhan (3.4 m) on the western coast of Java, but most of the gauges give values of less than 3 m for the highest wave. These values are far less than those observed during the 1883 Krakatau eruption, which reached an average value of 15 m on the coasts of Sumatra and Java (Symons 1888; Yokoyama 1981), with a local wave height of up to 30 m. Moreover,

Figure 5 shows that some parts of the coast are partially protected by the numerous islands in Sunda Strait (e.g. Rakata prevents the propagation of very high waves towards the large bay off Panimbang). Waves become smaller with increasing distance from the triggering event. During the 1883 tsunami, Jakarta was touched by a wave approximately 1.8 m high about 140 min after the eruption of Krakatau, whereas Merak and Anyer were touched by 15 m-high waves. Likewise, the 1883 tsunami also reached locations thousands of kilometres from the volcano (Choi *et al.* 2003, Pelinovsky *et al.* 2005). Considering that the maximum wave height recorded off Anyer and Merak is around 1.5 m in our simulation, we believe that the tsunami triggered by a flank collapse at Anak Krakatau would be negligible at Jakarta.

## Conclusion

Our numerical simulation shows that a partial destabilization (0.28 km$^3$) of Anak Krakatau Volcano towards the SW would possibly be dangerous on a local scale (tourist and fishing activities around the volcano) or even on a regional scale (coasts of Sumatra and Java). This event would trigger an initial wave of 43 m that would reach all of the islands in the Krakatau Archipelago in less than 1 min, with amplitudes ranging from 15 to 30 m, and would be extremely dangerous for boats in the Krakatau Archipelago. Waves would then propagate in a radial manner across Sunda Strait at an average speed of 80–110 km h$^{-1}$, the first wave reaching cities on the western coast of Java after 35–45 min, with a maximum amplitude of between 2.9 (Carita) and 3.4 m (Labuhan). These waves would be considerably smaller than those produced during the 1883 Krakatau eruption (average wave height of c. 15 m around the Sunda Strait).

Owing to the high population, the concentration of road and industrial infrastructure along some parts of the exposed coasts of Java and Sumatra, and the low elevation of much of this land, the tsunami might present a significant risk. However, as the travel time of the tsunami is several tens of minutes between the Krakatau Archipelago and the main cities along these coasts, a rapid detection of the collapse by the volcano observatory, coupled with an efficient alert system on the coast, could prevent this hypothetical event from being deadly. A tsunami preparedness project was initiated in 2006 by UNESCO and the Indonesian Institute of Sciences (LIPI). However, it should be noted that the ground deformation of the volcano is not permanently monitored, and the available data (e.g. bathymetry) are not sufficient to allow for an accurate assessment of slope instability.

The example of Krakatau Volcano illustrates the point that tsunamis generated by volcanic eruptions and flank instability are a neglected hazard. They represent 25% of all the fatalities directly attributable to volcanoes during the last 250 years (Latter 1981; Begét 2000). At least 115 volcanic tsunamis have been observed since 1600 AD (death toll >54 000), with 36 events during the nineteenth century and 54 events during the twentieth. Volcanic tsunamis can be dangerous because they can occur with little warning, and cause devastation at great distances. South Asian and South Pacific regions are particularly exposed to volcanic tsunamis because of the high density of active volcanoes located near the coasts (volcanic island arcs). Systematic monitoring of flank instability and the integration of tsunamis into volcanic hazard assessments (e.g. maps, evacuation routes) would reduce the impact of future events.

This work is part of the 'Vitesss' project (Volcano-Induced Tsunamis: numErical Simulations and Sedimentary Signature) supported by the French National Research Agency (ANR project 08-JCJC-0042) and whose leader is R. Paris (Geolab, CNRS). ASTER GDEM is a product of METI and NASA. We thank two anonymous reviewers for their constructive reviews of this manuscript. We are also grateful to Anaïs Ferot who first suggested we perform this study.

# References

BEGÉT, J. E. 2000. Volcanic tsunamis. *In*: SIGURDSSON, H., HOUGHTON, B., McNUTT, S. R., RYMER, H. & STIX, J. (eds) *Encyclopedia of Volcanoes*. Academic Press, New York, 1005–1013.

CAMUS, G. & VINCENT, P. M. 1983. Discussion of a new hypothesis for the Krakatau volcanic eruption in 1983. *Journal of Volcanology and Geothermal Research*, **19**, 167–173.

CAMUS, G., GOURGAUD, A. & VINCENT, P. M. 1987. Petrologic evolution of Krakatau (Indonesia): implications for a future activity. *Journal of Volcanology and Geothermal Research*, **33**, 299–316.

CAREY, S., SIGURDSSON, H., MANDEVILLE, C. W. & BRONTO, S. 1996. Pyroclastic deposits from flows and surges which travelled over the sea during the 1883 eruption of Krakatau volcano. *Bulletin of Volcanology*, **57**, 493–511.

CASALBORE, D., ROMAGNOLI, C., BOSMAN, A. & CHIOCCI, F. L. 2011. Potential tsunamigenic landslides at Stromboli Volcano (Italy): insight from marine DEM analysis. *Geomorphology*, **126**, 42–50, doi: 10.1016/j.geomorph.2010.10.026.

CHOI, B. H., PELINOVSKY, E., KIM, K. O. & LEE, J. S. 2003. Simulation of the trans-oceanic tsunami propagation due to the 1883 Krakatau volcanic eruption. *Natural Hazards and Earth System Sciences*, **3**, 321–332.

DADE, W. B. & HUPPERT, H. E. 1998. Long-runout rockfalls. *Geology*, **26**, 803–806.

DE LANGE, W. P., PRASETYA, G. S. & HEALY, T. R. 2001. Modelling of tsunamis generated by pyroclastic flows (ignimbrites). *Natural Hazards*, **24**, 251–266.

DEPLUS, C., BONVALOT, S., DAHRIN, D., DIAMENT, M., HARJONO, H. & DUBOIS, J. 1995. Inner structure of the Krakatoa volcanic complex (Indonesia) from gravity and bathymetry data. *Journal of Volcanology and Geothermal Research*, **64**, 23–51.

FRANCIS, P. W. 1985. The origin of the 1883 Krakatau tsunamis. *Journal of Volcanology and Geothermal Research*, **25**, 349–363.

FRITZ, H. M., HAGER, W. H. & MINOR, H. E. 2001. Lituya Bay case: rockslide impact and wave run-up. *Science of Tsunami Hazards*, **19**, 3–22.

FRITZ, H. M., KALLIGERIS, N. J., BORRERO, C., BRONCANO, P. & ORTEGA, E. 2008. The 15 August 2007 Peru tsunami runup observations and modeling. *Geophysical Research Letters*, **35**, L10604-4, doi: 10.1029/2008GL033494.

GIACHETTI, T., PARIS, R., KELFOUN, K. & PÉREZ-TORRADO, F. J. 2011. Numerical modelling of the tsunami triggered by the Güìmar debris avalanche, Tenerife (Canary Islands): comparison with field-based data. *Marine Geology*, **284**, 189–202, doi:10.1016/j.margeo.2011.03.018.

HARBITZ, C. B., LØVHOLT, F., PEDERSEN, G. & MASSON, D. G. 2006. Mechanisms of tsunami generation by submarine landslides: a short review. *Norwegian Journal of Geology*, **86**, 255–264.

HOFFMANN-ROTHE, A., IBS-VON SEHT, M. *ET AL.* 2006. Monitoring Anak Krakatau Volcano in Indonesia. *Eos Transactions of the American Geophysical Union*, **87**, 581, doi: 10.1029/2006EO510002.

KEATING, B. H. & McGUIRE, W. J. 2000. Island edifice failures and associated tsunami hazards. *Pure and Applied Geophysics*, **157**, 899–955.

KELFOUN, K. & DRUITT, T. H. 2005. Numerical modelling of the emplacement of Socompa rock avalanche, Chile. *Journal of Geophysical Research*, **110**, B12202.

KELFOUN, K., GIACHETTI, T. & LABAZUY, P. 2010. Landslide-generated tsunamis at Reunion Island. *Journal of Geophysical Research*, **115**, F04012, doi: 10.1029/2009JF001381.

LATTER, J. N. 1981. Tsunamis of volcanic origin: summary of causes with particular references to Krakatoa, 1883. *Bulletin of Volcanology*, **44**, 467–490.

LOCAT, J., LEE, H. J., LOCAT, P. & IRMAN, J. 2004. Numerical analysis of the mobility of the Palos Verdes debris avalanche, California, and its implication for the generation of tsunamis. *Marine Geology*, **203**, 269–280.

MADER, C. L. & GITTINGS, M. L. 2006. Numerical model for the Krakatoa hydrovolcanic explosion and tsunami. *Science of Tsunami Hazards*, **24**, 174–182.

MAENO, F. & IMAMURA, F. 2007. Numerical investigations of tsunamis generated by pyroclastic flows from the Kikai caldera, Japan. *Geophysical Research Letters*, **34**, L23303-1, doi: 10.1029/2007GL031222.

MAENO, F., IMAMURA, F. & TANIGUCHI, H. 2006. Numerical simulation of tsunami generated by caldera collapse during the 7.3 ka Kikai eruption, Japan. *Earth Planets and Space*, **58**, 1013–1024.

MARAMAI, A., GRAZIANI, L. *ET AL.* 2005. Near- and far-field survey report of the 30 December 2002 Stromboli (Southern Italy) tsunami. *Marine Geology*, **215**, 93–106.

MICHIUE, M., HINOKIDANI, O. & MIYAMOTO, K. 1999. Study on the Mayuyama tsunami disaster in 1792. *In*: *Proceedings of the 28th IAHR Congress, Graz, Austria, 22–27 August 1999*. International Association of Hydro-Environment Engineering and Research, Madrid (CD-ROM).

NOMANBHOY, N. & SATAKE, K. 1995. Generation mechanism of tsunamis from the 1883 Krakatau eruption. *Geophysical Researc. Letters*, **22**, 509–512.

OBA, N., TOMITA, K. *ET AL.* 1983. Geochemical study of volcanic products, in particular to pumice flow, of the Krakatau Group, Indonesia. *Report of the Faculty of Science, Kagoshima University (Earth Science, Biology)*, **16**, 21–41.

PELINOVSKY, E., CHOI, B. H., STROMKOV, A., DIDENKULOVA, I. & KIM, H. S. 2005. Analysis of tide-gauge records of the 1883 Krakatau tsunami. *In*: *Tsunamis: Case Studies and Recent Developments. Advances in Natural and Technological Hazards Research*, **23**, 57–77.

SELF, S. & RAMPINO, M. R. 1981. The 1883 eruption of Krakatau. *Nature*, **294**, 699–704.

SIGURDSSON, H., CAREY, S. & MANDEVILLE, C. 1991a. Submarine pyroclastic flows of the 1883 eruption of the Krakatau Volcano. *National Geographic Research and Exploration*, **7**, 310–327.

SIGURDSSON, H., CAREY, S., MANDEVILLE, C. & BRONTO, S. 1991b. Pyroclastic flows of the 1883 Krakatau eruption. *Eos Transactions of the American Geophysical Union*, **72**, 377.

SIMKIN, T. & FISKE, R. S. 1983. *Krakatau 1883: The Volcanic Eruption and its Effects*. Smithsonian Institution Press, Washington, DC.

STEHN, C. E. 1929. The geology and volcanism of the Krakatau Group. *In*: *Proceedings of the Fourth Pacific Science Congress, Batavia-Bandoeng (Java), May–June, 1929*. Martinus Nijhoff, The Hague, 1–55.

SUDRADJAT, A. 1982. The morphological development of Anak Krakatau Volcano, Sunda Strait. *Geology of Indonesia*, **9**, 1–11.

SYMONS, G. J. 1888. *The Eruption of Krakatoa, and Subsequent Phenomena. Report of the Krakatoa Committee of the Royal Society*. Trübner, London.

SYNOLAKIS, C. E., LIU, P. L. F., YEH, H. & CARRIER, G. F. 1997. Tsunamigenic seafloor deformations. *Science*, **278**, 598–600.

TINTI, S., BORTOLUCCI, E. & ROMAGNOLI, C. 1999. Modelling a possible holocenic landslide-induced tsunami at Stromboli volcano, Italy. *Physics and Chemistry of the Earth*, **24**, 423–429.

TINTI, S., BORTOLUCCI, E. & ROMAGNOLI, C. 2000. Computer simulations of tsunamis due to sector collapse at Stromboli, Italy. *Journal of Volcanology and Geothermal Research*, **96**, 103–128.

TINTI, S., PAGNONI, G. & ZANIBONI, F. 2006. The landslides and tsunamis of the 30th of December 2002 in Stromboli analysed through numerical simulations. *Bulletin of Volcanology*, **68**, 462–479.

TSUJI, Y. & HINO, T. 1993. Damage and inundation height of the 1792 Shimabara landslide tsunami along the coast of Kumamoto prefecture. *Bulletin of the Earthquake Research Institute, University of Tokyo*, **68**, 91–176.

VERBEEK, R. D. M. 1885. Krakatau. *In*: SIMKIN, T & FISKE, R. S (eds) *Krakatau 1883: The Volcanic Eruption and its Effects*. Smithsonian Institution Press, Washington, DC, 169–277.

WARD, S. N. 2001. Landslide tsunami. *Journal of Geophysical Research*, **106**, 11 201–11 215.

WARD, S. N. & DAY, S. 2003. Ritter Island Volcano-lateral collapse and the tsunami of 1888. *Geophysical Journal International*, **154**, 891–902.

WAYTHOMAS, C. F., WATTS, P., SHI, F. & KIRBY, J. T. 2009. Pacific Basin tsunami hazards associated with mass flows in the Aleutian arc of Alaska. *Quaternary Science Reviews*, **28**, 1006–1019.

WARTON, W. J. L. & EVANS, F. J. 1888. On the seismic sea waves caused by the eruption at Krakatau, August 26th and 27th, 1883. Part III. *In*: SYMONS, G. L. (ed.) *The Eruption of Krakatoa and Subsequent Phenomena. Report of the Krakatoa Commission of the Royal Society of London*, 89–151.

YOKOYAMA, I. 1981. A Geophysical interpretation of the 1883 Krakatau eruption. *Journal of Volcanology and Geothermal Research*, **9**, 359–378.

# An examination of hazard communication logs and public response during the 1946 and 1960 tsunamis that impacted Hilo, Hawaii

JEANNE B. JOHNSTON[1], DEANNE K. BIRD[2]*, JAMES R. GOFF[3] & WALTER C. DUDLEY[4]

[1]*Disaster Preparedness Solutions, Inc., Kailua, HI 96734, USA*

[2]*Risk Frontiers, Macquarie University, North Ryde, Sydney, NSW 2109, Australia*

[3]*Australia–Pacific Tsunami Research Centre and Natural Hazards Research Laboratory, School of Biological, Earth and Environmental Sciences, University of New South Wales, Sydney 2052, NSW, Australia*

[4]*Marine Science Department, University of Hawaii, Hilo, Hawaii 96720, USA*

*\*Corresponding author (e-mail: deanne.bird@gmail.com)*

**Abstract:** This paper examines communication methods used to inform the vulnerable community of Hilo, Hawaii of the impending tsunamis that struck in 1946 and 1960. These tsunamis caused tragic loss of life and enormous economic damage in Hilo and along the shores of the Hawaiian Island chain. Over 12 h notice of a possible large tsunami was given in 1960 *and* the siren warning system sounded more than 4 h prior to the event. The government agencies knew there was a tsunami alert and the media were broadcasting warnings. However, the 1960 tsunami took the lives of 61 people in Hilo only 14 years after 96 people were killed during the 1946 event. In order to discover why so many people perished, government agency logs recorded during the 1960 tsunami were examined and personal accounts from survivors of both the 1946 and 1960 tsunamis were analysed. Contributing to the tragic loss of life was a lack of communication between government agencies in addition to media inaccuracies and a public that was not educated in tsunami safety. Effective tsunami mitigation can only be accomplished through continual tsunami awareness education for the public, media and emergency personnel, and with accurate and timely tsunami warnings.

Residents living in tsunami-vulnerable regions have most probably never experienced a tsunami, and therefore lack knowledge of the hazard and understanding of how to behave (Murata *et al.* 2010). Despite many Hawaiian residents having direct or indirect experience of tsunami disasters in 1946 and 1960, most lack an understanding of tsunami hazard (Dudley & Lee 1998). It is also questionable whether or not people will take appropriate action in response to the next tsunami warning (Gregg *et al.* 2007).

Research conducted by Nishimoto (2000) and Johnston (2003) uncovered the depth of confusion and misunderstanding present during the 1946 and 1960 tsunamis that impacted Hilo, Hawaii. Comparing interview responses from survivors of both tsunamis also revealed that there was no heightened awareness of tsunami safety. Atwater *et al.* (2005) illustrated how people survived the 1960 tsunami in Chile, Hawaii and Japan through rational actions that reliably saved lives (e.g. heeding natural warnings, abandoning belongings, evacuating to higher ground until the hazard had passed)

and desperate actions of people caught unaware and/or unprepared (e.g. taking refuge in buildings or trees, floating on debris). Survivor stories, such as these, offer invaluable insight into the complexities of human behaviour prior to, during and after a disaster and therefore, provide important lessons for survival (Ripley 2008; Bird *et al.* 2011). To preserve life and maintain public safety, it is essential that these lessons be incorporated into ongoing public education programs in addition to, promoting increased preparedness among individuals, businesses and communities. Mitigating the effects of tsunami hazards also requires accurate and timely warnings, interagency communication and co-operation, and hazard knowledge and understanding among key emergency management and media personnel.

In this paper, we will demonstrate that continual education is an essential component of risk mitigation, not only with respect to the public but also in regards to emergency management agencies and the media. We achieve this by analysing communication logs obtained from the County of Hawaii

*From*: Terry, J. P. & Goff, J. (eds) 2012. *Natural Hazards in the Asia–Pacific Region: Recent Advances and Emerging Concepts*. Geological Society, London, Special Publications, **361**, 91–105, http://dx.doi.org/10.1144/SP361.8

Civil Defense Agency in Hilo, Hawaii, and examining interviews with survivors of the devastating 1946 and 1960 tsunamis, which are archived at the Pacific Tsunami Museum. A discussion on the implications of our findings in relation to risk communication and public education is provided. First, we describe the events of the 1946 and 1960 tsunamis, and the warning system, in the following sections.

## The 1946 tsunami

On 1 April 1946 a major earthquake centred about 90 miles (145 km) south of Unimak Pass, Alaska (Fig. 1) created a 100 ft (30.5 m) tsunami wave that swept away the lighthouse on Unimak Island in the Aleutian Islands, killing all five US Coast Guard personnel in the facility (Dudley & Lee 1998). The lighthouse, built in 1940, was nearly 100 ft (30.5 m) high and was sited 40 ft (12.2 m) above sea level.

The earthquake occurred at approximately 02:00 Hawaii local time (Hawaii Standard time) on 1 April 1946 in the Aleutian Trench (Shepard *et al.* 1949). The US Coast and Geodetic Survey at the University of Hawaii at Manoa, Honolulu, Oahu and the Hawaiian Volcano Observatory at Kilauea, Hawaii registered and recorded the Aleutian earthquake shortly after it occurred (Dudley & Lee 1998). A tsunami, however, travelling over 2300 miles

(3700 km) from the Aleutian Islands to Hilo at a rate of nearly 500 miles h$^{-1}$ (805 km h$^{-1}$) was not expected. The first wave reached Kaua'i at around 06:00, Honolulu at 06:33 and Hilo at approximately 07:00 (Shepard *et al.* 1949). A total of nine waves, varying from 17 to 25 ft (5.2–7.6 m) in height, inundated Hilo that day (Dudley & Stone 2000).

Dudley & Stone (2000) reported that as the tsunami approached Hilo, it inundated Laupahoehoe Peninsula (Fig. 2) killing 16 school children and eight adults. On all of the islands, almost 500 homes and businesses were totally destroyed, at least 1000 sustained damage and property damage was estimated at approximately $26 million (1946 US$) (Dudley & Stone 2000). The cost in relation to human life, however, was much worse. A total of 159 people lost their lives in the Territory of Hawaii and 96 of those lives were lost in Hilo.

Almost immediately, Hilo residents started to rebuild their homes and lives. Although some businesses were never rebuilt, most residential areas and businesses in Waiakea were rebuilt with some, once again, located in vulnerable, low-lying areas (Dudley & Stone 2000). However, Shepard *et al.* (1949, p. 392) noted:

If, moreover, a suitable system can be devised for warning of the approach of dangerous tsunamis even a few minutes in advance of their arrival, it should be

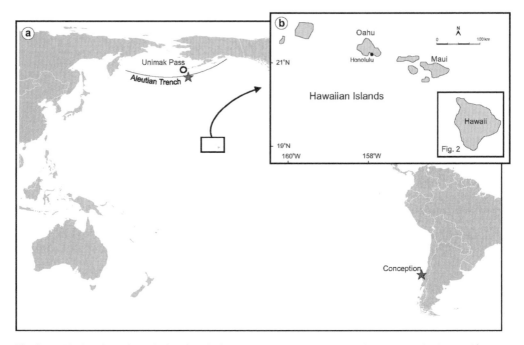

**Fig. 1.** (**a**) The locations of the 1946 earthquake in the Aleutian Trench and the 1960 earthquake in Concepción. (**b**) The Hawaiian Islands.

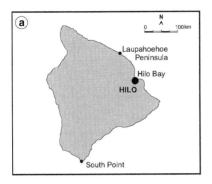

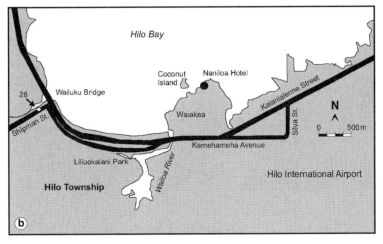

**Fig. 2.** (**a**) The Big Island, Hawaii showing Hilo, the Laupahoehoe Peninsula and South Point. (**b**) The township of Hilo showing the HFD headquarters at 28 Shipman Street (St.), located approximately 100 yards (91.4 m) from Hilo Bay and 100 ft (30.5 m) from the Wailuku River. Other prominent geographical points impacted by the 1960 include Coconut Island and Liliuokalani Park.

possible to effect a very considerable saving of life; and warnings an hour or more in advance would allow the saving of much easily movable property.

It is worth noting that much of the vulnerable, low-lying area rebuilt following the 1946 event was eventually set aside for recreational land use following damage caused as a result of the 1960 tsunami.

## The 1960 tsunami

Just after midnight, Hawaii local time, on 21 May 1960 an earthquake registering $M_w$ 7.5 struck near Concepción, Chile, 6600 miles (10 622 km) to the SE (Eaton *et al.* 1961) (see Fig. 1). The earthquake was registered at the US Coast and Geodetic Survey Observatory (warning centre) in Honolulu, Oahu and a tsunami watch was issued at 00:45. The warning centre started to monitor tide gauges throughout the Pacific but the alert was cancelled at 20:49 when only a small wave was recorded in Hilo Bay.

By 11:30 Hawaii time on 22 May 1960, it was known that a second, large earthquake had occurred near Concepción approximately 2.5 h earlier (Eaton *et al.* 1961). This event, however, was followed 15 min later by a huge $M_w$ 9.5 earthquake (Kanamori 1977). This was the largest instrumentally recorded earthquake of the twentieth century (Johnston *et al.* 2008).

Once again, a tsunami watch was issued and the expected time of arrival was predicted to be about 15 h later, at around midnight local time. News reports of destructive waves along the Chilean coast were received in Hawaii during the early afternoon. At 18:47 the warning centre issued a Seismic Sea Wave Warning and at 20:30 – the Hawaii Civil Defense Agency (HCDA) communication log states that the first siren sounded at 20:35 – coastal sirens signalled people in the low-lying areas of Hilo to evacuate to higher ground (Eaton *et al.* 1961). Lachman *et al.* (1961, p. 1406) reported that the warning sirens sounded 'for a 20-min period more than four hours prior to the impact of the wave'.

It was not until 22:23 that official notice of unusual wave activity was received from Tahiti, approximately 2800 miles (4506 km) south of Honolulu (Dudley & Lee 1998). This was the first official confirmation received by the warning centre since the first reports that tsunami waves had impacted the Chilean coast.

At 00:07 on 23 May 1960, rising water was noted beneath Wailuku Bridge (see Fig. 2) on the west edge of Hilo Bay (Eaton *et al.* 1961). The water crested at 00:13 at more than 4 ft (1.2 m) and began to fall slowly until 00:30 to a trough of −3 ft (−0.9 m). At 00:46, the second wave passed under Wailuku Bridge at a level of +9 ft (+2.7 m) (Dudley & Lee 1998). This wave flooded Kamehameha Avenue and the business district of Hilo. As the water withdrew, a trough of 7 ft (2.1 m) below normal was noted.

At 01:04, Eaton *et al.* (1961, p. 139) reported a '20-foot [6.1 m]-high nearly vertical front' as the tsunami wave flooded past Wailuku Bridge. At 01:05, the power plant at the southern end of Hilo Bay was impacted by the incoming waves and, after a brief moment, the city of Hilo and most of the Island of Hawaii went dark. Just over 1 h later, at 02:15, the height of the waves had diminished

sufficiently for people to re-enter the township of Hilo and assess the damage (Eaton *et al.* 1961) (Fig. 3).

## The tsunami warning system

According to Dudley & Lee (1998), Hawaii should have approximately 15 h notice of an impending tsunami generated from South America and only 5–10 min for locally generated tsunami. Tsunami disaster communication therefore requires a specialized strategy because of the potentially limited warning time and also due to their rare occurrence. It is imperative that the disaster response community, the media and the public have accurate information as quickly as possible. This is particularly important for locally generated tsunami with respect to preserving life and maintaining public safety.

On 1 April 1946 there was no early warning to the population but by 1960 a tsunami siren warning system was in place in the state of Hawaii. In addition to the sirens, there were warnings broadcast by radio and government agencies. This early warning system provided technically successful warnings of three large tsunamis on 4 November 1952, 9 March 1957 and 23 May 1960. However, a report from the Geophysical Society

**Fig. 3.** View WSW across Waiakea after the 23 May 1960 tsunami impacted Hilo, Hawaii. (Photograph courtesy of the Pacific Tsunami Museum, photograph number 1960.04, Polhemus Collection.)

of Hawaii (1960) found that improvement in the overall system and its acceptance by the public was still needed.

Based on Bonk *et al.* (1960), Dudley & Lee (1998) explained that many people did not understand the warning system because it was changed only a few months prior to the 1960 tsunami. The previous warning system consisted of three separate alarms: the first siren was to indicate that a tsunami warning was in effect; the second siren meant to evacuate; and the third was supposed to sound just prior to the arrival of the first wave. The new system, however, consisted of only one siren indicating immediate evacuation, although people may not have been aware of this change.

Nevertheless, the warning siren had been activated prior to 22 May 1960. Johnston (2003) reported that sirens signalling the arrival of relatively small tsunamis, such as the one on 21 May, were perceived by the public as 'false alarms' and residents were therefore complacent on 22 May.

In the next section we describe the methods used to analyse communication logs and examine interviews with survivors of the devastating 1946 and 1960 tsunamis.

## Methods

### Agency logs

An in-depth examination of the logs prepared by the three leading governmental agencies responsible for the safety of Hilo's citizens during the 1960 tsunami was performed. The information was collected from documentation located at the County of Hawaii Civil Defense Agency (HCDA) office in Hilo, Hawaii, and it included logs from the HCDA, the Hawaii Police Department – Hilo Station (HPD) and the Hawaii Fire Department (HFD). These logs were taken during the 28 h period from 11:58 on 22 May to 16:03 on 23 May 1960.

### Tsunami survivor interviews

Content analysis was conducted on recorded interviews with individuals who survived the 1946 and 1960 tsunamis in Hilo. All interviews were recorded on digital audio-tape (DAT) and video-tape for the Pacific Tsunami Museum, Hilo, Hawaii. The reader is referred to Dudley *et al.* (2009) for a detailed description of methods used during video interviewing.

The lead author (Johnston) conducted the interviews on a one-on-one basis, with the length of interviews averaging between 15 and 60 min. It is important to note that some of the survivors of these disastrous events found it difficult and emotional to talk about their experiences. For some, it was the first time they had shared their experience since the tsunami. In all cases, the interviewer respected the survivor's pace and content as they shared their stories, and all attempts were made to accurately report the information they relayed.

Copies of the transcriptions and original DATs are archived at the Pacific Tsunami Museum. All interviewees received copies of the transcripts and have released their interviews to the Pacific Tsunami Museum, where they are available to the public.

A total of 67 interview transcripts were reviewed in this study. This included 45 survivor interviews from the 1 April 1946 tsunami and 22 survivor interviews from the 23 May 1960 tsunami. Each transcript was examined in an effort to attain answers to the following three questions:

- Where were you when you heard about the tsunami?
- Where did you get the information?
- What did you do?

In addition to interviews archived at the Pacific Tsunami Museum in Hilo, Hawaii, interviews conducted by Bonk *et al.* (1960) and Nishimoto (2000) were reviewed and analysed.

## Results

### Agency logs: 22–23 May 1960

*Unofficial notification.* The first indication of the impending disaster recorded in the logs was the 'unofficial' report from the US Geological Survey's Volcano Observatory, received by the HPD at 11:58 on 22 May 1960. It was 17 min later, at 12:15, when an officer from the HPD notified the HCDA (Table 1). This notification indicated that the arrival time of the tsunami in the Hawaiian Islands would be midnight on 22 May 1960. The log for the HFD in Hilo did not begin until 20:05 on 22 May 1960.

*Tidal wave alert.* The logs of the HCDA disclose that, at 19:05, Hilo's KHBC radio announced that the Coast and Geodetic Survey had issued a tidal wave alert at 18:48. Six minutes later, at 19:11, the logs of the HPD declare that the Honolulu Police Department called and reported the warning. In addition, the account shows that the State Civil Defense Headquarters requested that the HPD notify all civil defence agencies. However, they were instructed to *not* sound the siren until advised. The HFD logs indicated the announcement of the 'tidal wave alert' occurred almost 1 h later at 20:05.

**Table 1.** *Critical communication events from 11:58 to 21:38 on 22 May 1960 (after Johnston 2003)*

| | 11.58 | 12.15 | 19.05 | 19.11 | 19.15 | 19.59 | 20.00 | 20.05 | 20.15 | 20.35 | 20.40 | 20.43 | 20.47 | 20.50 | 21.38 |
|---|---|---|---|---|---|---|---|---|---|---|---|---|---|---|---|
| Hawaii Civil Defense Agency (HCDA) | a | | | | | | | | | | | | | | d2 |
| Hilo Police Department | | a | b1 | b2 | b3 | c1 | c2 | | d1 | e1 e2 | f | g | h | i | |
| Hawaii Fire Department | | | | | | | | b4 | | e2 | | | | | |

Log entries:

a. Krivoy, Volcano Observatory reported unofficially that an earthquake was recorded on the coast of Chile at about 9.00 22/05/60 (local time). Magnitude of about 8.25. Feel sure that tsunami will result from this quake. Arrival time in the Hawaiian Islands around 12.00 midnight tonight 23/05/60. First place to strike would be Kalapana and Pohoiki area. Request that tidal wave gauge keeper be contacted and see if he can possibly change the recordings about 15.00 so that yesterday's recordings would not be lost.

b1. KHBC announced that the Coast & Geodetic Survey has issued a tidal wave alert at 18.48.

b2. Received from Sgt. Kitsuwa, Honolulu Police. Reported that according to McCaffery of the Honolulu Geodetic Survey, Honolulu, reported a tidal wave warning. A severe sea wave spreading over the Pacific. First wave will hit Hawaii at 00.00 midnight; Maui 00.15; Oahu 00.30; Kauai 00.45. Southern part of Hawaii will be affected first. Danger will last for several hours. Velocity of wave cannot be determined at present. Mr. Walker, State CD HQ, Honolulu. Notify all CD agencies to mobilise to an extent deputy directors CD agencies feels and to report action taken to CD HQ Honolulu. Telephone number 72161, and reverse charges. Don't sound siren until notified.

b3. Sgt Yuhas of the Hilo Police Department reported to Pakele that the Honolulu Police Dept. has issued tidal wave warning. Wave expected to hit the Big Island at 00.00 midnight and island of Oahu at 00.30.

b4. Tidal wave alert.

c1. Radio stations notified, no 20.00 sirens will be sounded.

c2. Asst. Chief George Martin of the Hilo Police Dept. called Pakele to notify him that he received a message from Mr. T.G.S. Walker, thorough the hotline that sirens are not to be sounded until notified by State CD Headquarters.

d1. Pakele phoned Mr. T.G.S. Walker at the State CD headquarters and was given the authority to sounds the sirens.

d2. Sgt. Molina' Honolulu Police . . . (message) 'Will you sound tidal wave warning now'.

e1. First siren sounded.

e2. Sirens sounded . . . Evacuation begins in lower areas.

e3. Tidal wave sirens sounded.

f. Second siren sounded.

g. Third siren sounded.

h. Fourth siren sounded.

i. Fifth siren sounded.

*Warning sirens and evacuation.* The HPD log indicated that local radio stations were told at 19:59 that no siren would be sounded at 20:00. At this time, the Assistant Chief of the HPD called the HCDA to notify them that he had received a message from the State Civil Defense that sirens were not to be sounded until notified by the State Civil Defense Headquarters.

At 20:15 the HCDA called the State Civil Defense Headquarters and was given the authority to sound the sirens. At 20:35, the HCDA log recorded 'First Siren Sounded', the HPD recorded 'Siren sounded ... Evacuation begins in lower areas' and the HFD recorded 'Tidal wave sirens sounded'. According to the HCDA, there were five separate sirens that sounded intermittently – at 20:35, 20:40, 20:43, 20:47 and 20:50.

At 21:38, the HPD log indicates that they received a call from the Honolulu Police Department asking them to sound the warning siren. However, no other records could be located to indicate whether this message was passed along to any other agency, nor was there any record of the sirens being sounded at or around 21:38.

The HPD log reports that they were 'instructed to evacuate lower areas immediately' at 21:56 (Table 2).

*Tahiti wave report.* At 22:31, the HCDA log reports: 'Wave hits Tahiti at 8:00 pm, 3 ft. high ...'. By this time, the HFD had sent one of their employees over to HCDA with a handheld radio. The employee reported the news of the Tahiti wave to the HFD at 22:35 just 4 min after the HCDA received the report. However, the HPD did not log the news until 20 min later, at 22:55, and their log reveals that they received their report from Hilo's KHBC radio. The HPD report stated: '... 3 ft 3 in [1 m] waves were recorded in Tahiti. First reports indicate no damage'.

At 23:00, the HCDA log reports that they called the Civil Defense in Honolulu. The Civil Defense confirmed to the HCDA that Tahiti had been impacted by a tsunami and that they should expect a wave to reach Hawaii as previously estimated. Four minutes later, the HPD was notified of the Tahiti wave and at 23:05 there is a second report of the Tahiti wave in the HCDA log.

*Tidal wave gauge.* The HPD log reported at 23:30 that 'the tidal wave gauge is normal'. Since there was no record of where the gauge was located in the records, a Hilo police officer at the time of the tsunami was contacted for the purpose of this study. This officer stated that the gauge was located at Pier One in Hilo Harbour 'on the breakwater [ocean] side of the harbor'. This officer also stated that whenever there was a tsunami warning

the police department would send an officer down to watch the gauge. He stated they would wait for the alarm to sound before taking off, and pray that they reached Silva Street and Kalanianaole Avenue before the water came.

*Christmas Island and Samoa wave reports.* The logs record that Samoa and Christmas Island were impacted by a tsunami at 20:40 and 22:58, respectively. This information was recorded in the HPD log at 23:47 and in the HFD log at 23:53. The HFD log also reports that an official notification had been given by the Governor of Tahiti stating that Tahiti had suffered no damage.

*The first wave.* At 00:09 on 23 May 1960, the HPD log indicates that the tidal wave gauge (presumably at Pier One) exceeded the normal high tide level. At 00:15, the HCDA log reports that the HPD notified them that the gauge 'went off' and that the water had not begun to recede.

Five minutes later, all three agencies became aware that the tsunami had impacted Coconut Island. Also, the HFD log at 00:20 states that the tidal wave alarm at Pier One had sounded and the HCDA log notes that the water had begun to recede at 00:22 (please note: this entry was logged in at 00:20).

At 00:25 the HCDA received a call from the US Coast Guard stating that they should be aware that the drop in wave height is just as important as the rise in water (Table 3). Also at 00:25, the HPD log states that the water was receding at Wailoa and at 00:33 the HCDA log notes: 'water receding 5' below normal'. According to the log entries at 00:35, the HFD received a report from the Coast Guard at Pier One that water had receded 5 ft (1.5 m) below normal and that it was continuing to drop.

*The second wave.* The second wave was logged by the HPD at 00:44: 'Coconut Island covered with water and now flowing into Liliuokalani Park'; at 00:47: 'Water coming over the pier'; and at 00:52 'Water entering Hawaiian village at Wailoa'.

At 00:53, the HCDA log states 'Secured headquarters at 60 Shipman Street' and that is the last logged entry until 01:40. The HCDA evacuated their Shipman Street headquarters and relocated to the HFD because at that time their headquarters was located approximately 100 yards (91.4 m) from Hilo Bay and 100 ft (30.5 m) from the Wailuku River.

The HFD log details at 00:53 that the Naniloa Hotel was surrounded by water at 00:48 and, at 00:58, that Kamehameha Avenue was covered with water from the Hilo Theatre to Waiakea. At 01:00, the HPD log relates that 'water went to

**Table 2.** *Critical communication events from 21:56 on 22 May to 00:20 on 23 May 1960 (after Johnston 2003)*

| | 21.56 | 22.31 | 22.35 | 22.55 | 23.00 | 23.30 | 23.47 | 23.53 | 00.09 | 00.15 | 00.20 |
|---|---|---|---|---|---|---|---|---|---|---|---|
| Hawaii Civil Defense Agency (HCDA) | j | k1 | | | k4 | l | | | | n2 | o1 |
| Hilo Police Department | | | | k3 | | | m1 | | n1 | | o2 |
| Hawaii Fire Department | | | k2 | | | | | m2 | | | o3 |

Log entries:
j. Instructed to evacuate lower areas immediately.
k1. Wave hits Tahiti at 20.00, 3 ft. High.
k2. Tidal wave struck Tahiti at 20.00, wave three (3) feet high. Via walkie talkie from fireman Edward Ahuna at Civil Defense Office.
k3. Harold Marques, KHBC reported via News Service that at 20.00 and 20.10, Hawaiian time, 3'3' waves were recorded in Tahiti. First reports indicate no damage. Report is being evaluated by US Coast and Geodetic Survey in Honolulu.
k4. Col. Byrnes, Hon advised message – Wave struck Tahiti at 20.10, 39 in high.
l. Sgt. Bellah reported that the tidal wave gauge is normal.
m1. Sgt. Molina, Honolulu, reported that at 22.58 tonight a wave 1.3 ft. High struck Christmas Island.
m2. Wave struck Samoa at 20.40, height of wave: six (6) inches. Report received via walkie talkie from Fireman Edward Ahuna at Civil Defense office. Wave struck Christmas Island at 22.58, height of wave 1'3' high. No damages at Tahiti as notified officially by Liaison Fire Dept. Man at Civil Defense office.
n1. Tidal wave gauge went off.
n2. Lt. Rosehill called in, he reported that at 00.09 gauge went off. It has not started receding as yet.
o1. Coconut Island fully covered. Pier at Naniloa with water – close to 3 ft. high. Mrs Santos Asst. Mgr. Naniloa reported.
o2. Pakele: Coconut Island covered – pier at Naniloa Hotel 3' – water receding at 00.22.
o3. Coconut Island covered by tidal wave at 00.20. Tidal wave alarm at pier No. 1 went off 00.09. Liaison man Edward Ahuna reporting from CD office via walkie talkie.

**Table 3.** *Critical communication events from 00:25 to 01:05 on 23 May 1960 (after Johnston 2003)*

| | 00.25 | 00.33 | 00.35 | 00.35 | 00.44 | 00.47 | 00.52 | 00.53 | 00.58 | 01.00 | 01.03 | 01.05 |
|---|---|---|---|---|---|---|---|---|---|---|---|---|
| Hawaii Civil Defense Agency (HCDA) | p | q2 | q4 | q5 | | | | t | Civil Defense moved to Fire Station | | x1 | x2 |
| Hilo Police Department | q1 | | | | r1 | r2 | s1 | | | v | | |
| Hawaii Fire Department | | | | q3 | | | | s2 | u | w | | |

Log entries:

p. Commander Yaergain called in to let Col. Pakele know that drop of wave height is just as important.

q1. Sgt. yuhas reported that water was receding at Wailoa.

q2. Water receding 5' below normal.

q3. Coast Guard reported from pier No. 1 that water has receded 5 ft below normal and still going down. Report received via walkie talkie from Edward Ahuna.

q4. Col. Byrne from Honolulu called for Pakele – Col. Pakele reported that 5' water receding as reported by Commander Yaegain.

q5. Lt. Rosehill called in that the water has been receding since 00.22 – Coconut island is not covered but water came up to the turntable.

r1. Coconut Island covered with water and now flowing into Liiiuokalani Park.

r2. Water coming over pier.

s1. Water entered Hawaiian village at Wailoa.

s2. Naniloa Hotel surrounded by water at 00.48, water has reached Uyeda Store, corner of kapean land and Lihiwai Streets. South Point normal. Report received via walkie talkie from Edward Ahuna.

t. Secured Headquarters at 60 Shipman Street.

u. Front street on Kamehameha Avenue covered with water from Hilo Theater to Waiakea at 00.55 a.m., Edward Ahuna reporting from CD Office via walkie talkie.

v. Water went into intersection of Kalanianaole & Silva Sts – 100 yards.

w. Water over road right up to Hilo Armory. Lights on front street went out. Evacuating all cars from Shipman Street. CD Office evacuated from Headquarters at Shipman Street and to set up temporary headquarters in the Fire Prevention Bureau Office 9 Edward Ahuna reporting from CD via walkie talkie).

x1. Lights went out.

x2. Electricity went out. No power in city. Tidal wave hit town area.

intersection of Kalanianaole and Silva Sts. 100 yards [91.4 m]'. Three minutes later at 01:03 the HFD log states that there is water on the road right up to Hilo Armory (28 Shipman Street): 'Lights on front street went out. Evacuating all cars from Shipman Street. CD Office [HCDA] evacuated from Headquarters at Shipman Street and set up temporary headquarters in the Fire Prevention Bureau Office [HFD]'.

At 01:05 on 23 May 1960, the HPD log attests that the lights went out and at that same time the HFD log states 'Electricity went out. No power in city. Tidal Wave hit town area'.

*After Hilo went dark.* At 02:20, the HCDA log states that a captain from the HPD initiated co-ordination between the HPD, HFD and the HCDA. This is the first indication in the logs that there is any attempt to co-ordinate interagency communication.

According to the HCDA log, at 02:30 Governor Quinn announced over the radio, KGMB [Honolulu] and KHBC [Hilo], that all people should stay away from the beach areas. Quinn mentioned the seriousness of the damage in Hilo.

The HPD log indicates that the power was back on at 06:02 and at 06:24 the following announcement was made: 'Director of State CD [Civil Defense] agency to all islands – NO FURTHER DAMAGES FOR THE PRESENT FROM THIS TIDAL WAVE. ALERT CALLED OFF – 6:10 AM'.

*South point, Island of Hawaii.* It appears that the HCDA and the HPD believed that the tsunami would impact South Point (see Fig. 2) prior to Hilo. As there was no telephone available at South Point, the HCDA instructed the Kau Police Station to position a police officer as a lookout at South Point and to signal the arrival of the tsunami with a flare. This instruction came from the HCDA at 21:38 on 22 May 1960.

At 22:43, there are two log entries. First, the HPD log states that the HPD contacted the Kau Police Station asking for the police officer stationed at South Point to locate a certain person. The HPD instructed that 'He is to remain with this man and pass on information on the tidal wave to the Kau Station and in turn to Hilo Station as soon as possible'.

The second entry was in the HCDA log and it revealed that the HCDA had spoken to the HPD about: 'whether there is any possibility of some flare signal from the South Point area to the phone. Time is the element – to notify Honolulu . . .'.

At 22:45, the HCDA log reports that a radio amateur operating from South Point is to notify Hilo and Honolulu. HPD notes, at 22:49, that the HCDA requests that any messages received from South Point regarding the tidal wave are transmitted immediately to the HPD in Honolulu via a special use telephone line.

At 22:50, the HCDA called HPD for further information. The HPD reported no change from South Point at that time. Then, at 23:55, the HCDA called the HPD for the latest report by midnight from South Point. The HCDA log notes at midnight 'No change at South Point' and, at 00:52, 'South Point – No Activity'. Similarly, the HFD log states, at 00:53, 'South Point normal'. The HCDA, HPD and HFD logs do not mention South Point again.

*General observations.* None of the logs were signed and it is therefore not possible to tell who made the records. The logs of the HCDA were disorganized and it was apparent that there was more than one person journaling in the HCDA as different typewriters were used for the logs as well as different forms. The HCDA logs are time-dated using 24 h time, although the time was out of sequence in some instances. The evacuation of the HCDA headquarters may account for the discrepancies in the time sequence but there is no notation in the logs as to who was transcribing. Overall, the HFD log is the most concise of the three logs.

## Tsunami survivor interviews

The Pacific Tsunami Museum, formerly known as the Hilo Tsunami Museum, was founded in 1993. In 1996, the museum began collecting and archiving tsunami survivor interviews. By that time, many of the people who had survived the 1946 tsunami had passed away. The majority of the survivors who were interviewed were therefore under the age of 40 years during the 1946 event (Table 4). The 23 May 1960 Hilo tsunami survivor interviews were also gathered after 1996. In this case, the majority of interviewees were over 31 years of age at the time of the tsunami.

*1 April 1946.* There was no official tsunami warning issued for the 1946 tsunami. As the first tsunami wave arrived in Hilo shortly before 07:00, most people were either at home or in the process of going to work or school (Table 5). The first inclination of a problem for many people was when they witnessed the actual tsunami. Sixteen of the 45 interviewees stated that they saw the water before they heard the news from another source. Others were informed by word-of-mouth, in most cases from a relative or friend, but some people were only made aware of the tsunami by people yelling in the street.

More than half of the survivors left immediately and began running for safety but there were seven

**Table 4.** *Interviewee demographics*

| Year of tsunami | Gender | Age at time of tsunami (years) | | | | |
|---|---|---|---|---|---|---|
| | | 0–9 | 10–20 | 21–30 | 31–40 | 41 + |
| 1946 | 26 male | 5 | 10 | 9 | 2 | 0 |
| | 19 female | 3 | 11 | 3 | 2 | 0 |
| 1960 | 12 male | 1 | 3 | 3 | 3 | 2 |
| | 10 female | 0 | 0 | 3 | 3 | 4 |

individuals who made a decision to watch what was happening. Not realizing the danger, six of the 45 interviewees decided to go back into their homes. Three of the survivors did not have a chance to respond to information because their first knowledge of the tsunami was when they saw the water. One interviewee, who was a policeman during the tsunami, stated that he drove to the police station as soon as he was informed of the tsunami.

*23 May 1960.* As with the 1946 tsunami, the first warnings of the 1960 tsunami were announced outside of work hours and, as a result, most of the interviewees were at home when they heard about the tsunami (Table 6). Most interviewees received information about the tsunami by word-of-mouth while a few mentioned the warning siren and even less stated a government agency. Upon hearing about the tsunami, most interviewees stated that they stayed at home and a little more than a quarter evacuated.

*Tsunami survivor interviews – Bonk* et al. *(1960).* Bonk *et al.* (1960) administered a questionnaire to 327 people who lived in the impacted region of Hilo. Although there is no information in the report as to where the individuals were when they *first* heard about the tsunami, their results indicate that 60% were at home when the tsunami impacted Hilo. This compares to 68% in the study presented above.

Bonk *et al.* reported that 95% of their respondents heard the 20:35 warning siren and, of these respondents, 41% evacuated and 59% did not. In comparison, results of the interviews presented in this paper show that only 14% of interviewees heard the siren.

In their study, Bonk *et al.* asked 'Did you have information about the wave before it hit other than the siren?'. They reported that 80% answered 'yes' and 20% responded 'no'. Those respondents who stated yes received information from radio/TV (68%); relatives or friends (17%); police, fireman or civil defence (3%); radio/TV and relatives and friends (8%); radio/TV and government (3%); and other (1%).

When asked directly 'Did you hear the siren?' nearly all respondents in the Bonk *et al.* study stated 'yes'. Whereas in the interviews presented in this study, the interviewees were asked 'Where did you get the information?' and, therefore, probably responded with the method of communication

**Table 5.** *Interviewee responses in relation to the 1946 tsunami (n = 45)*

| Question | Response | % |
|---|---|---|
| Where were you when you heard about the tsunami? | Home | 60 |
| | Work | 11 |
| | Standing on road waiting for bus | 9 |
| | Other | 20 |
| Where did you get the information? | Saw wave | 36 |
| | Parent | 29 |
| | Relative | 16 |
| | Other person | 20 |
| What did you do? | Left house and ran | 60 |
| | Went to watch | 16 |
| | Went into house | 13 |
| | Wave hit without notice | 7 |
| | Other | 4 |

**Table 6.** *Interviewee responses in relation to the 1960 tsunami (n = 22)*

| Question | Response | % |
|---|---|---|
| Where were you when you heard about the tsunami? | Home | 68 |
| | Work | 18 |
| | Other | 14 |
| Where did you get the information? | Word of mouth | 41 |
| | Radio | 18 |
| | Siren | 14 |
| | Civil Defense | 9 |
| | Saw wave | 9 |
| | Other | 9 |
| What did you do? | Stayed in house | 36 |
| | Evacuated | 27 |
| | Went to watch | 18 |
| | Stayed at work | 9 |
| | Other | 9 |

that made the greatest impact regardless of whether or not they had actually heard the siren. This is easily reconcilable since there had been several occasions in previous days when the sirens were used to warn of a tsunami and no destructive tsunami occurred.

Upon hearing the siren, respondents in the Bonk *et al.* study waited for further information (45%); evacuated (32%); went about normal activity (15%); or other responses (9%). Whereas, those who received information from other sources either evacuated (36%); prepared to evacuate (30%); awaited further instruction (19%); did not respond (10%); went to watch (3%); and continued their normal routine (1%). In the present study, however, only 27% evacuated while 18% went to watch and 36% stayed at home.

# Discussion

The research suggests that governmental agencies did not efficiently communicate or co-ordinate during the 1960 tsunami, which led to confusion between the agencies. Exacerbating the situation were media inaccuracies (Eaton *et al.* 1961) and a public naive of their vulnerability to tsunami hazard (Johnston 2003). These issues are discussed in the following sections.

## Procedures and co-ordination

One of the most interesting discoveries was the lack of communication between the agencies *and* to the public, and a lack of understanding of the phenomena. It took until 02:20 on 23 May 1960, more than 14 h *after* the HPD first notified the HCDA of the tsunami hazard warning, for the agencies to co-ordinate their efforts. It is noticeable from reviewing the logs that there was virtually no co-ordination between government agencies during the pre-impact period with one exception – the HFD sent one of their employees to the HCDA with a handheld radio so that he could report the latest news to them. Interagency communication and co-operation should be established long before a disaster occurs and much was learnt from this event.

The logs of the HCDA were understandably disorganized as they had to evacuate from their headquarters and move their operations to the HFD. Overall, the HFD log was the most concise and they received information in a timely manner because they sent one of their employees over to the HCDA to act as a liaison.

Although it appears that the HPD was the lead agency for response in Hilo during the tsunami, permission to sound the tsunami warning system had to come from the State Civil Defense on Oahu. It would have been, therefore, more expedient for the State Civil Defense to notify the HCDA directly. Also, the 'tidal wave alert' message was received by the HPD 23 min after the message had been issued by the US Coast and Geodetic Survey Observatory. It is apparent that there were no procedures in place and that any action taken was left to the discretion of the individual deputy director.

Another issue was that the authorities did not evacuate homes in the inundation zone. Eaton *et al.* (1961, p. 140) reported that some time after 02:15 on 23 May 1960, when they ventured back into Hilo that they found 'Hilo's streets had been evacuated, but its buildings had not'.

## Media misinformation

According to Eaton *et al.* (1961), at around 00:30 when the water from the first wave had begun to recede, a Honolulu radio station reported that the tsunami had not yet impacted Hawaii and the estimated time of arrival had been set back half an hour. It was then realized 'with growing uneasiness that communications between crucial observation points and public news media had broken down' (Eaton *et al.* 1961, p. 139).

However, other residents returned home after the first wave had impacted Hilo after hearing on the radio that the tsunami waves had already impacted the island (Atwater *et al.* 2005). Adding to the confusion, these residents were met by a police officer who informed them that the hazard had passed, but at around 01:00 they heard the low rumbling sound of the next tsunami wave impacting the coast.

## Tsunami awareness

A lack of tsunami awareness was clearly demonstrated by various government agencies. First, the HPD sending an officer down to watch the gauge whenever a tsunami warning was issued shows that the police department lacked understanding and awareness of tsunami hazard and vulnerability. Secondly, following the devastation that occurred in 1946, a more appropriate early warning system should have been installed other than the HPD sending a police officer as a lookout to South Point at the instruction of the HCDA. Thirdly, it should have been apparent that an agency such as the HCDA, whose function it was to respond to a tsunami, should not be located in the evacuation zone.

Furthermore, the US Army Engineer's Report (1960) testified that an employee from the Corps of Engineers was sent to Hilo to observe and report on the tsunami. Sadly, he lost his life in the 1960 disaster. As with the other lives lost, his life could have been spared if the authorities and population were educated on tsunami hazards and how to take appropriate action in response to the warning signal.

Governor Quinn's radio announcement at 02:30 on 23 May 1960, that people should stay away from the beach areas, should have been made in conjunction with the tsunami warning sirens which sounded between 20:35 and 20:50 on 22 May 1960. This time period presented a perfect opportunity to explain the new warning system to the public as it was changed only a few months earlier. The public needed to know that one siren indicated immediate evacuation. In a more recent study, Gregg et al. (2007) concluded that public understanding of the tsunami warning sirens in Hilo still remains low and, therefore, a major change in tsunami education is essential to increase public understanding of, and effective response to, future tsunamis.

Eaton et al. (1961) stated that the failure of nearly two-thirds of the residents to evacuate in spite of notice on 22 May 1960 that a tsunami would reach Hilo 'points up a fatal flaw in the public's understanding that low-lying seashore areas must be evacuated before the expected tsunami strikes' (p. 156). Adding to this misunderstanding is the fact that the area in Hilo impacted by the 1960 tsunami was not the same as in 1946. As a result, many people decided to stay home because they perceived that their area was not vulnerable or they did not understand the meaning of the warning sirens (Atwater et al. 2005). This further highlights the need to educate the public on tsunami hazard and warning, and to ensure that they are aware of their vulnerability in all regions.

An effective and compelling approach to tsunami education is through the use of the survivor video interviews. These videos provide immense value to education initiatives because they reveal visual emotive elements that other media sources lack (Dudley et al. 2009). Educational videos are also being used to retell traditional stories that relate to recognizing natural warning signs and suggesting appropriate behavioural responses. For example, the video Run to Higher Ground! uses a mix of traditional stories and contemporary approaches to educate schools and communities about tsunami hazards, warnings and response to warnings (Becker et al. 2008). These educational tools might also prove valuable in increasing awareness among emergency management and media personnel.

In a report written by the Geophysical Society of Hawaii (1960, p. 1) the need for tsunami awareness is emphasized:

The poignancy of this tragedy is intensified by the fact that it was obviously technically preventable. An

advisory bulletin on a possible tsunami had been made public nearly 12 h before a wave could arrive, and a formal warning was publicly issued four hours in advance. It appears certain that this information reached the people concerned, not only in Hilo but generally in shoreline areas of the state. Yet many failed to take adequate precautionary action and, worse, others, spurred by curiosity, placed themselves in unnecessary danger. This behaviour, and the testimony of many whose lives were spared, indicate a failure on the part of a large segment of the public to understand the nature of magnitude of the risks to which they subjected themselves.

Like other islands in the Pacific Ocean, the Hawaiian Islands are vulnerable to tsunami from both locally (e.g. earthquakes, volcanic eruptions and/ or submarine landslides) and distantly generated (e.g. circum-Pacific subduction zones) sources such as the recent 27 February 2010 Chilean Earthquake (Goff et al. 2011). Steps are being taken by government agencies to reduce the risk from the next catastrophic tsunami (e.g. Crawford 2005; Darienzo et al. 2005; Dengler 2005; Eisner 2005; Johnston et al. 2005). These efforts include enhancing collaboration between emergency management and scientific agencies, and providing media training workshops (Jonientz-Trisler et al. 2005). However, these efforts must be continued and improved upon in order to prevent the next tsunami hazard becoming a disaster in Hilo.

## Conclusion

No distant destructive tsunamis have impacted Hawaii since 1960 but the 26 December 2004 Indian Ocean tsunami showed that we, as a society, are complacent. This complacency has led to several generations of people who know very little about the phenomena of tsunamis. Tsunami preparation and increased awareness are essential to lessen the impact of future tsunami disasters (Johnston 2003).

Reports following the devastating 1960 tsunami emphasized the lack of public understanding of tsunami hazards and of the risks to which individuals subjected themselves. Fifty years on, events like the 29 September 2009 South Pacific tsunami and the 25 October 2010 Mentawai Islands, Indonesia tsunami, highlight the desperate need for continuing tsunami education for locals, visitors and hospitality staff in regions vulnerable to tsunami hazards.

Hawaii is an island state and, therefore, it is not only those who live and work in the inundation zones who are potential victims, but visitors too. In the case of a locally generated tsunami, anyone in the inundation zone would be at risk. An Australian tourist holidaying in Waikiki is just as vulnerable as a resident to losing their life due to lack of tsunami awareness, understanding and preparedness. Every person must therefore formulate an evacuation plan whether they live, work or occasionally use the beaches and parks for recreation. *Continuing* tsunami education is the key to creating a culture of awareness, understanding and preparedness.

Education campaigns must also focus on increasing awareness, understanding and preparedness among government officials, the media and hospitality staff. For example, it is the ignorance of the phenomena that leads the media to disseminate inaccurate information prior to the event, and during the watch and warning period – a time when concise and accurate information is *essential* to save lives. Fischer (1998) explained that disaster researchers have an obligation to the communities and to society at large to lead the educational process so that it will reach the public, the emergency managers and the reporters. In Hawaii, it is imperative that media agencies are included in disaster mitigation meetings and that a continuing programme of media education be instituted.

A catastrophic tsunami will occur in Hawaii in the future and, therefore, there will be a need for timely and accurate communication. An increasingly complex and diverse society with a growing population and commercial environment in the inundation zone increases the need for institutionalizing the dissemination of critical, life-saving information to the population.

# References

ATWATER, B. F., CISTERNAS, V. M., BOURGEOIS, J., DUDLEY, W. C., HENDLEY, J. W. II. & STAUFFER, P. H. 2005. *Surviving a Tsunami – Lessons from Chile, Hawaii and Japan*. United States Department of the Interior, United States Geological Survey Circular, **1187**.

BECKER, J., JOHNSTON, D., LAZRUS, H., CRAWFORD, G. & NELSON, D. 2008. Use of traditional knowledge in emergency management for tsunami hazard: a case study from Washington State, USA. *Disaster Prevention and Management*, **17**, 488–502.

BIRD, D. K., CHAGUÉ-GOFF, C. & GERO, A. 2011. Human response to extreme events: a review of three post-tsunami disaster case studies. *Australian Geographer*, **42**, 225–239.

BONK, W. J., LACHMAN, R. & TATSUOKA, M. 1960. *A Report of Human Behavior During the Tsunami of May 23, 1960*. Hawaii Division of the Hawaiian Academy of Science, Hilo, HI.

CRAWFORD, G. L. 2005. NOAA weather radio (NWR) – a coastal solution to Tsunami alert and notification. *Natural Hazards*, **35**, 163–171.

DARIENZO, M., AYA, A., CRAWFORD, G. L., GIBBS, D., WHITMORE, P. M., WILDE, T. & YANAGI, B. S. 2005. Local Tsunami warning in the Pacific Coastal United States. *Natural Hazards*, **35**, 111–119.

DENGLER, L. 2005. The role of education in the national tsunami hazard mitigation program. *Natural Hazards*, **35**, 141–153.

DUDLEY, W. & STONE, S. C. 2000. *The Tsunamis of 1946 and 1960*. Donning Press, Virginia Beach, VA.

DUDLEY, W., GOFF, J., CHAGUÉ-GOFF, C. & JOHNSTON, J. 2009. Capturing the next generation of cultural memories – the process of video interviewing tsunami survivors. *Science of Tsunami Hazards*, **28**, 154–170.

DUDLEY, W. C. & LEE, M. 1998. *Tsunami!*. University of Hawai'i Press, Honolulu.

EATON, J. P., RICHTER, D. H. & AULT, W. U. 1961. The tsunami of May 23, 1960, on the Island of Hawaii. *Bulletin of the Seismological Society of America*, **51**, 135–157.

EISNER, R. K. 2005. Planning for tsunami: reducing future losses through mitigation. *Natural Hazards*, **35**, 155–162.

FISCHER, H. W. 1998. *Response to Disaster: Fact versus. Fiction and its Perpetuation. The Sociology of Disaster*. University Press of America, Lanham, Maryland, 220.

GEOPHYSICAL SOCIETY OF HAWAII 1960. *Tsunami Warning System Review*. Geophysical Society of Hawaii Committee, Honolulu, HI, 14.

GOFF, J., CHAGUÉ-GOFF, C. *ET AL.* 2011. Palaeotsunamis in the Pacific Islands. *Earth-Science Reviews*, **107**, 141–146, doi: 10.1016/j.earscirev.2010.10.005.

GREGG, C. E., HOUGHTON, B. F., PATON, D., JOHNSTON, D. M., SWANSON, D. A. & YANAGI, B. S. 2007. Tsunami warnings: understanding in Hawai'i. *Natural Hazards*, **40**, 71–87.

JOHNSTON, D., PATON, D., CRAWFORD, G. L., RONAN, K., HOUGHTON, B. & BURGELT, P. 2005. Measuring tsunami preparedness in coastal Washington, United States. *Natural Hazards*, **35**, 173–184.

JOHNSTON, D., PETTERSSON, R., DOWNES, G., PATON, D., LEONARD, G., PISHIEF, K. & BELL, R. 2008. Developing an effective tsunami warning system: lessons from the 1960 Chile earthquake tsunami for New Zealand coastal communities. *Kōtuitui: New Zealand Journal of Social Sciences Online*, **3**, 105–120.

JOHNSTON, J. 2003. *Personal Accounts from the Survivors of the Hilo Tsunamis of 1946 and 1960: Toward a Disaster Communication Model*. Master of Arts in Communications thesis, University of Hawai'i, Hilo.

JONIENTZ-TRISLER, C., SIMMONS, R. S. *ET AL.* 2005. Planning for tsunami-resilient communities. *Natural Hazards*, **35**, 121–139.

KANAMORI, H. 1977. The energy release in great earthquakes. *Journal of Geophysical Research*, **82**, 2981–2987.

LACHMAN, R., TATSUOKA, M. & BONK, W. J. 1961. Human behavior during the tsunami of May 1960: research on the Hawaiian disaster explores the consequences of an ambiguous warning system. *Science*, **133**, 1405–1409.

MURATA, S., IMAMURA, F., KATOH, K., KAWATA, Y., TAKAHASHI, S. & TAKAYAMA, T. 2010. *Tsunami: to Survive from Tsunami*. World Scientific Publishing, Singapore, 302.

NISHIMOTO, W. S. 2000. *Tsunamis Remembered: Oral Histories of Survivors and Observers in Hawai'i*. Centre for Oral History. College of Social Sciences, University of Hawai'i at Manoa, 980.

RIPLEY, A. 2008. *The Unthinkable: Who Survives When Disaster Strikes – and Why*. Crown Publishers, New York.

SHEPARD, F. P., MacDONALD, G. A. & COX, D. C. 1949. The Tsunami of April 1, 1946. *Bulletin of the Scripps Institution of Oceanography*, **5**, 391–527.

US ARMY ENGINEER DISTRICT 1960. *Tsunami of 23 May 1960 in Hawaii, Final Post-flood Report*. US Army Corps of Engineers, Honolulu, HI.

# Towards better design and management of tsunami evacuation routes: a case study of Ao Jak Beach Road

ALAN D. ZIEGLER[1]*, ROY C. SIDLE[2], MANDY S. SONG[1], ZUO JIN ANG[1] &
DECHA DUANGNAMON[3]

[1]*Department of Geography, National University of Singapore, 1 Arts Link, Kent Ridge,
Singapore 117570*

[2]*US Environmental Protection Agency, Ecosystems Research Division,
960 College Station Road, Athens, GA 30605, USA*

[3]*Andaman Coastal Research Station for Development, Ranong, Thailand*

*\*Corresponding author (e-mail: adz@nus.edu.sg)*

**Abstract:** Among the thousands of people killed or reported missing in Thailand during the 2004 Indian Ocean Tsunami were villagers in small communities on the Andaman Coast. A combination of factors contributed to loss of life, including the lack of defined evacuation routes. This vulnerability to tsunami attacks has recently been addressed with the demarcation of evacuation routes, along both well-maintained arteries and native surface (unpaved) roads. However, poor location design and irregular maintenance will reduce the lifetime that the latter can provide safe egress from remote coastlines. In this work we identified 10 major gullies and 18 landslides along a critical 0.5 km section of a tsunami evacuation road accessing a remote beach of the Andaman Coast in southern Thailand. Erosion rates from landslides and gullies approached 9500 Mg ha$^{-1}$ in less than a year following widening of the road. Importantly, the degradation features, landslides in particular, reduced the effectiveness of the road to serve as a safe passageway to escape future tsunamis or large storm surges. This study demonstrates that greater attention should be given to appropriate road location, design and maintenance in integrated programmes aimed at reducing tsunami vulnerability in remote coastal areas, not only on the Andaman Coast, but worldwide.

A magnitude 9.1 earthquake off the NW coast of Sumatra early in the morning of 26 December 2004 generated a deadly tsunami that reached the coastlines of 14 Indian Ocean countries, killing an estimated 230 000 people and displacing almost two million more (Ziegler *et al.* 2009; USGS 2010) (Fig. 1a). The highest death toll was near the epicentre in Aceh (Sumatra), where 180 000 perished; and casualties from as far away as Africa were reported (Guerena-Burgueno *et al.* 2006; Obura 2006). In Thailand, more than 5000 died and thousands more were reported missing (Guerena-Burgueno *et al.* 2006). Most of the victims in coastal Thailand were tourists, but many villagers in small communities along the Andaman Coast also perished (Birkland *et al.* 2006; Rigg *et al.* 2008). A combination of factors are likely to have contributed to the loss of life on the southern coasts of Thailand, including insufficient early warning systems, poor education regarding tsunami risks, destruction of natural ecosystem defenses by human activities and the lack of defined evacuation routes leading from coastal waters to safe zones at higher elevations (Charnkol

& Tanaboriboon 2006; Cochard *et al.* 2008; Srivichai *et al.* 2009).

Reducing tsunami vulnerability has been a priority since the 2004 disaster (Rigg *et al.* 2005; Calgaro & Lloyd 2008). New evacuation routes, for example, have been established in many high-risk coastal areas in tsunami-prone areas of southern Thailand (TAT 2010). Most were established along well-maintained roads already in existence; however, in some cases native surface (unpaved) roads have become designated evacuation routes, especially for remote coastlines. Unlike paved roads near population centres, low-volume roads in developing areas are typically located with little regard for stability and they are often poorly designed and maintained, thereby reducing the lifetime that they can provide safe egress (Sidle *et al.* 2006). Only limited attention has been given to roads in the post-tsunami literature, with most given to road and bridge damage; others comment on the distances that must be traversed before reaching safety (e.g. Edwards 2004; Ziegler *et al.* 2009). Herein, we measure erosion and landslide features on a recently improved tsunami evacuation road in

*From*: TERRY, J. P. & GOFF, J. (eds) 2012. *Natural Hazards in the Asia–Pacific Region: Recent Advances and Emerging Concepts*. Geological Society, London, Special Publications, **361**, 107–114, http://dx.doi.org/10.1144/SP361.9

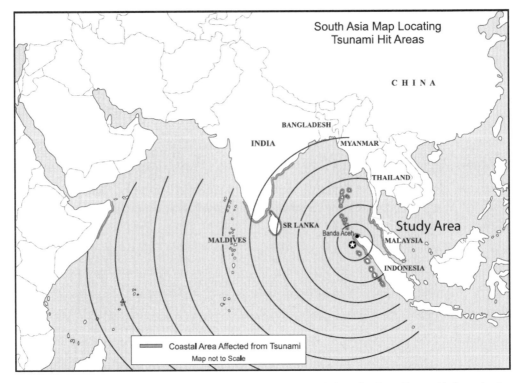

**Fig. 1.** Study area on the Andaman Coast of Thailand. The epicentre of the 2004 Indian Ocean Tsunami is shown (star). Map credit: Lee Li Kheng.

an attempt to understand how poor construction and irregular maintenance have reduced its effectiveness in providing long-term safe egress.

## Study area

The Ao Jak Beach Road in the Suksamran District of Ranong Province, Thailand, accesses a remote coastal area where farmers and fishermen outnumber tourists (Fig. 1). The road replaced a narrow native surface track following the 2004 tsunami, which claimed the lives of several residents of nearby villages who failed to escape inland. In the latter part of 2009, the road was widened to improve accessibility to the coast, thereby reducing vulnerability to future tsunamis (Fig. 2a). Currently, the road is primarily used by local villagers to access fields, orchards and fishing spots. Tourists are beginning to use the road to access a remote beach and a few sparsely located bed and breakfast lodges. Vehicle traffic is largely restricted to motorcycles and small pickup trucks.

Ideally, a balanced cut-and-fill construction approach is desired to increase the operational road width and promote slope stability (Fig. 3a).

Such an approach requires the excavated material to be carefully incorporated and compacted into the outer portion of the road prism (Fig. 3a). However, material excavated from the hill-slope during widening of the Ao Jak Beach Road was simply pushed to the outer side of the road prism where it created a berm, as well as a bed of unstable material on the fill-slope (Figs 2a & 3b). Some of the excavated material was incorporated onto the running surface of the road; other material remained near the cut-slope and some was eroded down-slope (Fig. 2). In general, no provisions were made for managing road drainage. Runoff water flowing on the road surface or within the inside ditch of the road prism was allowed to exit onto fill-slopes, which were inadequately prepared to receive runoff.

The impact of the widening process on the Ao Jak Road was akin to new construction, especially with respect to cut-slope stability. This manner of construction is common in locations throughout SE Asia where funding is limited. Excavating into the fractured and sheared sandstone bedrock over-steepened and removed support at the cutbank, destabilizing the upper hill-slope. Consequentially, in less than 1 year, many types of slope failures occurred on both the cut-slope and in the fill

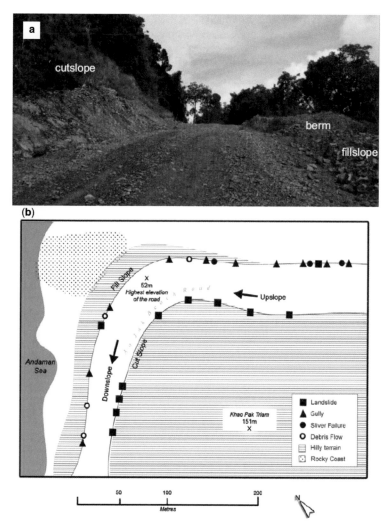

**Fig. 2.** (**a**) Crest of the Ao Jak Beach Road. Coarse gravel has been placed on the surface to improve traction. Unconsolidated material forms a berm on the fill-slope (right-hand side) after being excavated from the cut-slope (left). (**b**) Location on the Ao Jak Beach of observed landslides (boxes); debris flows (hexagon); sliver failures (circles); and gullies (stars). The road width is not drawn to scale.

materials; and gully erosion was prevalent on the fill-slope.

Ranong is the wettest province in Thailand – five of the wet-season months have a mean monthly rainfall of more than 500 mm (Table 1). Thus, the potential for surface erosion and mass failures in the area is very high (Degraff 1990; Phien-Wej *et al.*1993). The failures we observed on the Ao Jak Road were not caused by unusually large storms, rather by relatively small rain events between November 2009 and June 2010. The 967 mm of rainfall during this 8 month period is only about a quarter of the annual mean (Table 1).

## Measurements

In June 2010, we mapped gullies and slope failures on a critical 0.5 km road section that rises to about 50 m above the beach (Fig. 2b). The mean ($\pm 1$ SD) width of the road was $7.3 \pm 2.3$ m ($n = 25$); the mean road slope was $7.3° \pm 2.6°$ ($n = 25$). Three types of slope failures were identified: landslides on both cut-and-fill slopes, debris flows; and sliver failures (Fig. 4). Sliver failures are shallow slides in loosely or uncompacted fill material deposited on steep slopes (Sidle *et al.* 1985). The volume of material mobilized by most of these processes

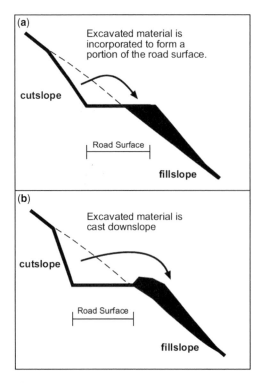

**Fig. 3.** (**a**) A balanced cut-and-fill road construction technique that incorporates compacted, excavated hill-slope material into the fill-slope to form a substantial portion the road width. (**b**) During road widening at Ao Jak, excavated material was side cast onto the fill-slope rather than being incorporated into the design of the operating portion of the road (adapted from FAO 1998).

was determined by estimating the volume of the geometrical shape of the deposited material (e.g. trapezoid, triangle or rectangle). In cases where the material had been eroded away, the scars were measured. Because we were interested in processes that were immediately threatening road accessibility, we did not quantify total erosion on the entire road prism. For example, we were unable to quantify the chronic process of road surface erosion by overland flow because it was greatly altered by the recent addition of coarse gravel to improve traction on steep sections.

## Results

The survey revealed 10 gullies and 18 slope failures that amounted to a total of 2664 m³ of material mobilized along the 0.5 km stretch of road (Fig. 2b; Table 2). Mass-wasting processes (landslide, debris flows and sliver failures) comprised nearly 98% of the volume of material displaced. Only about 2% of the sediment loss was attributed to gully erosion. There was no discernable relationship between drainage area and erosion or slope failure features (cf. Montgomery 1994). The gravel surfacing may have limited gully formation on the running surface but it did not prevent gullies from forming on other parts of the road prism.

Landslides represented the largest volume of displaced material (2178 m³). Eight of the 11 landslides occurred on hill-slopes steeper than 40° (Fig. 5). Most of the landslides were shallow debris slides that were initiated during rainfall events. These slides were characterized by a distinct scarp at the head, a translational failure plane and a

**Table 1.** *Mean (1961–1990), 2009 and 2010 rainfall for Ranong Province (TMD 2010)*

|  | Long-term mean | | 2009 | | 2010 | |
|---|---|---|---|---|---|---|
|  | Rainfall (mm) | No. of days | Rainfall (mm) | No. of days | Rainfall (mm) | No. of days |
| January | 19 | 4 | 10 | 1 | 31 | 5 |
| February | 13 | 3 | 0 | 1 | 10 | 4 |
| March | 34 | 5 | 141 | 18 | 46 | 6 |
| April | 140 | 12 | 305 | 20 | 30 | 6 |
| May | 513 | 23 | 586 | 27 | 307 | 24 |
| June | 734 | 26 | 778 | 26 | 454 | 26 |
| July | 654 | 27 | 809 | 24 | 615 | 27 |
| August | 809 | 28 | 684 | 27 | 615 | 27 |
| September | 675 | 26 | 641 | 23 | 296 | 21 |
| October | 393 | 23 | 360 | 21 | 540 | 26 |
| November | 165 | 15 | 74 | 10 | 211 | 18 |
| December | 38 | 7 | 15 | 5 | 162 | 11 |
| Total | 4187 | 199 | 4405 | 203 | 3315 | 201 |

**Fig. 4.** Slope failures and gullies on the Ao Jak Road: (**a**) landslide along a cut-slope; (**b**) debris flow on a fill-slope; (**c**) sliver failure in fill-slope material; and (**d**) gully formation from overland flow incising a rill on unconsolidated fill-slope material.

fan-shaped talus slope at the base (Fig. 4a). Because most landslides occurred on cut-slopes, mobilized material was often deposited on the road surface or carried across the road and deposited on the fill-slope.

The four debris flows that accounted for 389 m³ of sediment all occurred on the fill-slope (Table 2; Fig. 4b). These rapid mass-wasting features are characterized as a liquefied mass of sediment flowing down-slope with no scarp at the head of the failure. Sliver failures accounted for only about 40 m³ of material mobilized (Fig. 4c). Both debris flows and sliver failures occurred on relatively steep slopes of 30°– 45° (Fig. 5). The 10 measured gullies originated from rills that were incised by concentrated overland flow (Fig. 4d). They occurred across a wide range of slopes

(15°–40°); and they mobilized, on average, only about 6 m³ of material each (Fig. 5).

The estimated volume of material mobilized by nine cut-slope landslides was 2136 m³, compared with 528 m³ removed by 19 fill-slope failures and gullies (Table 2). Landslides, in particular, occurred on the unstable, oversteepened cut-slopes. In contrast, debris flows occurred exclusively on fill-slopes, where failure of unconsolidated material was triggered by the inflow of concentrated overland flow together with gravitational stresses on the steep unconsolidated slopes. Although numerous fill-slope failures were present, the volume of mobilized material was limited by the availability of unconsolidated material. Despite the disparity in the number and severity of degradation features above and below the road, all collectively threaten

**Table 2.** *Summary of number (n), slope, and volumes of the failures and gullies on cut- and fill-slopes*

| Type | n | Hill-slope gradient (°) | Total volume (m³) | Cut-slope (n) | Fill-slope (n) | Cut-slope volume (m³) | Fill-slope volume (m³) | Mean volume (m³) | Sediment yield (Mg ha⁻¹) |
|---|---|---|---|---|---|---|---|---|---|
| Landslide | 11 | 41 ± 4 | 2178 | 9 | 2 | 2136 | 42 | 198 ± 344 | 7757 |
| Debris flow | 4 | 37 ± 5 | 389 | 0 | 4 | 0 | 389 | 97 ± 72 | 1385 |
| Sliver failure | 3 | 37 ± 6 | 39 | 0 | 3 | 0 | 39 | 13 ± 6 | 139 |
| Gully | 10 | 31 ± 8 | 58 | 0 | 10 | 0 | 58 | 6 ± 9 | 207 |
| Total | 28 | 34 ± 7 | 2664 | 9 | 19 | 2136 | 528 | 95 ± 229 | 9488 |

*n* is the number of measurements made; gradient and mean volume are the mean ± 1 SD; all other values are totals. Sediment yield was determined assuming that the bulk density of material removed was 1.3 Mg m⁻³; the mean width of the 0.5 km stretch of road was 7.3 m.

the access and longevity of the road – although the road was still passable at the time of observation. Furthermore, gully erosion and slope failures were contributing to other environmental problems, such as sedimentation in down-slope residential areas and potentially sensitive coastal ecosystems (e.g. coral reefs).

The total erosion rate from the measured slope failures and gullies along the 0.5 km section of the Ao Jak Beach Road was nearly 9500 Mg ha⁻¹ year⁻¹, with the majority of this being associated with landslides (Table 2). This estimate was based on a mean road width of 7.3 m for the 0.5 km stretch of surveyed road. Although our assessment was carried within the first year following widening and we would expect the risk of additional failures to eventually reduce with time, secondary failures involving the remobilization of material from prior failures may still occur in the future (Sidle *et al.*

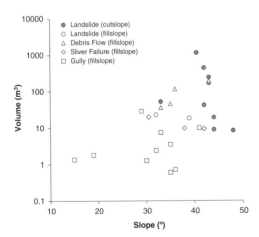

**Fig. 5.** Relationship between failure type, location (cut-slope or fill-slope) and the total volume of material mobilized (Table 2). Cut-slope landslides, which mobilized the most material, typically occurred on the steepest slopes (filled circles).

2011). However, the rate is a lower-bound annual estimate because it was determined for a period of time that did not include the four wettest months of the monsoon rainy season. It also does not include on-surface road erosion, which could not be quantified accurately.

The high value found at Ao Jak was similar to the 9600 Mg ha⁻¹ year⁻¹ rate reported for a 23.5 km stretch of road in Yunnan Province, China (Sidle *et al.* 2011). However, the rate is much lower than the maximum value of a severely affected stretch of road in the Yunnan study (33 000 Mg ha⁻¹ year⁻¹), which was the highest landslide rate ever reported along roads.

## Recommendations

To be effective tsunami evacuation corridors, such roads are often constructed in rugged terrain because of the need to rapidly transport people to higher elevations. In all cases of secondary road building, the location of the road must be carefully determined in order to avoid particularly unstable locations, paying close attention to unstable site indicators (Sidle *et al.* 1985). The route should also be evaluated by a geotechnical engineer or engineering geologist; and construction should follow recognized guidelines (e.g. Kellar & Sherar 2003). If not properly located, planned and constructed, as is often the case in rural remote areas in SE Asia, these roads may either fail completely or restrict access owing to the chronic sedimentation resulting from the unstable conditions. Furthermore, road-related landslides themselves pose a separate hazard to travellers (Sidle *et al.* 2011).

Cutbanks can fail when roads are excavated into steep hillslides, especially where bedrock dips parallel to the slope or where it is highly fractured or jointed (Sidle & Ochiai 2006). Slope failures also occur because of the disruption of equilibrium forces within the hill-slope following construction or because concentrated water is discharged onto unstable slope segments (Sidle & Ochiai

2006). Where possible, roads should not cut into steep and unstable slopes because of the risk of destabilizing the hill-slope. Our measurements showed that the largest volume of material came from cut-slope failures, and that these features often trigger fill-slope failures. Thus, consideration must be given to constructing cut-slopes at stable angles or in more stable substrate, based on the geotechnical properties of the hill-slope materials. For example, for the fractured sandstone found along the Ao Jak Road, a proper slope ratio (horizontal:vertical) would be 1:1–1.5:1 (Keller & Sherar 2003). Cut-slopes may also need to be stabilized with rock buttresses, gabions or mechanically stabilized earth structures (Keller & Sherar 2003). However, expensive mechanical stabilization structures along such secondary roads are generally prohibitively expensive, particularly in developing nations.

Fill-slope failures, such as those observed along the Ao Jak Road (Fig. 5), may be avoided by utilizing full bench construction when slopes exceed 30°–35°. This would require moving some excavated material offsite, rather than simply casting it down the hill-slope. If full bench construction is not possible, a series of small benches could be constructed. Fills should be properly compacted; and retaining structures, reinforced fills and mechanically stabilized earth structures can be utilized to maximize stabilization (Keller & Sherar 2003).

The frequency and intensity of slope failures can generally be reduced by preventing the build-up of positive pore-water pressure through adequate drainage of interflow and surface water to geologically stable locations (Sidle & Ochiai 2006). In addition, the removal of protective vegetation should be avoided to help limit the generation of concentrated overland flow that may erode the fill-slope or undercut the cut-slope (Montgomery 1994). Concentrated road runoff is common in mountainous terrain: it may be generated by the interception of subsurface flow by the cut-slope or initiated on the consolidated road surface as an excess infiltration process during most rainfall events (Ziegler et al. 2001, 2007).

The creation of a berm on the outside edge of the road should be avoided, as these features have the tendency to concentrate runoff, thereby increasing the likelihood of slope failures or gullying when the flow is finally discharged onto the hill-slope. On slopes exceeding 6°–7°, in-sloped or crowned roads with cross drain culverts, placed at appropriate distances, would help eliminate the development of high volumes of concentrated overland flow on the road surface (Keller & Sherar 2003). Ideally, inside ditches should be lined to prevent incision. Properly designed outlets with rock protection should be located on the fill-slope side to prevent

gullying and debris sliding (Sidle 1980). In most cases, the drainage of runoff directly onto the fill-slope should be avoided.

## Conclusion

Evacuation roads serving remote coastlines are problematic in the sense that the immediate success of reducing vulnerability is short-lived if slope failures and surface erosion degrade the road quickly following construction. Given the importance of secondary roads as evacuation routes, more attention is needed to ensure that proper location and design are integral components of tsunami vulnerability reduction and preparedness efforts. Poor road design often leads to chronic degradation that requires substantial maintenance. Steep grades, which are desirable to gain elevation rapidly to escape tsunami surges, are highly susceptible to landslide erosion. Deep cuts into unstable bedrock should be avoided whenever possible. Special attention should be given to road drainage in wet, unstable areas; and drainage water should be routed away from these and other potentially unstable sites down-slope of the road. In some locations, it may not be sensible to rely solely on low-maintenance roads for evacuation – for example, remote coastlines that are secluded by rugged terrain. In such situations other safety measures may be more appropriate, such as the construction of tsunami-proof evacuation structures; however, these types of interventions are prohibitively expensive for developing nations.

This study was funded by NUS grants #R-109-000-092-133 and Singapore–Delft Water Alliance (SDWA) JBE Part A (Joint Singapore Marine Programme–JSMP) research grant R-303-001-020-414. We also thank the detailed comments and suggestions by two anonymous reviewers.

## References

BIRKLAND, T. A., HERABAT, P., LITTLE, P. G. & WALLACE, W. A. 2006. The impact of the December 2004 Indian Ocean tsunami on tourism in Thailand. *Earthquake Spectra*, **22**, S889–S900.

CALGARO, E. & LLOYD, K. 2008. Sun, sea, sand and tsunami: examining disaster vulnerability in the tourism community of Khao Lak, Thailand. *Singapore Journal of Tropical Geography*, **29**, 288–306.

CHARNKOL, T. & TANABORIBOON, Y. 2006. Evacuee behaviors and factors affecting the tsunami trip generation model: a case study in Phang-nga, Thailand. *Journal of Advanced Transportation*, **40**, 313–330.

COCHARD, R., RANAMUKHAARACHCHI, S. L., SHIVAKOTI, G. P., SHIPIN, O. V., EDWARDS, P. J. & SEELAND, K. L. 2008. The 2004 tsunami in Aceh and southern Thailand: a review on coastal ecosystems, wave hazards and vulnerability. *Perspectives in Plant Ecology Evolution and Systematics*, **10**, 3–40.

DeGRAFF, J. V. 1990. Landslide dams from the November 1988 storm event in southern Thailand. *Landslide News*, **4**, 12–15.

EDWARDS, C. 2004. Thailand lifelines after the December 2004 Great Sumatra earthquake and Indian Ocean tsunami. *Earthquake Spectra*, **22**, S641–S659.

FAO. 1998. *Watershed Management Field Manual: Road Design and Conservation in Sensitive Watersheds.* FAO, Rome.

GUERENA-BURGUENO, F., JONGSAKUL, K., SMITH, B. L., ITTIVERAKUL, M. & CHIRAVARATANOND, O. 2006. Rapid assessment of health needs and medical response after the tsunami in Thailand, 2004–2005. *Military Medicine*, **171**, 8–11.

KELLER, G. & SHERAR, J. 2003. *Low Volume Roads Engineering: Best Management Practices Field Guide.* Produced for the US Agency for International Development. http://ntl.bts.gov/lib/24000/24600/24650/Index_BMP_Field_Guide.htm.

MONTGOMERY, D. R. 1994. Road surface drainage, channel initiation, and slope stability. *Water Resources Research*, **30**, 1925–1932.

OBURA, D. 2006. Impacts of the 26 December 2004 tsunami in Eastern Africa. *Ocean and Coastal Management*, **49**, 873–888.

PHIEN-WEJ, N., NUTALAYA, P., ZIN, A. & TANG, Z. 1993. Catastrophic landslides and debris flows in Thailand. *Bulletin of the International Association of Engineering Geologists*, **48**, 93–100.

RIGG, J., GRUNDY-WARR, C., LAW, L. & TAN-MULLINS, M. 2008. Grounding a natural disaster: Thailand and the 2004 tsunami. *Asia Pacific Viewpoint*, **49**, 137–154.

RIGG, J., LAW, L., TAN-MULLINGS, M. & GRUNDY-WARR, C. 2005. The Indian Ocean tsunami: socio-economic impacts in Thailand. *Geographical Journal*, **171**, 374–379.

SIDLE, R. C. 1980. *Slope Stability on Forest Land.* Pacific Northwest Extension (PNW), **209**. United States Department of Agriculture, Forest Service, Washington, DC.

SIDLE, R. C. & OCHIAI, H. 2006. *Landslides: Processes, Prediction, and Land Use.* American Geophysical Union, Water Resources Monograph, **18**.

SIDLE, R. C., FURUICHI, T. & KONO, Y. 2011. Unprecedented rates of landslide and surface erosion along a newly constructed road in Yunnan, China. *Natural Hazards*, **57**, 313–326, doi: 10.1007/s11069-010-9614-6.

SIDLE, R. C., PEARCE, A. J. & O'LOUGHLIN, C. L. 1985. *Hillslope Stability and Land Use.* American Geophysical Union, Water Resources Monograph, **11**.

SIDLE, R. C., ZIEGLER, A. D., NEGISHI, J. M., NIK, A. R., SIEW, R. & TURKELBOOM, F. 2006. Erosion processes in steep terrain – Truths, myths, and uncertainties related to forest management in Southeast Asia. *Forest Ecology and Management*, **224**, 199–225.

SRIVICHAI, M., IMAMURA, F. & SUPHARATID, S. 2009. A web-based online tsunami warning system for Thailand's Andaman coastline. *Journal of Earthquake and Tsunami*, **3**, 101–111.

TAT 2010. *Tourism of Thailand.* World Wide Web Address: http://www.tatnews.org; download date: 6 August 2010.

TMD 2010. Thai Meteorology Department. World Wide Web Address: http://www.tmd.go.th.

USGS 2010. *Earthquakes with 50 000 or More Deaths, Earthquake Hazards Program.* United States Geological Survey. World Wide Web Address: http://earthquake.usgs.gov; download date: 7 August 2010.

ZIEGLER, A. D., GIAMBELLUCA, T. W., SUTHERLAND, R. A., VANA, T. T. & NULLET, M. A. 2001. Contribution of Horton overland flow to runoff on unpaved mountain roads in northern Thailand. *Hydrological Processes*, **15**, 3203–3208.

ZIEGLER, A. D., NEGISHI, J. N., SIDLE, R. C., GOMI, T., NOGUCHI, S. & NIK, A. R. 2007. Persistence of road runoff generation in a logged catchment in peninsular Malaysia. *Earth Surface Processes & Landforms*, **32**, 1947–1970, doi: 10.1002/esp.1508.

ZIEGLER, A. D., WONG, P. P. & GRUNDY-WARR, C. 2009. Still vulnerable to killer tsunamis. *Science*, **326**, 1188–1189.

# GIS-based techniques for assessing the vulnerability of buildings to tsunami: current approaches and future steps

C. TARBOTTON[1]*, D. DOMINEY-HOWES[1], J. R. GOFF[1], M. PAPATHOMA-KOHLE[2], F. DALL'OSSO[1,3] & I. L. TURNER[4]

[1]*Australia–Pacific Tsunami Research Centre and Natural Hazards Research Laboratory, University of New South Wales, Sydney, NSW 2052, Australia*

[2]*Department of Geography and Regional Research, University of Vienna, Vienna, Austria*

[3]*Med Ingegneria S.r.l., Environmental Engineering, via P. Zangheri 16, 48100 Ravenna, Italy*

[4]*Water Research Laboratory, School of Civil and Environmental Engineering, University of New South Wales, Manly Vale, NSW 2093, Australia*

*Corresponding author (e-mail: cameron.tarbotton@student.unsw.edu.au)*

**Abstract:** The Papathoma Tsunami Vulnerability Assessment (PTVA) model offers a GIS (geographical information system)-based method of estimating the vulnerability of buildings to a potential tsunami threat. In the absence of fully validated building fragility curves, it provides an effective means of identifying vulnerable buildings/populations and estimating the loss associated with a tsunami. However, the PTVA model is limited by a number of factors, including a poor representation of the tsunami hazard, insufficient field testing/validation, and a data intensive and highly qualitative framework. These limitations significantly reduce its capacity as an accurate and practical tool for end users, such as emergency services and community planners. Presented in this paper is an extensive review of the PTVA methodology and recommendations on how the PTVA model can be improved to address the needs of end users. It is argued that the most recent version of the PTVA model, PTVA-3, offers the best available method for assessing the vulnerability of buildings to tsunamis. As such, the future development of new, and the refinement of existing, GIS-based tsunami vulnerability assessment techniques should consider the PTVA-3 model as the baseline.

The impacts of tsunamis can be devastating. The Indian Ocean Tsunami, on 26 December 2004 (2004 IOT), claimed at least 283 000 (USGS 2005) lives and caused widespread damage to coastal communities bordering the Indian Ocean. The 2004 IOT is a poignant example that tsunamis pose a very significant threat. In order to safeguard coastal communities, it is vitally important to develop tools that can predict the impact that future tsunamis will have on the built environment. This will help planners and emergency managers to quantify the risk posed by tsunamis, to introduce mitigative measures to reduce that risk, and to develop means of responding to and recovering from future events (Dall'Osso & Dominey-Howes 2010*a, b*).

Forecasting the impact of a tsunami on the built environment requires a careful consideration of both the hazard and the vulnerability of the buildings that are exposed to it. In this context, vulnerability represents the *susceptibility* of a building to damage, while risk – the potential for loss – arises when a vulnerable built structure is exposed to a physical hazard (Cardona 2003). However, in many cases, studies of tsunami risk and impact focus on the tsunami hazard without considering the extensive variations in vulnerability (Wood & Stein 2001; Papathoma & Dominey-Howes 2003).

Various engineering and statistically based attempts have been made to quantify the vulnerability of built structures to tsunamis. These include investigations into the forces sustained by tsunami-inundated buildings (Nistor *et al.* 2009) and the development of building fragility curves (Peiris 2006; Dias *et al.* 2009; Koshimura *et al.* 2009). Ultimately, the aim of this work is to develop fragility curves that quantitatively relate the intensity of a hazard to the probability that a particular damage state will be reached or exceeded. However, the large return period and unpredictability of tsunamis make it difficult to obtain the field data necessary for such an approach (Douglas 2007). Unlike other natural hazards, such as earthquakes (Rossetto & Elnashai 2003; Calvi *et al.* 2006) – where extensive quantitative post-event and laboratory data exist – there is limited such

*From*: TERRY, J. P. & GOFF, J. (eds) 2012. *Natural Hazards in the Asia–Pacific Region: Recent Advances and Emerging Concepts*. Geological Society, London, Special Publications, **361**, 115–125, http://dx.doi.org/10.1144/SP361.10

data for tsunamis. Where data are available, it is generally qualitative and shows great variation in the type and severity of damage (Ghobarah *et al.* 2006; Reese *et al.* 2007).

At present, the development of a fully validated and site-adaptable building fragility model looks to be far from completion. In the meantime, there is a need for tools that can assess the vulnerability of structures located within expected tsunami inundation zones and provide loss estimates for future events.

The Papathoma Tsunami Vulnerability Assessment (PTVA) model was developed for the expressed purpose of addressing this need. In contrast to more *quantitative* approaches (i.e. fragility curves), the PTVA model provides *qualitative* scenario-based estimates of building vulnerability and potential loss. These outputs contribute to the process of risk reduction by informing decisions regarding land-use policy, building codes, evacuation plans and public education. As such, the PTVA model has the potential for playing a central role in determining the risks faced by coastal communities. However, before this role can be realized, more work is required to improve and validate it. In light of this, the purpose of this paper is twofold: (1) to provide an in-depth review of the PTVA model; and (2) to outline the improvements that are required.

## The Papathoma Tsunami Vulnerability Assessment model

The PTVA model was first proposed in Papathoma & Dominey-Howes (2003), and later revised in Dominey-Howes & Papathoma (2007), Dall'Osso *et al.* (2009*b*) and Dominey-Howes *et al.* (2010). To date, three versions of the model have been published: PTVA-1, PTVA-2 and PTVA-3. Each of these have been applied to various study areas, including:

- PTVA-1 – Herakleio, Crete, Greece (Papathoma *et al.* 2003) and the Gulf of Corinth, and Greece (Papathoma & Dominey-Howes 2003);
- PTVA-2 – Seaside, Oregon, USA (Dominey-Howes *et al.* 2010);
- PTVA-3 – Sydney, Australia (Dall'Osso *et al.* 2009*a*) and the Aeolian Islands, Italy (Dall'Osso *et al.* 2010).

The central idea behind the PTVA model is that the vulnerability of a building can be described by combining the inundation results of a potential tsunami scenario with a series of measurable attributes relating to its design, condition and surroundings. Each attribute contributes in varying degrees to the overall vulnerability of a building and is seen as an indicator of the potential damage that would be sustained during a tsunami. By characterizing these vulnerability attributes, a relationship (i.e. building vulnerability equation) is established between them and the hazard. The building vulnerability equation provides the means of calculating the 'vulnerability score' of a building.

As illustrated in Figure 1, the building vulnerability equation is established via a four-step process. The first three steps involve the identification and ranking of the vulnerability attribute categories (e.g. building material, foundation type), and their various permutations (i.e. the possible variations in each attribute category). The ranking of the attributes represents an important aspect of the PTVA model, as it dictates the relative weight (i.e. importance) that an attribute has in contributing to the overall 'vulnerability score' of a building. In the final step, a vulnerability equation is established by integrating the attributes and weights determined in the first three steps.

Attribute identification and ranking is achieved via an in-depth analysis of inundation and building damage data from post-event tsunami surveys reported in the peer-reviewed scientific press. From this analysis, each attribute category is also assigned a series of possible numerical values corresponding to the various permutations that it represents. For example, if building material is identified as a vulnerability attribute category (as is the case in all versions of the PTVA model), it might have permutations such as wood, brick, reinforced concrete, etc. In this case, reinforced concrete would be assigned the lowest value because reinforced structures are the least vulnerable.

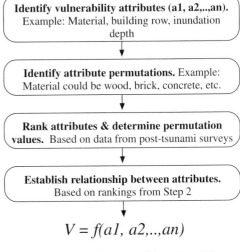

**Identify vulnerability attributes (a1, a2,...,an).** Example: Material, building row, inundation depth

**Identify attribute permutations.** Example: Material could be wood, brick, concrete, etc.

**Rank attributes & determine permutation values.** Based on data from post-tsunami surveys

**Establish relationship between attributes.** Based on rankings from Step 2

$$V = f(a1, a2,..,an)$$

**Fig. 1.** The PTVA model – establishing the building vulnerability equation.

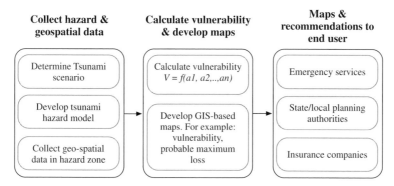

**Fig. 2.** The PTVA model – steps in conducting a vulnerability assessment.

The basic steps taken to conduct a PTVA model assessment are shown in Figure 2. They are conducted by combining the results of an inundation model with the vulnerability attribute data collected for each building. The outputs are presented via GIS (geographical information system)-based database/ maps, highlighting, among other things, buildings appropriate for vertical evacuation, possible evacuation routes and at-risk populations. In the majority of cases where the PTVA model has been used, the inundation scenario has been provided via a deterministic 'bathtub' inundation model. The one exception to this was in the Seaside, Oregon (Dominey-Howes *et al.* 2010) case study, where a probabilistic inundation scenario was used.

## PTVA-1

The first version of the PTVA model (PTVA-1) was developed in Papathoma 2003 and published in Papathoma & Dominey-Howes (2003). The methodology was tested in two coastal sites in Greece – Herakleio, Crete (Papathoma *et al.* 2003) and the Gulf of Corinth (Papathoma & Dominey-Howes 2003). Greece has a long record of tsunami events that dates back to at least 1628 BC (Papadopoulos 1998). As such, the probability of a tsunami occurring and devastating coastal areas in Greece is not only high, it is also likely to have a larger impact than in the past owing to the extensive development of coastal areas (Dominey-Howes 2002). The return period of tsunami events, however, was seen to be too low for Greece to invest money on mitigation measures such as sea walls, relocation of buildings and so on. Furthermore, tsunami source areas in Greece are generally close to the shore, leaving little time to issue a warning and evacuate at-risk areas.

PTVA-1 was developed to address these issues by providing a GIS-based method to estimate and present the vulnerability pattern within a predicted

tsunami inundation zone. The aim of this was to enable state and the local authorities to focus their limited resources more effectively, and to provide planners and emergency services with the information required to prepare for, and respond to, a tsunami.

Based on previous records of tsunami events and their impact, seven attributes affecting building vulnerability were identified. These were ranked according to their importance through an in-depth study of post-tsunami damage observations. The PTVA-1 attributes and their relative weightings are shown in Table 1.

The vulnerability of each building (BV) in the inundation zone is calculated via a weighted sum (Equation 1) of the vulnerability factors collected for each building.

$$BV = w_1 bv_1 + w_2 bv_2 + w_3 bv_3 + w_4 bv_4$$
$$+ w_5 bv_5 + w_6 bv_6 + w_7 bv_7. \tag{1}$$

For both case studies, a tsunami wave height of 5 m, such as was achieved during the tsunamis of 1650 AD in the Aegean Sea (Dominey-Howes *et al.* 2000) and 1963 in the Gulf of Corinth (Galanopoulos *et al.* 1964), was considered to be the worse-case scenario. The area between the 5 m contour and the coastline was identified as the potential inundation zone. The final product of the initial study using PTVA-1 included a GIS-based database and a series of vulnerability maps showing the location of vulnerable buildings (Fig. 3) within the inundation zone.

The GIS database developed for the two case study sites included data regarding the following.

- The buildings – number of floors, condition of building, building material, description of ground floor, surroundings, row of building, presence of movable objects.

**Table 1.** *PTVA-1 vulnerability attributes and their weightings*

| n | Attribute ($bv_n$) | Weight ($w_n$) |
|---|---|---|
| 1 | Building material | 7 |
| 2 | Building row | 6 |
| 3 | Surroundings | 5 |
| 4 | Condition of ground floor | 4 |
| 5 | Number of floors | 3 |
| 6 | Sea defence | 2 |
| 7 | Natural environment | 1 |

- The population – number of people, population density age.
- The local economy – land use
- The environment – vegetation, intertidal zone, physical or man-made barriers, sea defence.

The results of both studies demonstrated that in the case of a tsunami, the impact on the population and local economy would be significant. As such, the initial study using PTVA-1 not only met its aims but also it represented, at the time, a rare case where GIS was used in providing a comprehensive tsunami vulnerability assessment of the built environment.

## PTVA-2

A review of the PTVA-1 vulnerability attributes (Dominey-Howes & Papathoma 2007) using post-event data from the 2004 IOT led to the development of a revised version of the model: PTVA-2. This study confirms that many of the PTVA-1 attributes correlate well with the type and severity of the damage that was observed. PTVA-2 features some changes to the ranking and details of the attributes. The revised PTVA-2 vulnerability attributes and weighting are published in Dominey-Howes *et al.* (2010) (see Table 2).

The PTVA-2 attributes are combined in a weighted sum to provide estimates of building vulnerability. The primary change featured in the PTVA-2 framework is that inundation depth is explicitly included in the calculation of Building Vulnerability (BV). In PTVA-1, BV is exclusively related to a building's characteristics and surroundings, with the worst-case tsunami scenarios being incorporated as a separate layer into the GIS database.

## PTVA-3

A major criticism of both the PTVA-1 and PTVA-2 models is that the ranking of the vulnerability

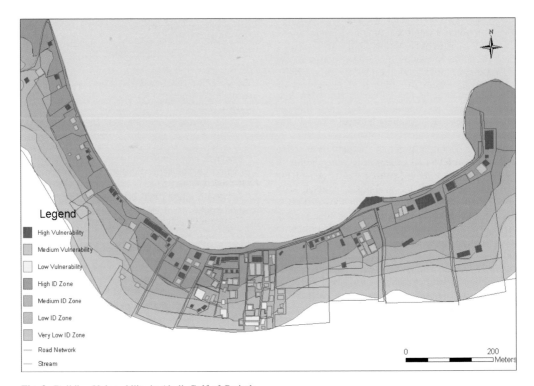

**Fig. 3.** Building Vulnerability in Akoli, Gulf of Corinth.

**Table 2.** *PTVA-2 vulnerability attributes and their weightings*

| n | Attribute ($bv_n$) | Weight ($w_n$) |
|---|---|---|
| 1 | Water depth above ground | 8 |
| 2 | Building row | 7 |
| 3 | Building material | 6 |
| 4 | Number of floors | 5 |
| 5 | Orientation of building | 4 |
| 6 | Condition of building | 3 |
| 7 | Building surrounding | 2 |
| 8 | Land cover | 1 |

attributes is based on a subjective procedure that relies heavily on the expert judgement of the authors. To address these concerns, a further version, PTVA-3, was proposed by Dall'Osso *et al.* (2009*b*). The PTVA-3 model introduces a more robust attribute ranking procedure via an Analytical Hierarchy Process (AHP), as well as additional vulnerability attributes and changes to the building vulnerability calculation. The PTVA-3 model has been applied at two pilot sites: Sydney, Australia (Dall'Osso *et al.* 2009*a*), and the Aeolian Islands, Italy (Dall'Osso *et al.* 2010).

In the PTVA-3 model, the vulnerability score of a building is calculated via the Relative Vulnerability Index (RVI) equation (Equation 2). The RVI equation is a weighted sum of two independent scores: the Structural Vulnerability (SV) – the capacity it has to sustain the hydrodynamic forces of a tsunami flow; and the Water Vulnerability (WV) – the extent to which it is submerged by water:

$$RVI = 2/3(SV) + 1/3(WV) \qquad (2)$$

The WV term represents the first innovative aspect of the PTVA-3 model, as it considers both the structural vulnerability of a building and the damage caused by its prolonged contact with water. According to Oliveri & Santoro (2000), a flooded building experiencing little or no structural damage could still lose up to 40–50% of its value.

A higher weighting coefficient is assigned to SV because structural damage generally results in expensive repair works or complete building replacement. However, the damage resulting from water contact causes a maximum loss smaller than half the value of the building (Oliveri & Santoro 2000).

WV is calculated simply as the percentage of the floors in a building that would be inundated by the tsunami, including possible underground storeys (Equation 3)

$$WV = (\# \text{ of inundated levels})/(\# \text{ of levels}). \quad (3)$$

Compared with WV, the computation of SV is significantly more articulated. It requires data on the building structure (BV), the expected inundation depth at the building (Ex) and the degree of protection provided by artificial and natural barriers (Prot). These three factors are multiplied together to obtain SV (Equation 4).

$$SV = (BV)(Ex)(Prot). \qquad (4)$$

The BV term is calculated via a weighted sum of seven attributes (the same as used for Equation 1) and the Prot term is calculated via a weighted sum of four attributes (Equation 5). The attributes and weightings for BV and Prot are shown in Tables 3 and 4.

$$Prot = w_1 Prot_1 + w_2 Prot_2 + w_3 Prot_3 + w_4 Prot_4 \qquad (5)$$

Many of the building vulnerability attributes used in the PTVA-3 model are the same as those used in previous model versions. However, PTVA-3 does introduce two new attributes: *foundation type* and *preservation condition*. The foundation type, in particular, was found to be very influential to the overall vulnerability of buildings (Dalrymple & Kriebe 2005; Reese *et al.* 2007). Furthermore, the manner in which the shielding term, Prot, is integrated into the vulnerability

**Table 3.** *PTVA-3 – Building Vulnerability (BV) vulnerability attributes and their weightings*

| n | Attribute ($bv_n$) | Weight factor ($w_n$) |
|---|---|---|
| 1 | Number of storeys | $w_1 = 0.236$ |
| 2 | Material | $w_2 = 0.189$ |
| 3 | Ground floor hydrodynamics | $w_3 = 0.149$ |
| 4 | Foundation strength | $w_4 = 0.142$ |
| 5 | Shape and orientation | $w_5 = 0.121$ |
| 6 | Moveable objects | $w_6 = 0.109$ |
| 7 | Preservation condition | $w_7 = 0.054$ |

**Table 4.** *PTVA-3 – Protection (Prot) vulnerability attributes and their weightings*

| n | Attribute ($Prot_n$) | Weight factor ($w_n$) |
|---|---|---|
| 1 | Building row | $w_1 = 0.332$ |
| 2 | Natural barriers | $w_2 = 0.243$ |
| 3 | Seawall | $w_3 = 0.243$ |
| 4 | Surrounding wall | $w_4 = 0.183$ |

calculation represents a significant departure from previous versions of the PTVA model. As opposed to *adding* the shielding attributes (i.e. building row) to the weighted BV calculation, the PTVA-3 model considers Prot as a separate *multiplying* factor. This approach is more consistent with the findings of Reese *et al.* (2007) who observed that well-shielded buildings in many cases suffer much lighter damage (up to four- or fivefold less) than buildings completely exposed to the tsunami impact. This is well represented by the SV equation (Equation 4), as a minimum score of Prot (i.e. Prot = 1 is very good protection) would reduce SV by up to fivefold.

As with previous versions of the PTVA model, the attribute weights in PTVA-3 correspond to the relative importance that an attribute has in contributing to the total vulnerability of a building. PTVA-3, however, features a much more robust and sophisticated ranking procedure than previous versions of the model. This is achieved via an Analytic Hierarchy Process (Saaty 1986), whereby a series of pair-wise comparisons are conducted between the various vulnerability attributes. Each pair-wise comparison provides a measure of the relative importance that one attribute has over another in contributing to the overall structural

vulnerability or level of protection of a building. A total of 21 comparisons were conducted for the seven BV attributes and seven for the four Prot attributes. Details of all the pair-wise comparisons are outlined in Dall'Osso & Dominey-Howes (2009). Comparisons between attributes were inputted into M-Macbeth, a specially designed computer program for multi-criteria analysis (Bana e Costa & Chargas 2004; Bana e Costa *et al.* 2004). The M-Macbeth software combines the pair-wise comparisons to determine the rankings of the attributes. This more rigorous mathematical approach avoids many of the biases typical of ranking procedure, and addresses concerns about the subjectivity and linearity of the weights used in the PTVA-2 model.

## Field testing PTVA-3

The PTVA-3 model has been successfully field tested in two coastal suburbs of the Sydney (Australia) metropolitan area: Manly Beach (Fig. 4); and Maroubra Beach. Results of these studies are described in detail in Dall'Osso *et al.* (2009*a*, *b*). More recently, the PTVA-3 model has been applied and validated in the Aeolian Islands, Italy (Dall'Osso *et al.* 2010). In this study, the model outputs were qualitatively compared with

**Fig. 4.** Tsunami inundation and water depth in the northern part of Manly. The RVI scores of buildings located within the inundation zone are indicated.

**Table 5.** *Comparison of the key aspects of currently available GIS-based tsunami vulnerability assessment models*

| Model | Representation of the hazard | No. of vulnerability attributes | Ranking procedure | No. of study locations used |
|---|---|---|---|---|
| Wood | Hydrodynamic, worst case | N/A | N/A | 1 |
| Omira | Hydrodynamic, probabilistic | 3 | Expert judgement | 1 |
| PTVA-1 | Bathtub, worst case, deterministic | 7 | Expert judgement | 2 |
| PTVA-2 | Hydrodynamic, probabilistic | 8 | Expert judgement | 1 |
| PTVA-3 | Bathtub, deterministic | 13 | AHP/Expert judgement | 3 |

post-tsunami damage data from the 2002 Stromboli Tsunami. Results of the comparison showed the PTVA-3 model to be fairly accurate, but simultaneously highlighted some of its main deficiencies – a simplistic representation of the tsunami hazard and a highly qualitative assessment framework.

## Discussion

### The PTVA model compared with other models

A review of the available literature (in English) suggests that only two other GIS-based attempts have been made to explore the vulnerability of buildings to tsunamis. These are documented in Wood *et al.* (2002), Wood & Good (2004) and Omira *et al.* (2009). Table 5 compares some of the key aspects of these models with PTVA-1, PTVA-2 and PTVA-3.

Wood & Stein (2001), Wood *et al.* (2002) and Wood & Good (2004) provide a framework for identifying broad areas of concern – termed as '*relative vulnerability hotspots*'. The approach focuses on: (1) identifying key assets and services within a community; and (2) representing the intersection of these community assets (using GIS) with worst-case hazard scenarios. This approach is effective at the regional scale but its ability to assess the structural vulnerability of individual buildings is limited.

The method outlined in Omira *et al.* (2009) offers an improvement in this respect. It provides an attribute-based methodology similar to PTVA in which three vulnerability factors are used to determine the vulnerability of a building: building condition; inundation depth; and the presence of a sea defence. The building condition attribute corresponds to four predefined building categories, ranging from very weakly resistant to strongly resistant. The attributes and weightings are indicated in Table 6. The pilot study used to test the model (Casablanca, Morocco) utilizes a probabilistic hydrodynamic inundation model to represent the tsunami hazard.

In comparison to the PTVA approach, Omira *et al.* (2009) requires significantly less input data regarding the design and condition of buildings. PTVA-3, for example, uses a total of seven attributes (Equation 1) to describe the structural vulnerability of a building, while Omira *et al.* (2009) uses only one: building condition. This significantly reduces the time required for field surveys but makes it less adaptable to study locations that do not feature buildings in the defined building categories (Dall'Osso *et al.* 2010).

In light of the other tsunami vulnerability assessment approaches discussed above, it is concluded that the PTVA model offers the best available technique for assessing the impact of tsunamis on the built environment. The PTVA-3 model, in particular, offers the most developed and flexible assessment framework. It can be used to analyse a wide range of different building types. As such, the future development of new, and the refinement of existing, GIS-based tsunami vulnerability assessment techniques should consider the PTVA-3 model as the baseline from which such work moves forward. However, it must be stressed that the PTVA-3 model also has significant shortcomings. These include: insufficient field validation; a qualitative and data intensive assessment framework; and a simplistic representation of the tsunami hazard. Together, these factors have lead to the development of a highly qualitative methodology, which can be impractical for some large study areas, and has difficulty in providing physically grounded, validated and quantitative results. In order to provide outputs that are relevant and

**Table 6.** *Omira* et al. *2009 vulnerability attributes and their weightings*

| Attribute | Weight |
|---|---|
| Building condition | 3 |
| Inundation zone | 2 |
| Presence of sea defence | 1 |

practical for planners and emergency managers, it is important that these limitations are addressed in the future. The following subsection discusses these limitations in detail and provides recommendations for the future development of the PTVA model

*Limitations and future steps*

The simplistic representation of the tsunami hazard in the PTVA model has, perhaps, the most significant affect on the accuracy of its outputs. The static 'bathtub' approach, mainly used to date, fails to account for the complex role that bathymetry, topography and buildings play in dictating the flow of an inundating tsunami (Liu *et al.* 1991). This has a profound affect on how the hazard exposure of buildings is incorporated into the model. In an attempt to account for variations in building exposure not represented by the static flood model, PTVA-3 uses a series of qualitative shielding factors in addition to the flood depth (the Prot and Ex term in Equation 4). The Prot term corresponds to shielding features in the vicinity of a building that act to reduce its exposure to inundation. This provides an approximation of how a tsunami would flow and impact the built environment without having to model it explicitly.

To improve this, it is recommended that the future development of the PTVA model should include the integration of hydrodynamic modelling results into its assessment framework. Hydrodynamic models are capable of representing (dynamically) a tsunami event from source (generation), via propagation to inundation (Synolakis & Bernard 2006). In models such as the Rivers and Coastal Ocean Model (RiCOM) (Walters 2005) and the MOST model (Titov & Gonzalez 1997; Titov & Synolakis 1998), the effects of bathymetry, topography and even aspects of the built and natural environment can be integrated directly into the numerical simulations. This provides a dynamic and much more physically accurate representation of a tsunami inundation than a static 'bathtub' model.

The integration of hydrodynamic modelling results could offer a number of important improvements for the PTVA model.

- The affect of shielding features, such as, walls, buildings and natural barriers could be integrated directly into the model of the hazard. This would provide the opportunity to remove aspects of the qualitative protection term (Prot), making estimates of building exposure less reliant on qualitative factors.
- Alternative methods of representing building exposure could be investigated, which not only utilize flood depth but also the other hydrodynamic quantities outputted by hydrodynamic tsunami models (e.g. flow speed and direction).
- Probabilistic vulnerability studies could be achieved by utilizing probabilistic source parameters (i.e. from subsea earthquake and landslide studies) as the initial conditions to tsunami simulations.
- It would build on a modelling tool that is already familiar and widely used by planners and emergency managers. The vulnerability assessments provided by the PTVA model would become a natural extension of inundation modelling efforts that are already taking place using hydrodynamic models. This would speed the adoption of PTVA as a planning resource for coastal communities, as well as extend the current capabilities of hydrodynamic models.

*Move towards a more quantitative assessment framework.* The qualitative approach utilized by the PTVA model imposes a number of limitations on the type and accuracy of results that can be provided. First, the relationship between building type, hazard and damage is based on a subjective interpretation of qualitative damage data. Despite significant efforts in PTVA-3 to reduce the subjectivity of attribute ranking procedure, it is unable to avoid the large uncertainties that are inherent in a qualitative methodology. Furthermore, the qualitative assessment framework makes it difficult to establish an absolute and quantitative measure of impact. Relative measures, such as the Relative Vulnerability Index (i.e. PTVA-3), are useful in determining the vulnerability of a building in relation to its surroundings, but are less suited to providing estimates of absolute building damage or economic loss. This leads to difficulties in conducting model calibration/validation, quantifying uncertainty and comparing the results of different study locations.

In order to provide outputs that are more absolute and comparable between study locations, a movement towards a more quantitative methodology is required. This would involve replacing/modifying the qualitative method used in PTVA to determine the exposure (the Ex and Prot terms) and the structural vulnerability of a building (BV: Equation 1). In the first case, this could be achieved by replacing the 'bathtub' inundation model with a more sophisticated hydrodynamic tsunami inundation model. Another option is to use tsunami fragility functions and tsunami building-load models, either to replace or to augment the qualitative scoring system used by the PTVA model. The outputs of a hydrodynamic inundation model (i.e. flow depth and velocity) would provide the required input data to develop these alternative techniques of representing the vulnerability of buildings.

As discussed previously, quantitative tsunami-building fragility models have been difficult to develop because of the limited availability of post-event data. While this is still a significant limitation, more extensive sets of damage and inundation data have started to become available as a result of the 2004 IOT. This has lead to the development of quantitative tsunami-building fragility functions (Peiris 2006; Dias *et al.* 2009; Koshimura *et al.* 2009). At present, these fragility functions only represent a limited number of building types in Banda Aceh, Indonesia and Sri Lanka. However, as the number of fragility functions increase in the future they could provide an alternative to, or at the very least augment, the qualitative scoring system that is currently used to assess structural vulnerability.

*Model validation and comparison.* While PTVA-3 features the most developed and robust framework for assessing the vulnerability of the built environment, it has undergone only limited field validations (Dominey-Howes & Papathoma 2007; Dall'Osso *et al.* 2010). Also, no effort has been made to compare the results of PTVA with other GIS-based techniques, such as Omira *et al.* (2009). This has lead to reasonable questions regarding the accuracy of its results. As such, it is important that field validations are made both of the PTVA model and of any new techniques that are developed in the future. Furthermore, the outputs of new techniques should be compared with existing methods (including previous versions of the PTVA model). This will help to determine the extent to which changes/improvements to the model structure have on its estimates of building vulnerability, providing a much-needed comparison between different methods and giving some direction to practitioners regarding the approach best suited to their study area.

*Reduce the data requirements.* The data collection requirements for some of the vulnerability attributes of the PTVA-3 model can be impractical for large study areas. In particular, building-to-building surveys are time-consuming and data-intensive. The integration of hydrodynamic models and a movement towards a more quantitative assessment framework would help to reduce the qualitative data requirements of the model. Furthermore, more extensive model validation and comparison with less data-intensive models could help indicate whether certain aspects of the PTVA model can be simplified. Less intensive data-gathering approaches should also be investigated. This could involve, for example, the extraction of building

characteristics and natural features from remotely sensed imagery and LiDAR (Light Detection And Ranging) data.

## Conclusion

The most recent version of the Papathoma Tsunami Vulnerability Assessment (PTVA) model, PTVA-3, has been identified as the best available technique for assessing the vulnerability of buildings to tsunami. Compared with other approaches, it offers the most developed and site-adaptable methodology for quantifying the vulnerability of buildings and providing estimates of Probable Maximum Loss (PML). The outputs of the model help to reduce the risk associated with tsunami by informing decisions regarding future land use, building codes and evacuation plans. The future development of new and the refinement of existing GIS-based tsunami vulnerability assessment techniques should consider the PTVA-3 model as the baseline.

However, at present, the value of the PTVA model as a practical tool for emergency managers and planners (the end user) is limited by: a simplistic representation of the tsunami hazard; a highly qualitative and data-intensive assessment methodology; and insufficient validation. In order for the PTVA model to provide more accurate outputs and become more widely adopted as a planning resource for coastal communities, it is important that these limitations are addressed. To achieve this, it is recommended that the future development of the model should include:

- the integration of hydrodynamic tsunami modelling results;
- more quantitative representations of exposure and vulnerability (e.g. via hydrodynamic quantities and building load/fragility models);
- an increased focus on validation and comparison with other tsunami vulnerability models (including previous versions of the PTVA model);
- reduced data requirements via more efficient data-collection techniques (e.g. from remotely sensed images/LIDAR) and model simplification.

## References

BANA E COSTA, C. A. & CHARGAS, M. P. 2004. An example of how to use MACBETH to build a quantitative value model based on qualitative value judgements. *European Journal of Operational Research*, **153**, 323–331.

BANA E COSTA, C. A., DA SILVA, P. A. & CORREIA, F. N. 2004. Multicriteria evaluation of flood control measures: the case of Ribeira do Livramento. *Water Resource Management*, **18**, 263–283.

CALVI, G., PINHO, R., MAGENES, G., BOMMER, J., RESTREPO-VELEZ, L. & CROWLEY, H. 2006. Development of seismic vulnerability assessment methodologies over the past 30 years. *ISET Journal of Earthquake Technology*, **43**, 75–104.

CARDONA, O. D. 2003. The need for rethinking the concepts of vulnerability and risk from a holistic perspective: a necessary review and criticism for effective risk management. *In*: BANKOFF, G., FRERKS, G. & HILHORST, D. (eds) *Mapping Vulnerability: Disasters, Development and People*. Earthscan, London.

DALL'OSSO, F. & DOMINEY-HOWES, D. 2009. *A Method for Assessing the Vulnerability of Buildings to Catastrophic (Tsunami) Marine Flooding*. Report prepared for the Sydney Coastal Councils Group Inc., Sydney.

DALL'OSSO, F. & DOMINEY-HOWES, D. 2010a. The emergency management implications of assessments of building vulnerability to tsunami. *Australian Journal of Emergency Management*, **25**, 24–30.

DALL'OSSO, F. & DOMINEY-HOWES, D. 2010b. Public assessment of the usefulness of 'draft' tsunami evacuation maps from Sydney, Australia – implications for the establishment of formal evacuation plans. *Natural Hazards and Earth System Sciences*, **10**, 1739–1750.

DALL'OSSO, F., GONELLA, M., GABBIANELLI, G., WITHYCOMBE, G. & DOMINEY-HOWES, D. 2009a. Assessing the vulnerability of buildings to tsunami in Sydney. *Natural Hazards and Earth System Sciences*, **9**, 2015–2026.

DALL'OSSO, F., GONELLA, M., GABBIANELLI, G., WITHYCOMBE, G. & DOMINEY-HOWES, D. 2009b. A revised (PTVA) model for assessing the vulnerability of buildings to tsunami damage. *Natural Hazards and Earth System Sciences*, **9**, 1557–1565.

DALL'OSSO, F., MARAMAI, A., GRAZIANI, L., BRIZUELA, B., CAVALLETTI, A., GONELLA, M. & TINTI, S. 2010. Applying and validating the PTVA-3 Model at the Aeolian Islands, Italy: assessment of the vulnerability of buildings to tsunamis. *Natural Hazards and Earth System Sciences*, **10**, 1547–1562.

DALRYMPLE, R. A. & KRIEBE, D. L. 2005. Lessons in engineering from the tsunami in Thailand. *The Bridge*, **35**, 4–13.

DIAS, W., YAPA, H. & PEIRIS, L. 2009. Tsunami vulnerability functions from field surveys and Monte Carlo simulation. *Civil Engineering and Environmental Systems*, **26**, 181–194.

DOMINEY-HOWES, D. 2002. Documentary and geological records of tsunamis in the Aegean Sea region of Greece and their potential value to risk assessment and disaster management. *Natural Hazards*, **25**, 195–224.

DOMINEY-HOWES, D. & PAPATHOMA, M. 2007. Validating a tsunami vulnerability assessment model (the PTVA model) using field data from the 2004 Indian Ocean tsunami. *Natural Hazards*, **40**, 113–136.

DOMINEY-HOWES, D., DUNBAR, P., VARNER, J. & PAPATHOMA-KÖHLE, M. 2010. Estimating probable maximum loss from a Cascadia tsunami. *Natural Hazards*, **53**, 43–61.

DOMINEY-HOWES, D., PAPADOPOULOS, G. A. & DAWSON, A. G. 2000. Geological and historical investigation of the 1650 Mt. Columbo (Thera Island) eruption and tsunami, Aegean Sea, Greece. *Natural Hazards*, **21**, 83–96.

DOUGLAS, J. 2007. Physical vulnerability modelling in natural hazard risk assessment. *Natural Hazards and Earth System Sciences*, **7**, 283–288.

GALANOPOULOS, A., DELIBASIS, N. & COMNINAKIS, P. 1964. A tsunami generated by an earth slump set in motion without shock. *Annales Geologique des pays Helleniques*, 93–110 (in Greek).

GHOBARAH, A., SAATCIOGLU, M. & NISTOR, I. 2006. The impact of the 26 December 2004 earthquake and tsunami on structures and infrastructure. *Engineering Structures*, **28**, 312–326.

KOSHIMURA, S., OIE, T., YANAGISAWA, H. & IMAMURA, F. 2009. Developing fragility functions for tsunami damage estimation using numerical model and post-tsunami data from Banda Aceh, Indonesia. *Coastal Engineering Journal*, **51**, 243–273.

LIU, P., SYNOLAKIS, C. & YEH, H. 1991. *Report on the international workshop on long-wave run-up*. Journal of Fluid Mechanics, **229**, 675–688.

NISTOR, I., PALERMO, D., NOURI, Y., MURTY, T. & SAATCIOGLU, M. 2009. Tsunami-induced forces on structures. *In*: KIM, Y. C. (ed.) *Handbook of Coastal and Ocean Engineering*, World Scientific, Singapore, 261–286.

OLIVERI, E. & SANTORO, M. 2000. Estimation of urban structural flood damages: the case study of Palermo. *Urban Water*, **2**, 223–234.

OMIRA, R., BAPTISTA, M., MIRANDA, J., TOTO, E., CATITA, C. & CATALO, J. 2009. Tsunami vulnerability assessment of Casablanca–Morocco using numerical modelling and GIS tools. *Natural Hazards*, **54**, 75–95.

PAPADOPOULOS, G. 1998. *A Tsunami Catalogue of the Area of Greece and the Adjacent Seas*. Institute of Geodynamics, National Observatory of Athens Publication, **17**.

PAPATHOMA, M. 2003. *Assessing Tsunami Vulnerability Using GIS with Special Reference to Greece*. PhD thesis, Coventry University.

PAPATHOMA, M. & DOMINEY-HOWES, D. 2003. Tsunami vulnerability assessment and its implications for coastal hazard analysis and disaster management planning, Gulf of Corinth, Greece. *Natural Hazards and Earth System Sciences*, **3**, 733–747.

PAPATHOMA, M., DOMINEY-HOWES, D., ZONG, Y. & SMITH, D. 2003. Assessing tsunami vulnerability, an example from Herakleio. Crete. *Natural Hazards and Earth System Sciences*, **3**, 377–389.

PEIRIS, N. 2006. Vulnerability functions for tsunami loss estimation. *Paper presented at First European Conference on Earthquake Engineering and Seismology*, Geneva, Switzerland, 3–8 September.

REESE, S., COUSINS, W., POWER, W., PALMER, N., TEJAKUSUMA, I. & NUGRAHADI, S. 2007. Tsunami vulnerability of buildings and people in South Java- field observations after the July 2006 Java tsunami. *Natural Hazards and Earth System Sciences*, **7**, 573–589.

ROSSETTO, T. & ELNASHAI, A. 2003. Derivation of vulnerability functions for European-type RC structures based on observational data. *Engineering Structures*, **25**, 1241–1263.

SAATY, T. L. 1986. Axiomatic foundation of the Analytic Hierarchy Process. *Management Science*, **32**, 841–855.

SYNOLAKIS, C. & BERNARD, E. 2006. Tsunami science before and beyond Boxing Day 2004. *Philosophical Transactions A*, **364**, 2231.

TITOV, V. & GONZALEZ, F. 1997. *Implementation and Testing of the Method of Splitting Tsunami (MOST) Model*. NOAA Technical Memorandum, **ERL PMEL-112**. Pacific Marine Environmental Laboratory, Seattle, WA.

TITOV, V. & SYNOLAKIS, C. 1998. Numerical modeling of tidal wave runup. *Journal of Waterway, Port Coastal and Ocean Engineering*, **124**, 157–171.

USGS 2005. *Summary of the Sumatra–Andaman Islands Earthquake and Tsunami of 26 December 2004*. United States Geological Survey. World Wide Web Address: http://neic.usgs.gov/neis/eq_depot/2004/eq_041226/neic_slav_summary.html.

WALTERS, R. 2005. Coastal ocean models: two useful finite element methods. *Continental Shelf Research*, **25**, 775–793.

WOOD, N. & GOOD, J. 2004. Vulnerability of port and harbor communities to earthquake and tsunami hazards: the use of GIS in community hazard planning. *Coastal Management*, **32**, 243–269.

WOOD, N. & STEIN, D. 2001. A GIS-based vulnerability assessment of Pacific Northwest ports and harbours to tsunami hazards. *In*: *Proceedings of the International Tsunami Symposium 2001*. NOAA/PEML, Seattle, 367–374.

WOOD, N., GOOD, J. & GOODWIN, R. 2002. Vulnerability assessment of a port and harbor community to earthquake and tsunami hazards: integrating technical expert and stakeholder input. *Natural Hazards Review*, **3**, 148.

# Impacts, recovery and resilience of Thai tourist coasts to the 2004 Indian Ocean Tsunami

POH POH WONG

*School of Social Sciences, University of Adelaide, Adelaide, SA 5005, Australia*
*(e-mail: wong3921@gmail.com)*

**Abstract:** A powerful earthquake off Sumatra on 26 December 2004 set off the most disastrous tsunami to impact on the coasts and coastal communities of the Indian Ocean. Coastal tourism in Thailand, Sri Lanka and the Maldives was significantly affected. Examples from Phuket Island, Khao Lak and Ko Phi Phi Don, Thailand, show the variation in the impacts, recovery and resilience of Thai tourist coasts, focusing primarily on beach recovery and the reconstruction of the tourist industry. As priority was given to Phuket Island, tourism recovered after 1 year. Khao Lak was the worst affected and has yet to fully recover. Ko Phi Phi Don recovered but is plagued by land-use problems. Various mitigation measures have been implemented to increase the resilience of the tourist coasts. However, the resilience of the Thai tourist coasts in the event of a future tsunami is questionable.

At 00:58:53 WTC (07:58:53 local time) on 26 December 2004, a powerful earthquake occurred with its hypocentre at 3.3°N and 96°E, and some 160 km west of Sumatra at a depth of 30 km (Kwata *et al.* 2005a). It was an undersea earthquake at the subduction zone associated with a 1200–1300 km-long rupture between the boundary of the Indo-Australian and SE Eurasian plates at NW Sumatra, the Nicobar Islands and the Andaman Islands. The quake was rated at $M_w$ 9.1–9.3 (moment magnitude) and the rupture lasted for more than 500 s (Lay *et al.* 2005). The slip was about 7 m, with a maximum slip of more than 20 m off the coast of NW Sumatra (Kanamori 2006).

The sudden displacement of the sea floor associated with the rupture propagated a series of waves that arrived at the shore of countries around the Indian Ocean. Tsunami waves have small amplitude as they travel across the ocean at a speed proportional to the square root of water depth (reaching 640 km h$^{-1}$), and increase in magnitude significantly upon reaching the shore. As the fault line is nearly north–south the greatest strength of the tsunami is from east to west. The actual height of the arriving tsunami waves is a function of many local factors. The attenuation of flow inland is influenced by local topography, and the density of buildings and vegetation (Rossetto *et al.* 2007).

The tsunami that occurred on the morning of 26 December 2004 was to become the most disastrous event in the Indian Ocean. More than 228 000 people died in 14 countries around the Indian Ocean and damages totalled nearly US$10 billion. Nearly 2.5 million people were affected in terms of loss of families, homes or livelihoods (TGLL Project 2009). The high number of fatalities was due to the lack of any warning system and the large number of coastal communities on the low-lying coasts of the Indian Ocean. The tsunami coincided with the height of the tourist season and thousand of tourists were killed in Thailand alone. With the rapid arrival of the tsunami, there was insufficient time for warnings in Aceh and Phuket. However, even with tsunami arrival times of 3 h or more, without any warning system Sri Lanka, India and the Maldives were all badly affected.

## Rationale

Since 2005 many studies have been carried out on earthquakes and the tsunami, with reviews covering geophysical, geological, engineering, and environmental aspects [see the special issues of *Disaster Prevention and Management* 2006 (15/1); *Earth Planets Space* 2006 (58/2); *Earthquake Spectra* 2006 (22/3); *Philosophical Transactions of the Royal Society A* 2006 (A364/1845); *Marine Geology* 2007 (242/1–3); *Journal of Environmental Management* 2008 (89/1)]. The studies included the coastal environmental impacts and the recovery of coastal communities.

Few studies have been carried out on tourism as past tsunamis have not impacted significantly on tourist coasts. Studies of the 2004 tsunami concerning tourism have been specific in nature and not integrative; that is, not considering the impacts on coasts and tourism, their recovery and long-term resilience. The majority focused on Thai coastal tourism–marine national parks (Marchand 2006; Meprasert 2006; Worachananant *et al.* 2007), a coastal community in Khao Lak (Calgaro 2005),

*From*: TERRY, J. P. & GOFF, J. (eds) 2012. *Natural Hazards in the Asia–Pacific Region: Recent Advances and Emerging Concepts.* Geological Society, London, Special Publications, **361**, 127–138, http://dx.doi.org/10.1144/SP361.11
© The Geological Society of London 2012. Publishing disclaimer: www.geolsoc.org.uk/pub_ethics

informal sector recovery (Handmer & Choong 2006) secondary impacts on inbound traffic (Ichinosawa 2005) and the recovery of the tourist industry (Ritti-chainuwat 2006). Luhrman (2005) dealt with the general recovery of the Maldivian tourist industry.

Within the Indian Ocean, coastal tourism is well developed in Thailand, Sri Lanka and the Maldives, and is based on the abundance of beaches and coral reefs. In the Maldives the resorts are located only on islands of the coral atolls. The beaches are season-ally influenced by the monsoons, and the tourist industry has a typical high season during the north-ern winter. Of the three countries, coastal tourism in Thailand suffered most from the tsunami in the coastal provinces of Ranong, Phang Nga, Phuket, Krabi, Trang and Satun. Thai coastal tourism in Pattaya, Ko Samui and elsewhere in the Gulf of Thailand was unaffected by the tsunami.

This paper examines the impacts of the tsunami on Thai coastal tourism in a more holistic perspec-tive by examining the impacts on the coastal environment and the tourism industry. A simple conceptual framework with three main components of impacts, recovery and resilience is adopted. For any given tourist coast, the impacts on the coastal environment depend mainly on the incoming tsunami wave height on the type of coastline; and the extent of structural damage depends on the density and layout of the tourism built-up area and type of structures. In recovery, the beach recovery depends on the normal coastal processes but the reconstruction relies more on socio-economic and political factors. Resilience is dependent on local measures and external or regional measures. On the Andaman coast, Thai tourism in three major locations – Phuket Island, Khao Lak and Ko Phi Phi Don – is examined using this framework to provide significant variations, relationships and generalizations. A conclusion is reached to answer the question of how resilient are the Thai tourist coasts in the event of a future tsunami.

## Study areas

At 570 km$^2$, Phuket is the largest Thai island and is connected to the mainland by a bridge in the north. Tourism started in the late 1960s, with numbers of tourists increasing to 20 000 in 1976, growing rapidly to reach 2.7 million in 2001 (Kontogeorgo-poulos 2004) and had reached 4.6 million at the time of the tsunami (Paphavasit et al. 2006). Phuket's tourism is based on beaches, corals and outstanding karst islands, and is complemented by other natural and cultural attractions. The most important tourist beaches are on the west coast bays – Nai Thong Beach, Bang Tao Beach, Surin Beach, Kamala Beach, Patong Beach, Karon

Beach, Kata Beach, Kata Noi Beach and Nai Harn Beach from north to south; the most developed is Patong Beach (Fig. 1).

The Khao Lak tourist coast refers to a stretch of about 20 km extending from Cape Pakarang in the north to Khao Lak Beach in the south (Fig. 1). Prior to the tsunami, it consisted of a number of distinct and relatively wide beaches separated by headlands and three sediment-filled tidal inlets. Immediately north of Cape Pakarang are Pak Weeb Beach and Bang Sak Beach. South of Cape Pakarang are Khuk Khak Beach, Bang Niang Beach, Nang Thong Beach and Sunset Beach, and passing south of the rocky headland is Khao Lak Beach. The tourism industry was characterized by a high proportion of small, family-run tourist hotels and restaurants.

Ko Phi Phi Don is the largest of six islands lying 50 km SE of Phuket Island (Fig. 1). It has an area of 28 km$^2$ and is one of the most touristic small islands in Thailand. An east–west low-lying tombolo, at 200 m at its narrowest, links two unequal parts to produce one bay in the north and another bay in the south. Tourism was mainly concentrated on the sandy tombolo.

Fieldwork on the tsunami-affected Thai tourist coasts began with an initial visit to Phuket Island on 5–7 January 2005, and Khao Lak and Ko Phi Phi Don on 3–5 August 2005. Subsequently, peri-odic trips to these coasts were made with an empha-sis on Bang Niang Beach in Khao Lak, which was recovering more slowly than other areas.

## Tsunami impacts

The tsunami impacts on the coastal environment and structural damage vary widely on Phuket Island, Khao Lak and Ko Phi Phi Don (Table 1). Several points need to be highlighted concerning the impacts on the coastal environment.

First, the impact of tsunami on the tourist coasts and subsequent damage depended on several factors influencing the run-up and wave height. The run-up reflects the effects of bathyme-try, coastal topography, coastline configuration and slope, the pattern and density of land use, and the biological and geomorphological characteristics of the offshore and nearshore areas of a particular beach or type of coast. The run-ups were relatively high and inundated further inland across shallower depths; for example, Bang Sak Beach and Bang Niang Beach (more than 2 km). Inundation extended inland across the coastal plains, and the mouths of canals and rivers. Pocket beaches with high hills, high coastal casuarinas or dense mangrove forests damped the advancing waves (Sir-ipong 2006). The sinuosity of bays also acts to

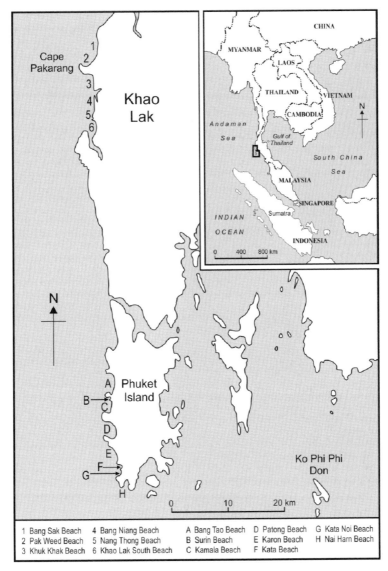

**Fig. 1.** Location map of Phuket Island, Khao Lak and Ko Phi Phi Don, which were the most tsunami-affected of all the Thai tourist coasts.

control the run-up of tsunami waves onto the land; the greater the curvatures of the shoreline, then the more the waves were focused on the bays (Choowong *et al.* 2007). At Ko Phi Phi Don, the tombolo is about 1 m above high tide, and illustrated the vulnerability associated with intensive tourist development on tombolos and sand spits (Bell *et al.* 2005).

Second, the extent of destruction on the Thai tourist coasts seems to be closely related to the tsunami wave height (Table 1). The tsunami wave height varied from 4 m near Phuket Airport to 6 m

at Patong Beach on Phuket, 5 m at Ko Phi Phi Don and 11 m on Khao Lak (Dalrymple & Kriebel 2005). The run-up height was 5–7 and 10–12 m at Cape Pakarang and Bang Niang Beach, respectively (Thanawood *et al.* 2008). The higher waves on Khao Lak contributed to the widespread destruction of resorts, and therefore it has taken a longer time for this area to recover. This was evident in the initial assessment of the extent of damage of hotels based on their projected reopening (Birkland *et al.* 2006).

Third, the destruction of coral reefs and boulders at Cape Pakarang is not seen elsewhere on the

**Table 1.** *Impacts – beach and structural damage*

| Location | Beach damage | Structural damage |
|---|---|---|
| Phuket Island | • Major tourist beaches on the west coast affected by the tsunami. Variations in impacts owing to varying tsunami wave height shoaling from sand bars and reefs, and beach orientation. Tsunami waves reached 480 m inland from the shoreline (Polngam *et al.* 2005)<br>• Other local factors are important. Kamala Beach was most extensively damaged owing to its extensive nearshore platform; even sea walls at its southern end collapsed. In contrast, Karon Beach was protected by its 3–4 m high dunes. Surin Beach, steep and with a low sea wall, and Nai Harn Beach, with a low sea wall, were relatively unaffected<br>• Scouring as tsunami floodwaters moved seaward; scour depths of less than 2 m and within 200 m of shore or less than half of the maximum inundation distance (Francis 2006). At Patong Beach scouring was related to the openings of low sea walls (Dalrymple & Krembel 2005)<br>• Some sedimentation features. Bedform dunes and small ripple sands at Bang Tao Beach (Choowong *et al.* 2007) | • 20% of hotels damaged, mainly at Patong and Kamala beaches Estimated damages at US$414 million (Alovisi *et al.* 2005)<br>• Dense tourism infrastructure at the coast was most affected, with physical damage confined to few hundred metres from the shore (WTO 2005). At Patong Beach, the density of buildings and the roads separating them constrained tsunami penetration. Side roads perpendicular to the beach and parallel to the flow direction became swift torrents. Less damage was in the alleyways off the side roads, which were perpendicular to the flow (Bell *et al.* 2005)<br>• Sea walls for protection from erosion and monsoon waves also ameliorated the impact of the tsunami waves. At Patong Beach, the coastal sea wall reduced the tsunami impact except where pedestrian openings existed. A well-constructed wall across the coastal road saved one building. At Karon Beach, the higher road level acted as a wall |
| Khao Lak | • Coast was impacted most severely with a tsunami wave height higher than 10 m (Kwata *et al.* 2005*b*)<br>• An estimated two-thirds of the beach surface area eroded (Choowong *et al.* 2009); leaving scarps of approximately 1 m, and beach widths diminished by 50 m or more in most areas (ASCE 2005)<br>• Tidal inlets were enlarged and deepened; inundation penetrated inland<br>• Tombolos removed from the outcrops at Nang Thong Beach<br>• At Cape Pakarang, the sandy terminus was removed with severe beach erosion, and damage occurred to the coral reefs and coastal forests. Three arcuate lines of boulders formed in the intertidal zone when three separate tsunami waves struck the reef rocks on the western side of the cape, and detached, transported and deposited them (Goto *et al.* 2007)<br>• Some distinct sedimentation features associated with tsunami inflows and return flows. Double-layered sand sheets at Ban Kheuk Khak, and unique circular holes 10–30 cm in diameter caused by vortices and coated with a thin layer of mud (Choowong *et al.* 2007) | • 80% of hotels suffered damage, with only a few left standing. Estimated damages at US$312 million (Alovisi *et al.* 2005)<br>• Completely destroyed beachfront hotels and infrastructure, which has a high proportion of small, family-run businesses<br>• Tourism at Bang Niang Beach was most intensively developed and virtually destroyed<br>• Only a few mid-rise larger hotels survived but were damaged (Rossetto *et al.* 2006) |
| Ko Phi Phi Don | • Some loss of sand from both bays north and south of the low-lying tombolo<br>• Low sea wall built with a core of sand bags and a hard outer covering on the south bay failed owing to scour and the hydrostatic force of the waves (Dalrymple & Kriebel 2005) | • 70% of hotels severely damaged. Estimated damages valued at US$312 million (Alovisi *et al.* 2005)<br>• The majority of cottages and hotels concentrated on the tombolo were destroyed; large RC buildings at the resorts were less affected |

Thai tourist coasts. The coastline at and near the cape was changed drastically by the tsunami (Table 1). Prior to the tsunami, Cape Pakarang was lined with casuarinas and coconut palms, and terminated in a sandy spit. It had a very shallow nearshore with coral boulders exposed at low tide (Siripong 2006).

As for the structural damage on the Thai tourist coasts, the primary damage caused by a tsunami can be the result of three main factors: inundation, wave impacts on structures and erosion (Bernard & Goulet 1981). The vulnerability of the tourist coasts was increased by extensive development close to the beaches, on sand spits and narrow coastal corridors, the absence of high ground for refuge, foreshores modified for coastal development by removing trees, the lowering of dunes to enhance ocean views and the hardened coastal defence structures that could exacerbate wave run-up (Bell et al. 2005).

On the tourist coasts, the tsunami onshore flow is difficult to predict as it is affected not only by local bathymetry and coastal topography but also the amount of entrained debris, and the density and pattern of buildings and structures in its path, as seen at Patong Beach (Table 1). Inundation can occur far inland and sometimes clashed with outwash flows. Coastal vegetation may offer some protection by reducing the power of waves but cannot prevent damage (Rossetto et al. 2006).

On the Thai tourist coasts, the tourist buildings were of different types. Large resort complexes of reinforced concrete (RC) with several storeys were constructed with the involvement of engineers. More common were low-rise RC buildings, and wooden and bamboo buildings constructed without the involvement of engineers. The bulk of tourist and commercial buildings was of low-rise RC type, which was easily destroyed by the tsunami.

According to the survey by RMS (2006), the relative damage to various buildings on the tourist coasts was related to the tsunami force or waves. Damage to structures is caused by several forces: lateral water flow; wave loading (pressure exerted on an object); ground scour; and debris impact of advancing waves (Rossetto et al. 2007). In their account of tsunami impact on beaches on Phuket Island, Khao Lak and Ko Phi Phi Don, Rossetto et al. (2006) concluded that the inundation height and tsunami onshore flow velocity were the two most important parameters in determining the potential tsunami hazard to the buildings.

From various surveys of the buildings (Dalrymple & Kriebel 2005; Saatcioglu et al. 2005; RMS 2006; Rossetto et al. 2006, 2007), it soon became quite clear that the typology of buildings on the tourist coasts was a major factor in determining

the severity of damage. In their initial report after the tsunami, Dalrymple & Kriebel (2005) stated that low-lying resorts, homes and fishing villages were severely damaged, whereas well-designed, RC buildings with good foundations generally survived; and results were even better for elevated buildings. The majority of buildings with two or three storeys survived with minor–moderate damage in wave heights of 3–6 m from ground level. Infill masonry walls without openings could not withstand waves of 2.5 m or more in height.

Rossetto et al. (2007) reported in more detail how the construction type of the buildings influenced the amount of damage. Low-rise reinforced RC buildings (one- or two-storey homes or beach bungalows/villas) suffered severe damage. The mid-rise RC structures (three- or four-storey non-residential and hotel buildings) performed even in areas where the tsunami reached the third storey and sustained extensive non-structural damage such as flooding, and cosmetic and content damage. Wood frame and bamboo buildings – for example, timber frame chalets in Phang Nga Province – were destroyed; many hotels and resorts near the beach took the full brunt of waves that were as much as 8 m or higher. In Phuket, mid-rise RC hotels survived but wooden structures could not withstand the waves of heights of up to 3 m (Rossetto et al. 2006, 2007).

## Beach and tourism recovery

The recovery of the tourist coast consists of two main components: recovery of the beaches and the reconstruction of the tourist industry (Table 2; Figs 2 & 3). There are basic differences between these two components.

For the major tourist beaches, such as Patong Beach, immediate recovery measures included pushing sand from the foreshore to fill scours on the backshore and the base of coastal forests. The severely eroded beach at Bang Niang Beach saw lateritic material trucked to the coast in February 2005 and then covered by a layer of sand.

Overall, the recovery of beaches was expected to take place under conditions influenced by the monsoons and involved the landward transport of material from the nearshore zone to the beach. The SE Monsoon from May to October is onshore and stormy, while the NW Monsoon from November to April is considered as the calmer period.

Other restoration measures were carried out, including: the reinforcement of natural barriers; replanting or enhancing coastal vegetation belts, such as large casuarinas south of Cape Pakarang; enhancing dunes in Karon Beach; and regulating channels on many beaches (Table 2). In a few cases, beach recovery is interfered with by human

**Table 2.** *Recovery – Beach and tourism*

| Location | Beach recovery | Tourism recovery |
|---|---|---|
| Phuket Island | • Initial measures included pushing beach sand to fill erosion scars, raising the backshore and replanting coastal vegetation<br>• Natural beach recovery by the landward migration of sand bars from the nearshore zone; for example, the southern end of Patong Beach<br>• Karon Beach: seasonal channels behind dunes were filled up with earth except for the last channel in the south, which was regulated (Fig. 2)<br>• Kamala Beach: the channel at the southern end was strengthened and regulated; some degraded scars are still left in the backshore and used by tourists to reach the beach | • In rehabilitation, priority given to Phuket Island compared to other tourist coasts<br>• Priority for Patong Beach: a rehabilitation plan with distinct zones – beach, green strip, coastal road, permanent construction landward of the coastal road<br>• Kamala Beach: also has a rehabilitation plan; provision of a pedestrian walk along the backshore; structures landward of it; no permanent structures close to the foreshore |
| Khao Lak | • Beaches away from the tidal inlets recovered slowly; after 2 years two-thirds of the beach surface area has recovered (Choowong *et al.* 2009)<br>• Beaches near the tidal inlets did not recover uniformly; the tidal inlets themselves have not recovered and probably will take several decades (Choowong *et al.* 2009)<br>• Tombolos have been rebuilt on outcrops at Nang Thong Beach<br>• Cape Pakarang: terminus has been rebuilt as refracting waves moved sand and gravels to the eastern and western sides of cape. Coral gravels formed a distinct series of ridges with a broad base attached to the coast, tapering seaward and terminating in few recurves that are highly mobile. As the ridges merged, the intervening depressions became narrower and disappeared in some cases. Pioneering coastal vegetation such as coconut seedlings and *Rhizophora* established in the depressions but many did not survive owing to the desiccating condition on the gravel ridges | • Slow recovery, especially for all small enterprises that virtually had no insurance cover<br>• Large chain hotels repaired and rebuilt<br>• Bang Niang Beach: fill material was trucked in during February 2006 to the eroded beach and covered by sand (*Phuket Gazette 2005*). This resulted in a reddish scarp up to 3 m high along the beach. Series of sea walls (simple rubble, gabion, precast structures, cylindrical pipes) constructed along the upper foreshore. By September 2010 the majority of lots were protected by sea walls. Further enhanced at two lots: one lot constructed of pipe-pile infill walls further seaward to protect an earlier sea wall; another had a sea wall with elevated beaches at two levels (Fig. 3) |
| Ko Phi Phi Don | • Beach recovered in the subsequent monsoon seasons owing to the small loss of sand | • Slow recovery in tourism. Land-use problems even before the tsunami occurred (Rittichainuwat 2006). Delayed local government action. More rigorous controls and zoning were not enforced |

action in the form of sea-wall construction and channel retraining.

Immediately after the tsunami, two major strategies were taken to rebuild the tourist industry. The first was the immediate response from the tourism industry, where the WTO (World Tourism Organization) opened its first-ever emergency session on Phuket Island on 1 February 2005 to consider a plan of action. The Phuket Action Plan identified assistance for Sri Lanka, the Maldives, Thailand and Indonesia. The second was the application of the Cairo principles, which consist of 12 guiding principles for post-tsunami rehabilitation and reconstruction (UNEP 2005). The overarching principle is to reduce the vulnerability of coastal communities by establishing a regional early warning system and the application of a science-based reference line that defines a no-build zone seaward of it.

The reconstruction of the tourist industry is not uniform and varies from location to location. While beach recovery is more dependent on fairly predictable physical variables, tourism recovery is more complex as it depends on factors ranging from economic, to social, to political. A marked difference is therefore expected in the reconstruction

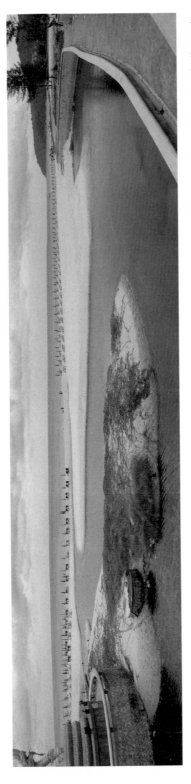

**Fig. 2.** The mouth of the southernmost channel at Karon Beach with its golden dragon statue on its left bank, viewed directly west. Two lines of deckchairs and umbrellas on the beach are interrupted by the sand bar.

**Fig. 3.** The recovery of Bang Niang Beach seems to be characterized by a coastal protection syndrome in which owners construct a variety of sea walls to protect their properties. One example is using pipe-pile infill wall to enhance the height of an existing sea wall in order to provide an elevated beach in front of a previous one.

of hotels and business than in the recovery of beaches. As priority was given to Phuket Island and especially Patong Beach for tourism recovery, the island was back in business almost 1 year later while construction had stalled on Ko Phi Phi Don and barely even started on Khao Lak (WTO 2005) (Table 2).

Bang Niang Beach represents an example of an attempt by the local tourist industry to rehabilitate the tourist coast quickly without proper evaluation of the measures implemented. The beach lies in a moderately eroded coast and is eroding at a rate of $1-5$ m year$^{-1}$, with its implications for coastal protection (Phantuwongrai 2006), and was eroded badly by the time of the tsunami. The initial landfill created a 3 m scarp that had to be protected by a series of sea walls, with some lots increasing the height of sea walls and extending them further into the foreshore. With the sea walls extending into the foreshore, the beach undergoes erosion during the strong SW Monsoon, with waves overtopping some of the sea walls. Beach nourishment and rehabilitation of facilities are necessary for the tourist season that peaks at the end of the year during the weaker NE Monsoon.

## Coastal resilience

Tourist coasts can be considered to be highly vulnerable as there is the need to protect not only the coastal resources and local communities but also tourists and tourist infrastructure. Central to reducing the vulnerability at the coasts is the simple concept of coastal resilience – how to reduce vulnerability and protect coastal communities. Ahmed (2006) contains a more in-depth discussion of the concept of resilience and related concepts, including the protection offered by vegetation. In more general terms, the recovery from the 2004 tsunami is also an example of social–ecological resilience to natural disasters (Adger *et al.* 2005). Various measures can be taken for increasing the social–ecological resilience of these tourist coasts; the more significant local mitigation measures fall into several groups (Table 3; Fig. 4).

Not all local measures were implemented easily. The necessity for resorts to be near the coast and dealing with a hazard of unknown return period were the usual arguments for the slack implementation of the setback line. Hotels were not rebuilt as tsunami-proof structures because of the high costs involved. Thus, the tourism industry would prefer to rely on alternative local measures – reinforced natural and artificial barriers, local warning systems, evacuation routes and tsunami escape towers.

Apart from the local tsunami-mitigation measures, a regional early warning system is both logical and important for the Indian Ocean. Intensive efforts were made by various stakeholders to support the development of an early warning

**Table 3.** *Local tsunami-mitigation measures*

| Measures | Comments |
| --- | --- |
| Safety zone or setback lines: minimum distance of permanent structures from the shoreline, which is the mean high-water mark | Followed by a few large hotels. This measure is difficult to implement for tourism, as the proximity to the beach is an attraction. The argument is that it is unreasonable to require a setback line from a hazard whose return period is unknown (Birkland *et al.* 2006). Also, a uniform setback may be ineffective because the tsunami torrent causes damage for a considerable distance inland, and especially at estuaries and rivers (Bell *et al.* 2005) |
| Tsunami-proof structures: reinforced concrete columns, deeper scour-resistant foundations, strategic placing of openings, anchored precast floor slabs, buildings on piles along waterways (Dalrymple & Kriebel 2005; Lukkunaprasit & Ruangrassamee 2008) | No hotel is totally tsunami-proof but improvements have been made. Some rebuilt with more reinforced concrete; some elevated from the ground; some have built a low wall separating the hotel from the beach. One resort on the northern Khao Lak coast has chalets built on concrete piles within a mangrove environment |
| Natural barriers: preservation of coastal dunes, replanting of coastal forests and mangroves, protecting coral reefs. Mangrove replanting at appropriate locations (Dalrymple & Kriebel 2005) | Field observations showed that green belts, such as dunes and dense coastal forests, could significantly reduce tsunami wave force if the wave height does not exceed a few metres |
| Proposed large-scale modular planting of mangroves (Wong 2010) | |
| Escape routes: designated escape routes with signature for tourist beaches; for example five evacuation routes for Patong Beach | Some routes are fairly long (several km) before high ground is reached. Some signage needs maintenance |
| Warning towers in the major tourist beaches and along the coast | Eighteen built on Phuket Island; some not functioning owing to rapid corrosion |
| Tsunami-escape buildings: three-storey high structures with the shelter on the highest floor | Several built on the Khao Lak coast (Fig. 4) |

system in the Indian Ocean. The Intergovernmental Oceanographic Commission (IOC) of UNESCO initiated two meetings in Paris and Mauritius in 2005 to establish the Intergovernmental Coordination Group for the Indian Ocean Tsunami Warning and Mitigation System (ICG-IOTWS). The IOTWS involves all countries around the Indian Ocean in six working groups (Lauterjung *et al.* 2010). From 2005, the National Tsunami Warning Centre (NTWC) of each country is linked to a simple interim warning system with tsunami-related information provided by the Pacific Tsunami Warning Center (PTWC) and the Japan Meteorological Agency (JMA) (ESCAP 2009). Eventually this role will be taken over by several Regional Tsunami Watch Providers (RTWP), with full implementation in 2011. The NTWCs are free to negotiate bilateral agreements with the RTWP (ESCAP 2009; IOC 2010). Australia, India and Indonesia have agreed to take on their role as RTWPs.

Several issues need to be resolved before the IOTWS is fully operational. These include system integration and co-ordination, risk assessment, and community resilience and sustainability (IOC 2010). There are, however, some problems in funding, upgrading and sustaining some equipment

for sea-level monitoring. In addition, sea-level measurement at deep ocean stations (tsunameters) is critical but the major problems are vandalism and accidental damage, particularly arising from fishing activities. The warning system has been tested in a few countries and requires effective channels of communication down to the community level (ESCAP 2009).

It should be noted that the coasts of Sumatra and the Thai coasts in the Andaman Sea are close to an active earthquake belt and have little time to evacuate should a tsunami occur. This puts the pressure on alternative local measures, which include effective land use and rehabilitation measures, master planning, developing functional escape routes, and constructing physical barriers and escape buildings (NGI 2006). In recent years, new tsunami escape shelters have been constructed along the Khao Lak coast.

## Discussion and conclusion

As a non-seismic zone, buildings on the tourist coasts of Thailand were not designed for earthquakes let alone tsunamis. On some tourist beaches – for

**Fig. 4.** Although warning towers have been built on the tourist coasts, new three-storey tsunami escape buildings have been constructed on the Khao Lak coast. These are built to withstand the tsunami waves as their reinforced pillars are strengthened and mounted on a concrete base.

example, Patong and Surin – low retaining walls (or sea walls), 1 m in height, had been constructed to prevent erosion by tide- or storm-induced waves. Many beaches – for example, Karon in Khao Lak – were separated by streams, without any means of reinforcement being put in place. Resorts were also established close to large streams that were also used by fishing boats.

The resilience of the tourist coasts has not been further strengthened by the reconstruction of hotels and tourist infrastructure themselves. Prior to the tsunami, tourist construction had been at the coast or very near to the coast. The tourism industry violated safety regulations and was responsible for environmental degradation (NGI 2006). The tsunami was supposed to have represented an opportunity to further avoid the overexploitation of resources leading to environmental degradation (WTO 2005). However the post-tsunami tourism recovery has been criticized (Rice 2005) as business and profit still prevails over good environmental practice. New setback requirements in hotel construction were less evident and followed only by some large hotels.

The question is how resilient are the Thai tourist coasts in the event of a future tsunami? Of course, much depends on the source and direction of the tsunami, which determines the time taken to reach the Thai tourist coasts and the magnitude of the waves reaching the Thai beaches. While it is difficult to predict the extent of damage, the Thai tourist coasts seem now to be in a better position in the event of a future tsunami. They would be more resilient than before, as a result of the following measures: the raising of land along some parts of the beach, including the infilling of depressions where waves can surge inland; the removal of wooden and unnecessary structures on the beaches, which could be lethal debris during a tsunami; the planting or re-establishment of biobelts; proper designated escape routes provided at various beaches, provided that these are also maintained; improved infrastructures to protect properties, that is sea walls and channelized streams; some better constructed resorts, and some hotels and chalets elevated above the ground; an increased awareness among the local population and tourists; the provision of high-storey tsunami shelters along the coast; and an early warning system in place in the Indian Ocean, assuming that the system is being maintained.

From the planning perspective, a basic plan on coastal restoration and rehabilitation could not be drawn as there were different goals and objectives at each tourist coast. There is more of a need to design a plan specific to suit the local conditions (Paphavasit *et al.* 2006). No single measure is expected to provide adequate protection, and much depends on the early warning system and its effectiveness.

The Thai tourist coasts were not resilient or never prepared for any tsunami before 26 December

2004. With post-tsunami reconstruction, the socio-ecological resilience is still questionable. However, the beaches have, no doubt, recovered and been made physically more resilient through the upgrading of beaches and biobelts. At Bang Niang Beach, more sea walls have been built but these, unfortunately, have implications for encouraging coastal erosion. Overall, the reconstruction of hotels has not made the tourist coast any more resilient. Although many local measures have been implemented as part of a general mitigation system, it will take many more years to develop a resilient tourist coast to the tsunami threats. Much depends on the early warning system and its effectiveness. A tsunami is not an easy event to predict and its return period is such that many will forget the events of 26 December 2004.

The fieldwork was carried out while the author was employed at the National University of Singapore. The author is grateful to Mrs L.K. Lee for drafting Figure 1 and two anonymous referees for their helpful comments.

# References

ADGER, W. N., HUGHES, T. P., FOLKE, C., CARPENTER, S. R. & ROCKSTRÖM, J. 2005. Social-ecological resilience to coastal disasters. *Science*, **309**, 1036–1039.

AHMED, A. K. 2006. *Concepts and Practices of 'Resilience': A Compilation from Various Secondary Sources*. US IOTWS (Indian Ocean Tsunami Warning System) Program Document, **05-IOTWS-06**.

ALOVISI, J., HASSAM, N., LOGAN, D. & MILLIGAN, A. 2005. *Tsunami: Indian Ocean Event and Investigation into Potential Global Risks*. Guy Carpenter, London.

ASCE 2005. *Seaports and Coastal Aspects*. American Society of Civil Engineers, **8**. World Wide Web Address: http://www.asce.org/files/pdf/tsunami/2-8.pdf.

BELL, R., COWAN, H., DALZIELL, E., EVANS, N., O'LEARY, M., RUSH, B. & YULE, L. 2005. Survey of impacts on the Andaman coast, Southern Thailand following the Great Sumatra–Andaman Earthquake and Tsunami of December 26, 2004. *Bulletin of the New Zealand Society for Earthquake Engineering*, **38**, 123–148.

BERNARD, E. N. & GOULET, R. (ed.). 1981 *Tsunami Research Opportunities: An Assessment and Comprehensive Guide*. NSF, USDOC/NOAA joint publication, Seattle, WA.

BIRKLAND, T. A., HERABAT, P., LITTLE, R. G. & WALLACE, W. A. 2006. The impact of the December 2004 Indian Ocean tsunami on tourism in Thailand. *Earthquake Spectra*, **22**, S889–S900.

CALGARO, E. 2005. *Paradise in Tatters: An Analysis of the Vulnerability of the Tourism Community of Khao Lak, Thailand to the 2004 Indian Ocean Tsunami*. Stockholm Environment Institute, Stockholm.

CHOOWONG, M., MURAKOSHI, N. ET AL. 2007. Erosion and deposition by the 2004 Indian Ocean tsunami in Phuket and Phang-nga provinces, Thailand. *Journal of Coastal Research*, **23**, 1270–1276.

CHOOWONG, M., PHANTUWONGRAJ, S., CHAROENTITIRAT, T., CHUTAKOSITKANON, V., YUMUANG, S. & CHARUSIRI, P. 2009. Beach recovery after 2004 Indian Ocean tsunami from Phang-nga, Thailand. *Geomorphology*, **104**, 134–142.

DALRYMPLE, R. A. & KRIEBEL, D. L. 2005. Lessons in engineering from the tsunami in Thailand. *The Bridge*, **35**, 4–13.

ESCAP 2009. *Tsunami Early Warning Systems in the Indian Ocean and Southeast Asia*. United Nations Economic and Social Commission for Asia and the Pacific, Bangkok.

FRANCIS, M. J. 2006. *Tsunami Inundation Scour of Roadways, Bridges and Foundations – Observations and Technical Guidance from the Great Sumatra Andaman Tsunami*. 2006 EERI/FEMA NEHRP Professional Fellowship Report, Final Draft.

GOTO, K., CHAVANICH, S. A. ET AL. 2007. Distribution, origin and transport process of boulders deposited by the 2004 Indian Ocean tsunami at Pakarang Cape, Thailand. *Sedimentary Geology*, **202**, 821–837.

HANDMER, J. & CHOONG, W. 2006. Disaster resilience through local economic activity in Phuket. *The Australian Journal of Emergency Management*, **21**, 8–15.

ICHINOSAWA, J. 2005. Reputational disaster in Phuket: the secondary impact of the tsunami on inbound tourism. *Disaster Prevention and Management*, **15**, 111–123.

IOC 2010. *Intergovernmental Coordination Group for the Indian Ocean Tsunami Warning and Mitigation System, Steering Group Meeting, Final Report*. International Oceanographic Commission, Paris.

KANAMORI, H. 2006. Lessons from the 2004 Sumatra-Andaman earthquake. *Philosophical Transactions of the Royal Society A*, **364**, 1927–1945.

KAWATA, Y., TSUJI, Y. ET AL. 2005a. Preface. In: *Comprehensive Analysis of the Damage and its Impact on Coastal Zones by the 2004 Indian Ocean Tsunami Disaster*. Special Purposes Research Report by Kyoto University for the Ministry of Education, Culture, Sports, Science and Technology of Japan, 1–3. World Wide Web Address: http://www.tsunami.civil.tohoku.ac.jp/sumatra2004/report.html.

KAWATA, Y., TSUJI, Y. ET AL. 2005b. Field survey and numerical simulation on the 2004 off-Sumatra earthquake and tsunami in Thailand. In: *Comprehensive Analysis of the Damage and its Impact on Coastal Zones by the 2004 Indian Ocean Tsunami Disaster*. Special Purposes Research Report by Kyoto University for the Ministry of Education, Culture, Sports, Science and Technology of Japan, 49–76. World Wide Web Address: http://www.tsunami.civil.tohoku.ac.jp/sumatra2004/report.html.

KONTOGEORGOPOULOS, N. 2004. Conventional tourism and ecotourism in Phuket, Thailand; Conflicting paradigms or symbiotic partners?. *Journal of Ecotourism*, **3**, 87–108.

LAUTERJUNG, J., KOLTERMANN, P., WOLF, U. & SOPAHELUWAKAN, J. 2010. The UNESCO-IOC framework – establishing an international early warning infrastructure in the Indian Ocean region. *Natural Hazards and Earth System Sciences*, **10**, 2623–2629.

LAY, T., KANAMORI, H. ET AL. 2005. The Great Sumamtra-Andaman earthquake of 26 December 2004. *Science*, **308**, 1127–1133.

LUHRMAN, D. 2005. *Post Tsunami Review Workshops and Seminar, 24–31 May 2005*. Ministry of Tourism, Maldives.

LUKKUNAPRASIT, P. & RUANGRASSAMEE, A. 2008. Building damage in Thailand in the 2004 Indian Ocean tsunami and clues for tsunami-resistant design. *The IES Journal Part A: Civil & Structural Engineering*, **1**, 17–30.

MARCHAND, H. 2006. Impacts of the tsunami on a Marine Natonal Park area – Case Study of Lanta Islands (Thailand). *Ocean and Coastal Management*, **45**, 923–946.

MEPRASERT, S. 2006. *The 2004 Indian Ocean Tsunami: Tourism Impacts and Recovery Progress in Thailand's Marine National Parks*. Unpublished PhD dissertation, Oregon State University.

NGI. 2006. *Tsunami Risk Reduction Measures with Focus on Land Use and Rehabilitation*. Report No. 20051267-1. Norwegian Geotechnical Institue, Oslo, Norway World Wide Web Address: http://www.ccop.or.th/download/pub/tsunami_final_report.pdf.

PAPHAVASIT, N., CHOTIYAPUTTA, C. & SIRIBOON, S. 2006. Pre- and post-tsunami coastal planning and land-use policies and issues in Thailand. *In*: *Proceedings of the Workshop on Coastal Area Planning and Management in Asian Tsunami-affected Countries, 27–29 September 2006, Bangkok, Thailand*. FAO Regional Office for Asia and the Pacific, Bankok.

PHANTUWONGRAI, S. 2006. *Shoreline Change after the 26 December 2004 Tsunami Between Laem Pakarang-Khao Lak Area, Changwat Phang-nga, Thailand*. Unpublished MSc thesis, Chulalongkorn University.

PHUKET GAZETTE. 2005. One Year On. *Phuket Gazette*, **12**, Special Supplement, 24–30 December.

POLNGAM, S., SANGUANTRAKOOL, T., PRICHARCHON, E. & PHOOMPANICH, S. 2005. Remote sensing technology for tsunami disasters along the Andaman Sea, Thailand. *In*: ADAMS, B. (ed.) *Proceedings of the International Workshop Series on Remote Sensing: A Compilation of Materials from Workshops held in 2003 (California), 2004 (California) and 2005 (Japan)*. Multidisciplinary Center for Earthquake Engineering Research, Buffalo, USA, **MCEER-05-SP03** (CD-Rom).

RICE, A. 2005. *Post-tsunami Reconstruction and Tourism: A Second Disaster?* Tourism Concern, London.

RITTICHAINUWAT, B. N. 2006. Tsunami recovery: a case study of Thailand's tourism. *Cornell Hotel and Restaurant Administration Quarterly*, **47**, 390–404.

RMS 2006. *Managing Tsunami Risk in the Aftermath of the 2004 Indian Ocean Earthquake and Tsunami*. Risk Management Solutions, Newark, CA.

ROSSETTO, T., PEIRIS, N., POMONIS, A., WILKINSON, S. M., DEL RE, D., KOO, R. & GALLOCHER, S. 2007. The Indian Ocean tsunami of December 26, 2004: observations in Sri Lanka and Thailand. *Natural Hazards*, **42**, 105–124.

ROSSETTO, T., WILKINSON, S., POMONIS, A. & KOO, R. 2006. Thailand. *In*: POMONIS, A., ROSSETTO, T., PEIRIS, N., WILKINSON, S., DEL RE, D., KOO, R., MANLAPIG, R. & GALLOCHER, S. *The Indian Ocean Tsunami of 26 December 2004: Mission Findings in Sri Lanka and Thailand*. Earthquake Engineering Field Investigation Team (EEFIT), Institution of Structural Engineers, London, 125–173.

SAATCIOGLU, M., GHOHARAH, A. & NISTOR, I. 2005. *Reconnaissance Report on the December 26, 2004 Sumatra Earthquake and Tsunami*. Canadian Association of Earthquake Engineering, Ottawa.

SIRIPONG, A. 2006. Andaman seacoast of Thailand field survey after the December 2004 Indian Ocean tsunami. *Earthquake Spectra*, **22**, S187–S202.

TGLL PROJECT 2009. *The Tsunami Legacy – Innovation, Breakthroughs and Change*. Tsunami Global Lessons Learned Project Steering Committee, UN Office of the Recovery Coordinator for Aceh and Nias, Banda Aceh, Indonesia.

THANAWOOD, C., YONGCHALERMCHAI, C. & DENSIREREEKUL, O. 2008. Effects of the December 2004 tsunami and disaster management in southern Thailand. *Science of Tsunami Hazards*, **24**, 206–217.

UNEP 2005. *Guiding Principles for Post-Tsunami Rehabilitation and Reconstruction*. United Nations Environment Programme, Nairobi. World Wide Web Address: http://www.gdrc.org/oceans/tsunami_coastal-guidelines.html.

WONG, P. P. 2010. Coastal communities in Asia Pacific: Vulnerability and adaptation (abstract). *In*: *Coastal Zone Asia Pacific Conference – CZAP 2010, 18–22 October 2010, Bangkok*, 13–14.

WORACHANANANT, S., CARTER, R. W. & HOCKINGS, M. 2007. Impacts of the 2004 tsunami on Surin Marine National Park, Thailand. *Coastal Management*, **35**, 399–412.

WTO 2005. *Tsunami: One Year On – A Summary of the Phuket Action Plan*. World Tourism Organization, Madrid.

# Earthquake catastrophe models in disaster response planning, risk mitigation and financing in developing countries in Asia

NIGEL WINSPEAR[1]*, RADE MUSULIN[2] & MOHAN SHARMA[3]

[1]*Aon Benfield Asia, #42-01 UOB Plaza 1, 80 Raffles Place, Singapore 048624*

[2]*Aon Benfield Analytics Asia Pacific, Aon Tower, Level 29, 201 Kent Street, Sydney, NSW 2000, Australia*

[3]*Catalytics Pte Ltd, UOB Plaza 1, 80 Raffles Place, #36-00, Singapore 048624*

*Corresponding author (e-mail: nigel.winspear@aonbenfield.com)*

**Abstract:** Earthquake catastrophe models combine simulated earthquake hazard intensity parameters, such as ground-shaking intensity and liquefaction potential, with spatial data layers describing the geography and vulnerability of exposed assets at risk (property, populations and infrastructure) to calculate the probability of loss. There is significant scope for applying catastrophe models to disaster relief planning, risk mitigation and financing, especially for earthquake-prone developing economies in Asia. Potential uses of earthquake catastrophe models in these areas include the following.

- Estimating probable levels of damage across an area resulting from a range of possible earthquake events. These estimates are useful in assessing the scale of the response required when an earthquake event actually occurs and for devising a realistic plan for the disaster response effort.
- Quantifying the humanitarian and economic benefit of introducing or upgrading existing risk mitigation measures in advance of their introduction; and assessing the loss potential of possible sites for future infrastructure and/or industrial facilities.
- Quantifying risk metrics fundamental to the pricing of financial risk transfer solutions that enable the transfer of the cost of relief and reconstruction away from the damaged national economy, thereby cushioning it from financial shock caused by major earthquake damage.

Catastrophe (cat) models have been widely used in the insurance and reinsurance industries for nearly 20 years for calculating the amount of insured loss expected from natural catastrophes (such as earthquakes or typhoons) at an annual probability of exceedance (e.g. such as 1/250, see Fig. 1). Prior to the advent of catastrophe models, the insurance industry's usual approach was to estimate the maximum percentage of total insured value in an area that might suffer loss from a realistic earthquake event. This estimation was either based on experiential knowledge or, in many cases where such knowledge was inadequate, the estimation was based on the subjective judgement of industry experts; for example, seismologists from leading reinsurers typically defined earthquake scenarios and their associated losses that were followed by the rest of the industry. Unfortunately, however, using this method there was no way to estimate the actual probability of each loss scenario. The introduction of fully probabilistic cat models in the late 1980s represented a major step forward by providing a scientific basis for assessing both the frequency and severity of earthquake catastrophe

risk. Catastrophe models gained rapid acceptance in the insurance and reinsurance industries after Hurricane Andrew devastated parts of Miami in 1992, causing the largest insured loss experienced worldwide at that time (estimated at about US$15.5 billion in 1992 prices: AIR Worldwide 2005).

Earthquake catastrophe models are created by combining four separate modules: exposure, hazard, vulnerability and financial. The exposure module is set up to capture the attributes of the exposed assets primarily in terms of location, sum insured, occupancy type (residential, commercial office, etc.), coverage type (buildings, contents), construction type (e.g. timber frame, brick, masonry, reinforced concrete frame, steel frame) and policy terms (size of deductible and limit). The earthquake hazard module typically comprises a probabilistic event catalogue containing tens of thousands of physically realizable earthquake scenarios, each of which is assigned an annual probability of occurrence or allocated to a specific simulation year (out of tens or hundreds of thousands). The vulnerability module contains a set of mathematical relationships describing the damageability of the

*From*: TERRY, J. P. & GOFF, J. (eds) 2012. *Natural Hazards in the Asia–Pacific Region: Recent Advances and Emerging Concepts*. Geological Society, London, Special Publications, **361**, 139–150, http://dx.doi.org/10.1144/SP361.12

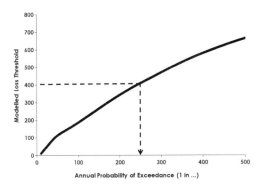

**Fig. 1.** Loss Exceedance Probability Curve produced by an earthquake catastrophe model for a portfolio of property exposure in SE Asia. This curve gives the annual probability of loss exceeding particular thresholds (e.g. a loss of 400 is expected to be exceeded at an annual probability of 1 in 250, also known as the '1 in 250 year return period'). The area under the curve, when annualized, gives the annual loss cost. Both the loss exceedance thresholds and the annual loss cost are essential to the pricing of catastrophe insurance.

exposed assets to earthquake ground shaking of varying severities, and is usually sensitive at a minimum to differences in occupancy and construction type. The financial module calculates the monetary value of the physical damage and insured loss expected from each stochastic earthquake event to the portfolio as a whole, and calculates the probability of exceedance of a range of loss thresholds (Fig. 1) from different financial perspectives (the insured, the insurer, the reinsurer, etc.).

One of the main advantages of probabilistic catastrophe models is that they simulate loss from earthquake events with recurrence intervals that are much too long to be present in the historical record. As such they consider the loss potential from a much wider range of possible earthquake events than would be the case if only the historical record were available. However, models are imperfect representations of reality, being limited by: (a) typically sparse sampling in the instrumental and historical record of large magnitude earthquakes that usually occur on a much longer timescale (making it difficult to accurately constrain the activity rate and maximum credible earthquake magnitude on a particular fault); (b) where faults are either thought to be inactive or are not previously known (either due to lack of geological mapping or because the faults involved are blind; i.e. without surface expression, as caused the January 1994 Northridge Earthquake in California, and the September 2010 and February 2011 Christchurch earthquakes in New Zealand); (c) where the location of seismic activity is time

dependent (i.e. where the main geographical loci of earthquake productivity and earthquake event parameters develop in a non-random manner over time); (d) where there are no locally applicable seismic attenuation relationships available (as is the case throughout much of Asia); (e) where local site soil conditions are poorly represented (these can have a very strong influence on landslide, liquefaction and seismic amplification potential); and (f) where exposed assets (i.e. property, infrastructure or populations) are difficult to define in terms of location, value and vulnerability to earthquake damage.

The objective of this paper is to outline the potential application of earthquake catastrophe models to: (1) disaster response planning; (2) mitigation of loss; and (3) disaster risk financing, as a means for cushioning the national economy from the adverse financial consequences of a seriously damaging earthquake. It is anticipated that this paper will stimulate the application of catastrophe models in all three of these areas.

## Earthquake catastrophe models in disaster response planning

Catastrophe models can produce outputs that are useful for the planning of disaster response and mitigation. This is achieved by combining earthquake intensity parameters (such as maps of ground-shaking intensity) with data layers describing the location, value and vulnerability of the exposed assets at risk (i.e. property, populations and infrastructure) to produce estimates of physical damage. This can be undertaken: (a) for an actual earthquake event to indicate what emergency response teams can expect; (b) for a number of postulated scenario earthquakes used for emergency service training purposes; or (c) for thousands of postulated scenario earthquakes from the probabilistic event set, in order to estimate probabilities of damaging effects on the asset portfolio (e.g. annual probability of casualties exceeding a threshold value).

Systems for real-time earthquake loss estimation and response are already in existence in a small number of developed countries, principally the United States (e.g. Eguchi *et al.* 1994; FEMA 2010), Japan (e.g. Nakamura 1996; Yamazaki *et al.* 1998; Hosokawa *et al.* 2008) and Taiwan (e.g. Yeh *et al.* 2006), and a small number of other territories including Central America (e.g. GFDRR 2008) and Colombia (Yamin *et al.* 2004). The authors are not aware of any such systems that have been created to date specifically for developing countries in Asia, noting that certain territories such as Indonesia and the Philippines are particularly at risk of damaging earthquake and hence in need of such systems. Whilst both of these territories are already covered by earthquake loss estimation systems with worldwide scope (e.g. USGS PAGER and WAPMERR systems: see USGS 2010b and WAPMERR 2010), there is significant potential for locally developed, locally focused systems to be created that will: (a) provide considerably greater spatial resolution of the modelled earthquake hazard; (b) utilize locally applicable data for earthquake hazard modelling (e.g. attenuation relationships and high-resolution soil mapping); (c) employ local experience in developing asset vulnerability relationships; (d) generate additional bespoke, customizable model outputs of use in disaster planning; and (e) allow direct integration of these outputs with decision support systems used to train and guide emergency response units. These models will also differ from existing catastrophe models available for these territories from established commercial model vendor companies because they will: (a) reflect the vulnerability of the entire building stock (rather than just the insured building stock; the two can be quite different in developing economies), populations and infrastructure; and (b) produce outputs that are of use in disaster response planning (such as those outlined below).

To ensure consistently high quality of the underlying earthquake hazard model, it is recommended that any such model spanning multiple territories utilizes a globally standardized earthquake hazard model which has benefited from significant local input during development, such as the Global Earthquake Model (GEM 2010) or the USGS SHAKEMAP model (USGS 2010a) (Fig. 2). Equally important is a finely resolved definition of the exposed assets at risk, ideally with these data defined at a horizontal resolution of 1 km or less to allow relatively fine-scale variation in ground-shaking intensity to be represented.

Commercial earthquake catastrophe models currently in use for most Asian territories currently simulate only ground-shaking damage and do not explicitly consider major secondary perils, particularly fire following the earthquake and tsunami inundation. At present, the only exception to this is in Japan where commercial catastrophe models have the capability to estimate losses arising from fire following the earthquake (but not tsunami). Both of these are important secondary perils that need to be considered in a full catastrophe risk assessment, noting that in some instances, such as for the $M$ 9.0 Tohoku earthquake of 11 March 2011, damage from tsunami significantly exceeded that from ground shaking.

Fire following the earthquake is a possibility whenever and wherever a major earthquake strikes

(a) where there are available ignition sources, such as lit cooking fires (in Asia today these are often fed by bottled kerosene) or where LPG tanks are damaged and their contents ignite in (b) areas dominated by high-density wooden housing with few fire barriers (such as in older parts of some major Asian cities and in many informal housing areas) where (c) the fire fighting service is either overwhelmed by the sheer scale of the disaster or is unable to reach areas affected by fire because of the damage sustained. Major fire does not accompany every major earthquake, however. The few large fires that do occur tend to affect high-value industrial facilities storing flammable petrochemicals (e.g. Izmit, Turkey in 1999; and Hokkaido, Japan in 2003). Fortunately, no widespread earthquake-triggered conflagration scenario affecting tens of thousands of residential properties has occurred anywhere in the world since the 1923 Great Kanto Earthquake and conflagration devastated the Tokyo–Yokohama area of Japan, killing more than 100 000 people. Smaller-scale fires have, however, occurred more recently as a result of earthquakes, including fires that consumed thousands of homes in an 82 ha area of Kobe, Japan after the 17 January 1995 Great Hanshin Earthquake (RMS 2005); the 30–50 significant fires following the 17 January 1994 Northridge Earthquake in California (Evans *et al.* 1997); and the 12 fires in Kaohsiung City and Pingtung County, southern Taiwan, in the aftermath of two major earthquakes on 26 December 2006 (Wen *et al.* 2008). When modelling the effect of fire following the earthquake, catastrophe models must probabilistically simulate multiple different outcomes for each ground-shaking event, taking into account the number of initial locations in which fire starts and the subsequent development of each fire either as it burns out or as it merges with other fires to form a larger fire. This is clearly a very complex modelling problem requiring a detailed understanding not only of the local built environment but also of the dynamics of fires in these environments; and is tackled at only a cursory level by the few commercial earthquake catastrophe models available that consider this secondary peril.

Tsunami is also a known peril in Japan, and in the Indonesian and Philippine archipelagos. Earthquake-triggered tsunamis most recently affected Japan in 2011, and Indonesia in 2004, 2006 and 2010. In the Philippines, local earthquake-triggered tsunamis were generated in 1976 and 1994. However, other territories bordering the South China Sea are also at risk from tsunami caused by failure of the subduction zone located offshore from Manila (Megawati *et al.* 2009; Lau *et al.* 2010). Sieh (2009) predicted that another extremely large ($M$ 8.8) subduction-related earthquake is likely

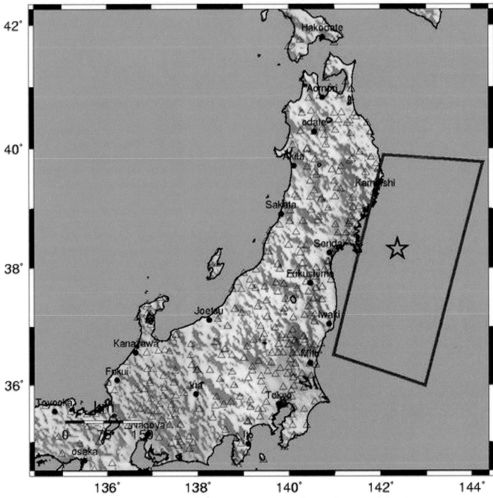

**Fig. 2.** USGS SHAKEMAP (©USGS 2011) for the *M* 9.0 Tohoku Earthquake epicentred offshore from NE Japan on 11 March 2011. The box shows the approximate area of rupture of the subduction zone that began with this earthquake. As an indication of the likelihood of damage, MMI VI intensity shaking is expected to cause damage to poorly constructed masonry buildings.

to occur in the next few decades on the subduction zone west of Sumatra, Indonesia, which could result in a tsunami that devastates the south-central part of western Sumatra. In both of these cases it is possible that damage from tsunami may outweigh that from ground shaking, particularly where the area affected by tsunami is a long way from the earthquake epicentre. For this reason, any earthquake catastrophe model developed for disaster response planning for these territories needs to be capable of simulating damage from either or both of ground shaking and tsunami inundation. It is worth noting that no commercial catastrophe model developed for the insurance industry currently available takes tsunami into account in its damage calculations for any Asian territory.

A number of catastrophe model outputs useful for disaster planning are listed below. It is envisaged that these would be implemented as spatial data layers in a geographical information system (GIS), in order to enable the following.

- Visualization of the spatial data by disaster relief co-ordinators at control locations and by emergency response units in the field.
- GIS analysis and ad hoc querying of spatial relationships in the modelled output data (e.g. in order to identify population centres that can be accessed by road with modelled ground-shaking intensity of MMI VI or more, with at least 500 predicted casualties).
- Integration with other related resources, such as satellite and aerial photographic imagery, and third-party data products providing an alternative independent view on the risk, such as WAPMERR, USGS SHAKEMAP and PAGER estimates of ground-shaking intensity, number of fatalities and populations affected by severe ground shaking.
- Assessment of uncertainty surrounding modelled parameters by comparing with actual measured parameter values, such as ground-motion observations from seismic accelerometers, changes in land surface elevation, tilt and shift in horizontal location recorded by ground-based GPS stations, and airborne/satellite-based synthetic aperture radar (SAR) and light detection and ranging (LiDAR) surveys. Once differences have been quantified, it is then possible to adjust the modelled values to take account of measured parameter values via a statistical routine such as kriging. Maps of modelled, measured and adjusted values, and the differences between them, can then be displayed and queried in the GIS.

The GIS and its accompanying data would form part of a decision support system designed to guide the disaster response services in making more effective use of resources available by providing forewarning of what to expect in the aftermath of a major earthquake. Useful data layers, including outputs from catastrophe models, which should be implemented in the GIS as spatial data layers include the following.

(1) *Hazard maps*: base maps describing the modelled magnitude of the earthquake or earthquake-induced hazard, including (a) ground-shaking intensity (e.g. peak ground acceleration or displacement, Modified Mercalli Intensity (MMI) scale); (b) average or peak tsunami inundation velocity and depth; and (c) estimates of ground deformation (i.e. areas likely to have undergone uplift or subsidence, liquefaction, lateral spreading of gently sloping ground, settlement or landslide). These maps can potentially be generated in real time following an actual earthquake scenario or in advance to represent one or more events carefully chosen from the event set of a probabilistic catastrophe model, as would be useful for emergency service training. As noted above, for an actual event it is important to also overlay measured values onto the modelled hazard base maps, where available, to provide a means by which the accuracy of the modelled estimates can be assessed and if necessary improved. A catalogue of previous earthquake events would also be very useful.

(2) *Assets*: maps and lists of the exposed known assets at risk. These include population and housing density by administrative zone, digitized outlines of buildings and/or registered land allotments, and location of utility lifelines (e.g. water mains, piped gas, electrical systems and telephone trunk lines). Asset schedules should also be updated at periodic intervals to reflect population growth and changes in the built environment. Note that there may be a mismatch between the coarser spatial resolution of asset inventory data (which may be available by administrative zone) and the underlying hazard mapping; in such cases possible resolutions include disaggregating the asset data to match the finer hazard resolution or aggregating the hazard data to match the resolution of the assets.

(3) *Estimates of property damage*: maps and lists of modelled likelihood and severity of damage to property (e.g. residential, commercial and industrial property), infrastructure (e.g. schools, health clinics, roads, bridges, tunnels, water and sewerage infrastructure, pumping stations, etc.) and utility lifelines. These outputs may be generated either for scenario earthquakes or using the entire probabilistic event set, allowing estimation of the probability that damage will exceed a threshold value(s) over 1 year or several consecutive decades chosen at random. Maps of field observations concerning damage to

infrastructure (such as ruptured gas or water mains, fallen lengths of high-tension power lines or damage to telephone and electrical substations) should also be overlain onto these modelled damage maps to provide a means by which the accuracy of the modelled estimates can be assessed and, if necessary, improved.

(4)  *Estimates of casualties*: maps and lists of esti-mated populations and population centres exposed to hazard of varying levels of inten-sity, together with estimates of resulting casualties and fatalities. For example, the USGS's PAGER product (USGS 2010*b*) pro-vides estimates of populations and settlements affected by ground shaking of various intensi-ties together with estimated number of fatal-ities from previous earthquakes in the area. These products do not consider temporal vari-ation in the human populations of affected areas, which can sometimes be significant, and there is therefore scope for improving such estimates by considering temporal vari-ation not only in the gross population of an area but also how it splits into populations housed within buildings and those located without. Again, these outputs could be gener-ated either for scenario earthquakes or using the entire probabilistic event set, as noted in (3) above.

(5)  *Key location estimates*: values for the par-ameters listed in (1)–(4) above for key prede-fined static locations (such as major towns or cities) and for locations dynamically chosen defined by the user.

(6)  Locations identified as being safer (for pre-evacuation assembly) and land-based evacua-tion routes to be used by disaster response teams in the aftermath of a damaging earthquake.

(7)  Data enabling logistical support for the ensu-ing disaster relief effort; for example, identify-ing areas likely to require some or all of:

- immediate emergency food and medical assistance (via land, sea or air including air drop);
- estimates of displaced households and associated shelter requirements;
- dispatch of military troops to re-establish law and order, and to assist in the search for survivors;
- dispatch of rescue assistance and fire-fighting teams;
- land-based routing to overcome impassa-ble bridges, tunnels or roads.

(8)  Backdrop maps including topography, veg-etation cover, land use, hydrology, soil type, precipitation isohyets, satellite and/or aerial photographic imagery.

These outputs would be very useful both for: (a) dis-aster response planning (both in the immediate aftermath of an event and for training the emergency response services prior to an event); and (b) guiding longer-term efforts to mitigate the effects of dama-ging earthquakes (e.g. when evaluating and priori-tizing options for future extension of utility lifeline systems to minimize exposure to potential lique-faction). In the event of a damaging earthquake, it is envisaged that a catastrophe model would be employed to estimate the damage resulting from an event with the parameters specified (e.g. magnitude, location, depth, focal plane solution), producing outputs consistent with the data resources listed above. These could be used to create a damage assessment report, which in turn would be used to assess the scale of the disaster response required and as the basis for manually creating an initial plan for the actual response effort. In this way the emergency response co-ordinator would have access to a working response plan up to several days in advance of disaster relief teams reaching a remote affected area. It took several days, for example, before ground-based response teams could reach the Indonesian Mentawai islands affected by the recent 25 October 2010 $M_w$ 7.7 earthquake and tsunami because of seasonally rough seas.

It is important to note that differences are always expected between the modelled and the actual damage situation on the ground because of uncer-tainty in the form of: (a) incomplete representation in the catastrophe model of a more complex and detailed reality, as the real world is far more compli-cated in detail than is possible to represent in models; (b) ground-shaking intensity at the location of each exposed asset (reflecting uncertainty in the detailed characterization of the earthquake hazard); (c) the damage response of each individual asset to this ground shaking (reflecting the ability of the model to accurately simulate damage to the asset); (d) estimation of damage caused by second-ary perils (such as fire following the earthquake, or tsunami and flood caused by failure of natural or man-made river dams); and (e) lack of detailed accurate descriptions of the exposed assets at risk (e.g. the location of an asset may be specified by street address or postal code rather than by an actual co-ordinate location; its replacement value may only be estimated; and its construction may be incompletely or incorrectly listed). These sources of uncertainty cause deviation of the mod-elled hazard and damage from actual values experi-enced. As a way of improving confidence in the model predictions, it is essential to quantify differ-ences between original modelled and actual parameters (making them available for display and query within the GIS system). Actual measured values can also be used to improve the accuracy of the modelled predictions by adjusting the modelled values, as already noted.

Training exercises based on a handful of realistic earthquake scenarios are also essential for preparing the emergency response services and testing existing disaster response plans. Owing to the physical effort involved in each training exercise, including co-ordinating numerous different disaster response agencies, it is essential to limit these to a handful of realistic earthquake disaster scenarios representing a small number of both relatively extreme hypothetical scenarios and/or actual historical events. Hypothetical scenarios would be defined as: (a) specific individual events, defined by expert judgement and/or by identifying the maximum credible event likely to affect an area using a probabilistic earthquake hazard model; and/or (b) in terms of maximum ground-shaking intensity expected to be exceeded with a fixed probability in a given period (e.g. 10% chance of exceedance in 50 years).

## Earthquake catastrophe models in disaster risk mitigation

One way for a country damaged by earthquake to enhance its ability to recover from major earthquake damage is to purchase catastrophe insurance to provide guaranteed financing for relief and reconstruction. Another alternative is to make far-sighted investments in disaster risk mitigation that will progressively lessen the effect of a damaging earthquake when it occurs, thereby reducing the loss (both humanitarian and economic) experienced by the economy, and eventually the amount of catastrophe insurance required (because economic loss expectations will become lower with time). Examples of earthquake disaster mitigation measures potentially include: (1) upgrading the existing minimum seismic design code for engineered buildings; (2) making engineered design of buildings compulsory (together with adequate enforcement) throughout the economy as a whole (noting that this is not currently the case with the majority of single-family housing in Asia); (3) retrofitting major buildings with lateral structural bracing and lifeline infrastructure systems (water, gas, electricity) with automated tremor-induced shut-offs (this step may exceed minimum design code specifications); (4) choosing routes for new lifelines and infrastructure that are less likely to experience severe ground shaking, ground deformation or tsunami inundation (e.g. routing of lifelines away from areas that may liquefy during shaking or

amplify the ground motions, such as reclaimed land or soft alluvial soils); (5) identifying zones in which to build that are likely to be safe from tsunami inundation (and, conversely, zones that are not safe to build in and in which future major developments that would give rise to serious consequences should they fail, such as nuclear power plants, should be reconsidered); and (6) enforcing the use of steel-framed construction (rather than timber frame, which is easily demolished by tsunami) in areas at risk of tsunami inundation. Bespoke catastrophe models can be used to estimate the benefit gained from such improvements in advance of their implementation, as outlined later.

Investments in loss mitigation ultimately enhance the ability of the economy to recover from unexpected major earthquake damage. Of these, it is the extent to which suitable engineered design is required and enforced in the economy as a whole that is, perhaps, the single most important from an overall economic perspective as this directly affects not only the level of property damage incurred but also humanitarian and consequential (loss of family members, medical expenses for casualties, loss of livelihood, loss of breadwinner, etc.) losses. This is of significance to the economy as a whole because major earthquakes can kill and injure tens or hundreds of thousands of people and can damage hundreds of thousands of properties. This level of damage cannot be easily absorbed into the normal building capacity of an economy because the diversion of material and labour to post-event reconstruction from other activities would cause severe stress and disruption (Musulin et al. 2009). Note that the provisions made when designing a seismic code governing lateral building strength depend on accurate assessments of the ground-shaking intensity likely to be encountered. This is often expressed as the shaking intensity likely to be exceeded only once in a fixed period of time (such as a 10% chance of exceedance in a 50 year period, which corresponds to a return period of 475 years) at a specific location. Earthquake catastrophe models can be used for this purpose because, by default, they already perform similar calculations; that is, they calculate the probability of exceedance of loss to a combined portfolio of locations. All that is needed is an adjustment to allow them to calculate the probability of exceedance of ground-shaking intensity at each location in turn. As private commercial catastrophe models do not currently allow adjustment in this way, it is anticipated that public open-source models will be developed that are not so constrained in the adjustments that can be made. Catastrophe models will also be developed specifically for the purpose of disaster relief planning and risk mitigation in Asia in the future.

Catastrophe models also have a key role to play in quantifying the financial benefit of introducing disaster risk mitigation measures. For example, Kunreuther & Michel-Kerjan (2009) used a catastrophe model to determine the economic benefit of mandating the use of residential loss mitigation measures for insured household property in several hurricane-exposed US states. The analysis suggested that this could reduce damage by up to 61% in Florida at a return period of 100 years, equivalent to about US$51 billion in losses. Earthquake catastrophe models can and should be used in a similar way to evaluate the financial benefit of proposed disaster risk mitigation measures (examples of which are listed earlier) in advance of their introduction; and also for assessing (in order to minimize) the loss potential of possible sites for future infrastructure and/or industrial facilities. Perhaps the most significant advance developing economies in Asia can make is to take measures to strengthen existing non-engineered buildings to prevent (or at least significantly delay) their collapse in order to purchase time to allow their inhabitants to escape. As there are literally millions of non-engineered buildings requiring reinforcement in Asia, a multi-stage process is suggested below that when coupled with active enforcement of the seismic building design code would assist greatly in reducing the vulnerability of the building stock in coming decades.

- Focus initially on retrofitting public buildings such as government buildings, public hospitals and large schools to help to ensure that core public services remain operational in the aftermath of a major earthquake (noting that government effectively ceased to function in the immediate aftermath of the 2010 Haiti Earthquake in part because of widespread collapse of government buildings). Large school buildings are included here because of the number of casualties that could potentially result should they collapse.
- Dramatically increase enforcement of compliance to the seismic design code for new building construction. Obviously, there are corruption issues to first overcome in certain developing countries in Asia that prevent this from happening. However, enforcing this step would mean that the problem of the lack of earthquake resistance of buildings would gradually diminish as the building stock is gradually renewed on a timescale spanning multiple decades.
- Identify areas known to be dominated by non-engineered buildings that are unlikely to comply with existing seismic design regulations and focus on developing low-cost simple solutions for reinforcing these buildings to allow

their occupants to escape. Because this describes the majority of buildings in most developing Asian countries, some form of prioritization will be necessary, such as focusing initially on the most vulnerable buildings; for example, adobe and poorly constructed masonry buildings located in areas with soft soils that may enhance ground-shaking intensity or liquefy.

Earthquake catastrophe models can be used to estimate in advance the considerable long-term financial benefit to the economy of such improvements.

## Earthquake catastrophe models in disaster risk financing

The financial consequences of a damaging earthquake can be mitigated in multiple ways, both before the event (*ex ante*) and after the event (*ex post*) (Table 1). A consistent shortcoming in the disaster risk management strategies of developing economies in Asia is their reliance on *ex post* disaster financing solutions, preferring for various reasons (such lack of affordability of alternative *ex ante* solutions) to rely on their own, often limited, financial resources to cover as best they can the majority of disaster losses (e.g. by emergency reallocation of budget), and on international assistance for major disasters. This contrasts with developed countries, where *ex ante* disaster financing solutions are instead the norm (ADB 2008).

*Ex ante* disaster risk financing solutions are generally preferable because the guarantee of payment of a pre-agreed amount (which in some instances can be rapid) reduces dependence on ad hoc sources of post-disaster funding. Catastrophe insurance is often a key component of *ex ante* disaster risk financing solutions, providing the buyer with the significant advantage of leverage in which a smaller insurance premium can result in a much larger payout. Catastrophe models enable the quantification of risk metrics that are fundamental to the pricing of catastrophe insurance and reinsurance, and other forms of alternative risk transfer that seek to transfer financial risk to non-traditional risk carriers such as the capital markets (e.g. via catastrophe bonds). Risk metrics include estimates of the limit of catastrophe insurance coverage needed, the technical price (i.e. the annual loss cost) of the insurance and the probabilities of the insurance cover being activated and exhausted, at which point the spillover in excess of the insurance limit falls back to the government or public.

The leverage provided by catastrophe insurance provides the policyholder (in this case, the national or local government) with a greater ability to meet heavy unexpected disaster relief and reconstruction obligations than might otherwise be the case.

**Table 1.** *Summary of the main disaster risk financing options available at governmental level*

| # | Type | Option | Remarks |
|---|------|--------|---------|
| 1 | *Ex post* | Donor assistance (for relief/ reconstruction) | Often too little, too late; not guaranteed; not timeous; may be given instead in the form of debt cancellation; donor fatigue if several major events occur worldwide in same year |
| 2 | *Ex post* | Emergency reallocation of budget to provide funds for disaster relief and reconstruction | Budgetary reallocations will divert funds from other longer-term development objectives. However, the margin available for reallocation is often limited |
| 3 | *Ex post* | Increased governmental borrowing (domestic and international). | Sovereign national rating may suffer a downgrade if an earthquake damages the capital city or an area of major industrial infrastructure on which the economy is dependent. Ability to borrow will consequently be reduced at a time of need |
| 4 | *Ex post* | Tax increases or new taxes | On the taxable population and commercial economy |
| 5 | *Ex ante* | Contingencies in budget – enabling the retention of relatively small amounts of fiscal risk | Draw down from pre-allocated national reserves to finance small but recurrent disasters. Contingencies are unlikely to be enough to cover damage from major earthquakes |
| 6 | *Ex ante* | Contingent credit (either on its own or together with other forms of *ex ante* funding) from international or domestic sources. Also known as Catastrophe Deferred Drawdown Option (Cat DDO) | Long-term deferred credit facility to cover relief, recovery and reconstruction demands and/or to provide funding whilst a catastrophe fund begins to accumulate. Arranged in advance but the loan is drawn down only after a qualifying loss event |
| 7 | *Ex ante* | National catastrophe reserves fund | Accumulating reserves fund set aside specifically for disaster relief and reconstruction purposes |
| 8 | *Ex ante* | Catastrophe insurance (either on its own or together with other forms of *ex ante* funding) | Benefit of insurance leverage provides the ability to meet volatile and occasionally very heavy demands for relief and reconstruction funds. Indemnity or parametric trigger basis |
| 9 | *Ex ante* | Catastrophe reserves fund + catastrophe insurance + contingent credit | As the catastrophe reserves fund accumulates, the need for catastrophe insurance decreases. The contingent loan facility provides bridging finance whilst the catastrophe fund is accumulating |
| 10 | *Ex ante* | Catastrophe bond(s)/Insurance Linked Securities | Investment-grade bond issued to secure the issuer by accessing guaranteed disaster finance from the international capital markets. Payout trigger usually has a parametric basis, although indemnity bonds do exist |

*Ex post*, arranged after the event; *Ex ante*, arranged before the event. *Ex ante* solutions are preferred because the amounts involved are arranged in advance and can, in some instances, be paid rapidly.

Figure 3 shows considerable volatility in calculated payout for an earthquake disaster relief risk financing scheme in a SE Asian country over the past 6 years. Disaster funding in this territory at present consists of simply a budgetary allocation that does not accumulate year to year. In years with major earthquake-triggered catastrophes there may be a significant disaster funding shortfall, requiring emergency reallocation of budget that was previously allocated to other longer-term development objectives. Catastrophe insurance provides a means of meeting these enhanced obligations, in a way that can be allowed for in advance in the annual budget,

thereby significantly reducing the need for emergency budgetary reallocation after the event. In this way, the economy can be protected to some degree from unexpected fiscal shocks caused by earthquakes that could interrupt, delay or even halt its development.

In developing Asian countries, earthquake catastrophe insurance penetration is usually highest in the commercial and industrial sectors of the economy, and lowest in the residential and municipal (i.e. government) sectors. The commercial and industrial sectors can, therefore, expect to be indemnified to the limit of their insurance coverage in the

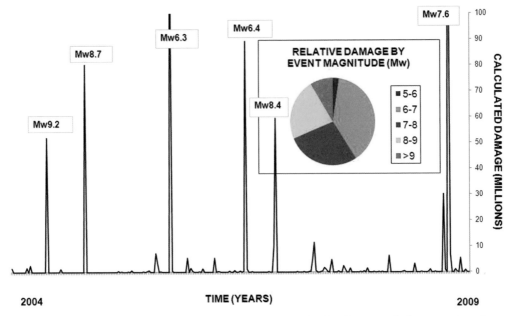

**Fig. 3.** Example of volatility in calculated damage covered by a proposed earthquake catastrophe insurance scheme in a major Asian territory for the period 2004–2009. Spikes represent damage from particularly damaging earthquakes. It is envisaged that catastrophe insurance payouts would have been made for most, if not all, of these major events had such a catastrophe insurance scheme been in place at the time. Note that some of the most damaging events are caused by smaller ($M_w$ 6–7) earthquakes; these events occurred onshore in proximity to major population centres.

event of a damaging earthquake, whereas the uninsured parts of the economy will obviously not benefit from any payment from the insurance industry. This means that across the economy as a whole a major 'disaster financing gap' exists between the total economic loss and the amount recovered from insurance. This gap can be very large. For example, only a tiny portion (less than 2%) of the US$85–120 billion economic loss from the 2008 Wenchuan Earthquake in China was insured; and even in Japan only about 3.5% of the US$100–130 billion economic loss (1995 prices) from the 1995 Great Hanshin Earthquake was insured. A disaster risk financing solution, such as catastrophe insurance, can potentially fill some of this gap where it is specifically designed to cover segments of the economy that are currently mostly uninsured, such as the residential and municipal sectors. Since it is difficult to enforce the purchase of residential earthquake insurance in developing economies in Asia, the premium for such insurance cover would need to be paid instead either by the national or local government itself and/or by international donors. The municipal sector is the responsibility of the local and national governments, and hence funding for earthquake insurance would need to be drawn from their respective budgets and/or by donor assistance. In both cases, it is envisaged that

a single earthquake catastrophe insurance policy could be issued to the national government on behalf of a particular economic sector as a whole. Payouts from the insurance policy would subsequently be disbursed by the government at its discretion to assist in disaster relief and/or reconstruction. It is worth noting here that there are currently only a few examples worldwide of catastrophe insurance being used to provide funds directly to government or government agencies (rather than directly to individuals such as homeowners) because of earthquake damage, all of which employ catastrophe models as the basis for loss estimation. In both cases outlined below, the amount of insurance coverage and hence the payout is calibrated to a proportion of the total economic loss and is not tied to a specific economic sector.

- Caribbean – the Caribbean Catastrophe Risk Insurance Fund (CCRIF) covers 16 island nations in the Caribbean for earthquake and hurricane windstorm peril up to the limit of each island's catastrophe insurance policy. The original CCRIF scheme used a parametric index (i.e. an index constructed from modelled event characteristics, such as ground-shaking intensity, across an array of island locations) to calculate the insurance payout. An upgraded loss estimation methodology is now being adopted involving modelling of actual event damage using a bespoke catastrophe model. The CCRIF scheme has made payouts to policyholders several times since its inception, most recently to the Government of Haiti within 3 weeks of the devastating 12 January 2010 earthquake. Note that the payout received was about 20 times the premium paid by the Haitian Government into the CCRIF.

- Mexico – the Mexican Government's disaster agency FONDEN has issued multiple Catastrophe Bonds to institutional investors to enhance its ability to meet relief obligations arising from an earthquake similar to the 19 September 1985 magnitude 8.1 'Mexico City' Earthquake. In each case, a fixed payout is made to FONDEN if a qualifying earthquake (i.e. one that exceeds a threshold magnitude within predefined areas during the fixed lifetime of the bond). No payouts to FONDEN have yet been made because, fortunately, no major earthquakes have yet occurred in the areas specified.

An important consideration when designing a disaster risk financing scheme is that developing countries are naturally keen to maximize retention of funds within their national economies; for example, by minimizing payments made internationally to third parties such as reinsurers. This can be accommodated by combining selected risk financing options (outlined in Table 1) in such a way as to retain more risk (and, hence, premium) within the national economy by only transferring exceptionally large losses to international reinsurers. For example, smaller, more frequent, losses might be tackled using domestic catastrophe reserves and/or budget contingencies set aside specifically for this purpose. Larger, less frequent, losses could be handled using funds drawn only when required from a guaranteed contingent credit facility from an international agency. Infrequent exceptionally large losses could be covered by catastrophe insurance (backed by international reinsurance) with a deductible set at a level to ensure that only losses exceeding a certain size are covered by the insurance. By covering only very large losses, catastrophe insurance would be considerably less expensive than if it were to also cover smaller, higher frequency, losses as well. This means that less premium would be paid onwards to international reinsurers, helping to maximize the domestic retention of premium within the territory.

A call is made here for disaster risk financing schemes covering vulnerable economic sectors that are currently mostly uninsured (such as the residential and municipal sectors) to be set up in collaboration with the governments of highly earthquake-prone developing countries in Asia, such as Indonesia and the Philippines. This would help to significantly cushion these economies from the fiscal risk arising from unexpected major earthquake disasters. Catastrophe models enable the pricing of catastrophe insurance, which provides the capability to cover occasional extreme loss events; and, as such, underpin the development of such schemes.

## Conclusions

There is significant scope for applying earthquake catastrophe models to disaster relief planning, risk mitigation and disaster financing operations in earthquake-prone developing territories in Asia, and a call is therefore made here for the development and application of bespoke catastrophe models to support these purposes. Catastrophe model outputs can be deployed within decision support systems designed specifically to enable disaster relief planning, for use in training the emergency services on scenario earthquakes and to give advance warning of what to expect in the aftermath of an actual earthquake. Catastrophe models can also be used to quantify the financial benefit of proposed risk mitigation measures prior to their introduction as part of a wider cost–benefit analysis. Finally, catastrophe models have a more traditional application in loss estimation and pricing for insurance and reinsurance, including enabling the development of disaster risk financing schemes for developing countries that are prone to damaging earthquakes.

The authors wish to thank the following colleagues at Aon Benfield for their assistance in reviewing this manuscript: Prof. R. Blong, Dr W. Gardner, Mr N. Mathison, Mr G. Attard and Mr B. Weir.

## References

ADB. 2008. *Natural Catastrophe Risk Insurance Mechanisms for the Asia and Pacific Region*. Asian Development Bank Regional Technical Assistance Report, August 2008. Project Number 42103. World Wide Web Address: http://www.adb.org/Documents/ TARs/REG/42103-REG-TAR.pdf. Accessed 8 November 2010.

AIR WORLDWIDE. 2005. *1992 Hurricane Andrew Anniversary*. AIR Worldwide, Boston, MA. World Wide Web Address: http://www.air-worldwide.com/PublicationsItem.aspx?id=14642. Accessed 24 March 2011.

GFDRR. 2008. *GFDRR Case Study: Central American Probabilistic Risk Assessment (CAPRA)*. Global Facility For Disaster Reduction and Recovery, Washington, DC. World Wide Web Address: http://www.gfdrr. org/docs/Snapshot_CAPRA.pdf. Accessed 4 April 2011.

EGUCHI, R., GOLTZ, J. D., SELIGSON, H. & HEATON, T. H. 1994. Real-time earthquake hazard assessment in California: the early post-earthquake damage assessment tool and the Caltech–USGS broadcast of earthquakes. *In*: *Proceedings of the 5th US National Conference on Earthquake Engineering, July 10–14, 1994, Chicago, Illinois: Earthquake Awareness and Mitigation Across the Nation*, Volume 2. Earthquake Engineering Research Institute, Berkeley, CA, 55–63.

EVANS, D. D., WALTON, W. D. & MOWRER, F. W. 1997. Progress report on fires following the Northridge earthquake. *In*: BEALL, K. A. (ed.) *Thirteenth Meeting of the UJNR Panel on Fire Research and Safety, March 13–20, 1996*, Volume 2. Building and Fire Research Laboratory, National Institute of Standards and Technology, Gaithersburg, MD. World Wide Web Address: http://www.fire.nist.gov/bfrlpubs/fire97/PDF/f97088.pdf. Accessed 14 April 2011.

FEMA. 2010. HAZUS: *FEMA's Methodology for Estimating Potential Losses from Disasters*. Federal Emergency Management Agency, Hyattsville, MD. World Wide Web Address: http://www.fema.gov/plan/prevent/hazus/. Accessed 8 November 2010.

GEM. 2010. *Global Earthquake Model*. Global Earthquake Model, Pavia, Italy. World Wide Web Address: http://www.globalquakemodel.org. Accessed 1 November 2010.

HOSOKAWA, M., JEONG, B., TAKIZAWA, O. & MATSUOKA, M. 2008. Disaster risk evaluation and damage detection using remote sensing data for global rescue operations. *In*: *Proceedings of Commission VIII ISPRS Congress, Beijing, China, July 2008*. International Society for Photogrammetry and Remote Sensing, Beijing. World Wide Web Address: http://www.isprs.org/proceedings/XXXVII/congress/8_pdf/2_WG-VIII-2/06.pdf. Accessed 4 April 2011.

KUNREUTHER, H. & MICHEL-KERJAN, E. 2009. *At War with the Weather: Managing Large-scale Risks in a New Era of Catastrophes*. MIT Press, Cambridge, MA.

LAU, A. Y. A., SWITZER, A. D., DOMINEY-HOWES, D., AITCHISON, J. C. & ZONG, Y. 2010. Written records of historical tsunamis in the northeastern South China Sea – challenges associated with developing a new integrated database. *Natural Hazards and Earth Systems Science*, **10**, 1793–1806.

MEGAWATI, K., SHAW, F. *ET AL.* 2009. Tsunami hazard from the subduction megathrust of the South China Sea: Part 1. Source characterization and the resulting tsunami. *Journal of Asian Earth Sciences*, **36**, 13–20.

MUSULIN, R., LIN, R. & FRANK, S. 2009. Dealing with the axis of financial destruction: demographics, development and disasters. *In*: *Beyond PML: Frequency vs. Severity. Proceedings of a Conference sponsored by Aon Benfield Australia Limited*. Aon Benfield Australia, Sydney, 43–58.

NAKAMURA, Y. 1996. Research and development of intelligent earthquake disaster prevention systems UrEDAS and HERAS. *Journal of Structural Mechanics and Earthquake Engineering, JSCE*, **537**, 1–33 (in Japanese).

RMS. 2005. *1995 Kobe Earthquake 10-Year Retrospective*. Risk Management Solutions, Newark, CA. World Wide Web Address: http://www.rms.com/Reports/KobeRetro.pdf. Accessed 14 April 2011.

SIEH, K. 2009. *Next Big One Will Strike Sumatra Within Decades*. Earth Observatory of Singapore, Singapore. World Wide Web Address: http://www.earthobservatory.sg/index.php?option=com_content&view=article&id=213&Itemid=105. Accessed 28 March 2011.

USGS. 2010a. *SHAKEMAPS*. US Geological Survey, Reston, VA. World Wide Web Address: http://earthquake.usgs.gov/earthquakes/shakemap. Checked 1 November 11 2010.

USGS. 2010b. *PAGER –- Prompt Assessment of Global Earthquakes for Response*. US Geological Survey, Reston, VA. World Wide Web Address: http://earthquake.usgs.gov/earthquakes/pager. Accessed 1 November 2010.

WAPMERR. 2010. *World Agency of Planetary Monitoring and Earthquake Risk Reduction. Real-time Loss Estimates after Earthquakes*. World Agency for Planetary Monitoring and Earthquake Risk Reduction, Geneva. World Wide Web Address: http://www.wapmerr.org/realtime.asp. Accessed 30 March 2011.

WEN, K.-L., CHANG, Y.-W., LIN, C.-M., CHIANG, H.-J. & HUANG, M.-W. 2008. Damage and ground motion of the 26 December 2006 Pingtung earthquakes, Taiwan. *Terrestrial Atmospheric and Oceanic Sciences*, **19**, 641–651.

YAMAZAKI, F., MEGURO, K. & NODA, S. 1998. Developments of early earthquake damage assessment systems in Japan. *In*: SHIRAISHI, N., SHINOZUKA, M. & WEN, Y. K. (eds) *Structural Safety and Reliability*. Balkema, Rotterdam, 1573–1580.

YAMIN, L. E., ARÁMBULA, S., REYES, J. C., BELAGE, S., VEGA, A. & GIL, W. 2004. Earthquake loss estimation for a gas lifeline transportation system in Colombia. *In*: *13th World Conference on Earthquake Engineering, Vancouver, B.C., Canada, August 1–6, 2004*. World Conference on Earthquake Engineering, Tokyo, paper 2941. World Wide Web Address: http://www.iitk.ac.in/nicee/wcee/article/13_2941.pdf. Accessed 03 April 2011.

YEH, C.-H., LOH, C.-H. & TSAI, K.-C. 2006. Overview of Taiwan Earthquake Loss Estimation System. *Natural Hazards*, **37**, 23–37.

# Geological hazards of SW Natib Volcano, site of the Bataan Nuclear Power Plant, the Philippines

A. M. F. LAGMAY[1]*, R. RODOLFO[1], H. CABRIA[1], J. SORIA[2], P. ZAMORA[2], C. ABON[1],
C. LIT[1], M. R. T. LAPUS[1], E. PAGUICAN[1,3], M. G. BATO[1,3], G. TIU[1,3], E. OBILLE[4],
N. E. PELLEJERA[1], P. C. FRANCISCO[1], R. N. ECO[1] & J. AVISO[1]

[1]*National Institute of Geological Sciences, College of Science, University of the Philippines,
Diliman, Quezon City 1101, the Philippines*

[2]*Marine Science Institute, College of Science, University of the Philippines, Diliman,
Quezon City 1101, the Philippines*

[3]*Clermont Université, Université Blaise Pascal, Laboratoire Magmas et Volcans, BP 10448,
F-63000 Clermont-Ferrand, France*

[4]*National Institute for Science and Mathematics Education Development, University of the
Philippines, Diliman, Quezon City 1101, the Philippines*

*\*Corresponding author (e-mail: mlagmay@nigs.upd.edu.ph)*

**Abstract:** The SW sector of Mount Natib, a potentially active volcano in the Bataan volcanic arc in western Luzon, is the site of a mothballed nuclear power plant that members of the national legislature have proposed to activate. Detailed geological fieldwork was conducted to assess the capability of the volcano and to identify any volcanic hazards it might pose to the nuclear plant. The nearest eruptive centre is 5.5 km away from the plant. SW Natib Volcano is underlain by lava flows, lahar deposits and at least six pyroclastic density current (PDC) deposits, three directly underlying the nuclear reactor facility. A fault trending N30°E is aligned with the Lubao Fault, a capable fault NE of the volcanic edifice. Radon emissions at the traces of these faults are high and comparable to those at known active faults. An associated thrust fault at the nuclear site cuts through lahars up to the ground surface. The results presented here can be used for general hazard preparedness of local communities, and may assist the government to decide whether or not to recommission the nuclear power plant.

Natib Volcano is one of several calderagenic volcanoes comprising the Bataan volcanic arc (Fig. 1) in west Luzon, in the Philippines (Defant *et al.* 1988). The most famous of these volcanoes is Pinatubo, which erupted in 1991 after 540 years of dormancy (Newhall & Punongbayan 1996). Reaching plume heights of up to 35 km (Koyaguchi & Tokuno 1993), the Plinian eruption left $11 \times 10^9 \pm 0.5 \times 10^9 \text{ m}^3$ of tephra (Siebert & Simkin 2002) and a caldera 2.5 km wide. To the south, separated from Pinatubo by about 17 km of intervening Cenozoic volcanic terrain, are the mountains of Natib and Mariveles, which together comprise the entire Bataan Peninsula. Natib and Mariveles are less famous, but nonetheless equally impressive in their edifices, and have even larger calderas. The largest of Natib's two summit calderas has three times the diameter of Pinatubo's, and that of Mariveles is nearly 1.5 times larger.

Mount Natib is also well known locally because its SW slope is the site of the Bataan Nuclear Power Plant (BNPP). Construction began in 1976 and was temporarily suspended in 1979, following the Three Mile Island nuclear accident and a subsequent safety inquiry into the plant. Construction was resumed later but, before it was activated, the nuclear plant was mothballed in 1986. In 2008, 26 years later, a Congressional Bill 'mandating the immediate recommissioning and commercial operation of the Bataan Nuclear Power Plant' was filed (Cojuanco 2008).

When the BNPP was built in the late 1970s and early 1980s (Volentik *et al.* 2009), the planning of nuclear power plant facilities did not involve well-established, internationally accepted guidelines to set criteria and procedures for assessing potential volcanic hazards (McBirney *et al.* 2003). Permits for constructing the BNPP were granted based on investigations carried out according to local practices (EBASCO 1977, 1979; Newhall 1979) and based on science that necessarily could not take into account many relevant aspects of volcanology

*From:* TERRY, J. P. & GOFF, J. (eds) 2012. *Natural Hazards in the Asia–Pacific Region: Recent Advances and Emerging Concepts.* Geological Society, London, Special Publications, **361**, 151–169, http://dx.doi.org/10.1144/SP361.13

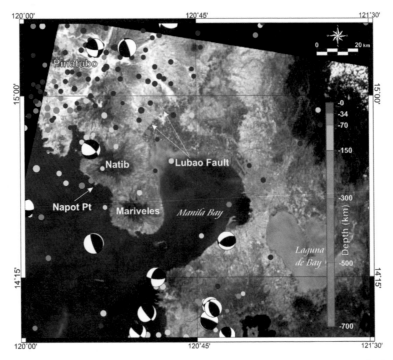

**Fig. 1.** The Bataan Arc, composed in part of Pinatubo, Natib and Mariveles volcanoes, and plots of seismic epicentres, focal mechanism solutions of earthquakes and lineaments. Data sources: Advanced National Seismic System Catalogue, Global Centroid Moment Tensor (Dziewonski & Gilbert 1976) and USGS Global Land Cover Facility (USGS 2004).

that have rapidly developed only over the past 30 years (Schmincke & Sumita 2008).

Even today, adequate geological maps of Natib Volcano do not exist, the same criticism of the original hazard assessment for the BNPP given by experts of the International Atomic Energy Agency (1978), volcanologist C. G. Newhall (1979) and oversight panels in the Philippines. Prior to the present report, the best available geological assessments of Natib Volcano were those of Almero (1989), Ruaya & Panem (1991) and Payot *et al.* (2008). However, Ruaya & Panem's work, which delineates the summit caldera deposits, springs and faults, was narrowly focused on the geothermal prospects of the Bataan volcanic arc. For the purposes of the present report, the most significant result of that work was to determine geochemically the relationship to an active volcanic hydrothermal system of the water in some of the 16 hot springs. The maps of Almero and Payot *et al.* are either too generalized or do not assess the volcanic hazards. Without detailed geological maps that identify the stratigraphy and distribution of Natib's eruptive products, the volcanic hazards at the site cannot be assessed properly.

Considering the importance of this controversial site for a nuclear power plant only 80 km away from

Metro Manila, and in view of the recent cataclysmic eruption of Pinatubo only 60 km away, it is puzzling that Natib remains so poorly understood. Part of the reason is the difficulties posed to geological mappers: the large size of the volcano, its steep slopes, highly weathered exposures and dense vegetation. Thus, our field data were gathered mainly on Natib's midslopes and footslopes during five field campaigns conducted from May 2009 to January 2010, three of which were severely hampered by continuous heavy rain.

Nevertheless, the rapidity with which the legislation to activate the BNPP is proceeding necessitated the improved understanding of the volcanic hazards that even a preliminary map of the geology of the SW sector of the volcano and its stratigraphy could provide. The work was guided by the IAEA volcanic and seismic guidelines (IAEA 2002, 2003, 2005, 2009) and the recommendations of Hill *et al.* (2009) for evaluating the volcanic hazards at sites for nuclear installations. Although the work is still in progress, enough scientific data have been gathered to assist the Philippine government in deciding whether or not to activate the BNPP, and to improve the general hazard preparedness of the communities on the volcano slopes.

# Methodology

## Remote sensing and lineament analysis

Very near infrared (VNIR) images from the AVA ASTER (Advanced Spaceborne Thermal Emission and Reflection) archive (NASA 2009) were downloaded and draped over an ASTER digital elevation model (DEM) using ERDAS (Earth Resources Data Analysis System) processing software. River drainage patterns, lava ridges, levees, summit calderas and a flank eruptive centre were identified in the three-dimensional (3D) images and aerial photographs. Lineaments were also delineated from the VNIR images, and from shaded relief and slope aspect maps derived from the DEM, to identify target sites for structural mapping.

European Space Agency (ESA) Environmental Satellite (ENVISAT) Advanced Synthetic Aperture Radar (SAR) descending radar images were processed using the Stanford Method for Persistent Scatterers-Multi-Temporal InSAR (STAMPS-MTI: Hooper 2006). Twenty-one time-series images from 19 March 2003 to 8 March 2006 were used in the persistent scatterer interferometry to evaluate the ground movement of the area adjacent to the Lubao Fault.

## Structural and lithological field mapping

Before the fieldwork, sites of structural outcrops were selected using the lineament map. In the field, the orientation of joint and fault structures encountered at the target sites were measured, and geometric and kinematic fabrics were recorded for microtectonic analysis. Thick vegetation and soil cover developed from moderate to extreme weathering of the deposits limited access to good rock exposures, limiting most fieldwork to outcrops at quarries, coasts and road cuts. Where tephra deposits cropped out, slope faces were scraped cleaned before examining and describing deposit sequences and lithologies. Mapping of outcrops with pyroclastic deposits and faults was carried out at a scale of 1:2500.

## Radon measurements

Two short-lived isotopes of radon gas have found useful application in evaluating active faults (Crenshaw et al. 1982). Radon 222 ($^{222}$Rn) is generated naturally by the decay of $^{238}$U, and has a half-life of only 3.8235 days; Radon 220, also called thoron ($^{220}$Rn or $^{220}$Tn), with an even shorter half-life of only 55.6 s, is the natural decay product of $^{232}$Th, the most stable thorium isotope (Holden 2004). Both isotopes decay by emitting alpha radiation, detectable by their unique emission energies

of 6.3 MeV for $^{220}$Tn and 5.5 MeV for $^{222}$Rn (Sexton 1994; Papastefano 2002).

Ajari & Adepelumi (2002) and Burton et al. (2004) attributed the high content of these radon isotopes in soils underlain by faults and fractures to increased surface-to-volume ratios in the fracturing rock, and increased soil permeability, which facilitate radon release from the solid matrix. The short half-lives of these isotopes require that measurable quantities must be escaping from free surfaces of the rock.

Radon gas was measured at flatland sites where lineament traces appear in the remotely sensed images. At discrete points along transect lines perpendicular to the lineaments, a soil probe was driven 0.4 m into the soil and connected to an RAD7$^{TM}$ Durridge Co. portable radon detector. Two 5 min readings were taken at each point. Concentrations were reported in Bq m$^{-3}$ units. Radon background values also were measured at a quarry site 4 km north of the perimeter fence of the nuclear power plant facility.

## Seismicity

Earthquake hypocentres of the Bataan region for 1976 to the present were obtained online from the Advanced National Seismic System (ANSS), and focal mechanism solutions from 1929 to the present from the Global Centroid Moment Tensor archives (Fig. 1). Earthquake plots were created using the Generic Mapping Tools (GMT$^{TM}$) software (Wessel & Smith 1991).

# Results

## Remote sensing/geomorphological and morphotectonic analyses

The remotely sensed images and DEMs show that Natib's summit, 1233 m above sea level, rises between two calderas. The largest is 7.5 × 5 km$^2$ in plan (Fig. 2). East of it is a younger volcanic cone with a smaller summit caldera measuring 2 × 1.8 km. Large channels occupy the eastern slopes of this younger volcanic cone, forming a prominent curved feature that resembles a landslide scar. The southern half of the concavity has been filled by a circular planform of rugged terrain.

Several ridges originate from the western rim of the larger caldera and extend towards the South China Sea (Fig. 2). Along their axes, these ridges are steepest near the Natib summit, their slope angles of about 30°–40° decreasing to 0°–15° as they reach a break in slope at approximately the 114 m elevation. Below this break, single ridges splay out towards the coast, with flatlands

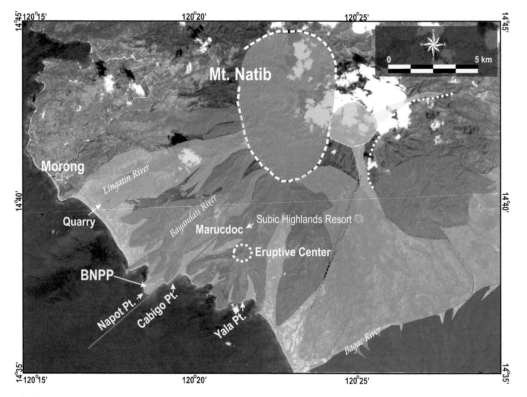

**Fig. 2.** Morphological interpretation of the summit area and SW flanks of Mount Natib. Napot Point is the location of the Bataan Nuclear Power Plant (BNPP).

occupying the spaces between them. At the coast, they terminate as headlands that form cliffs as high as 30 m. The BNPP is located in one of these headlands, named Napot Point.

About 4.2 km SSW of the larger caldera rim (Fig. 2), a high point 348 m in elevation protrudes from the lower midslopes of the edifice. From this topographical high, finger-like ridges emanate and reach the coast near Napot Point. A relatively smooth fan-like feature occupies most of the southern portion of the Natib edifice, terminating where it meets the Bagac River at the base of Mariveles Volcano.

Closely spaced lineaments trend S30°–35°W from the southern rim of the large caldera towards the coast, a prominent one defining the SE coast of Napot Point (Fig. 3). An offshore extension is expressed on bathymetric charts as a submarine scarp at least 10 km long (Fig. 3).

The processing of persistent scatterers in the 21 descending radar images reveal a sharp linear boundary of ground movement separating the western and eastern blocks of the Lubao Fault (Fig. 4). Persistent scatterers in the western block of the Lubao Fault show a decrease in the line-of-sight (LOS) of the radar signal by as much as 2.5 cm year$^{-1}$. The eastern block, however, is characterized by an increase in LOS with a rate of $-2.5$ cm year$^{-1}$. The change in LOS across the Lubao Fault is most pronounced in transect 4 (Fig. 4), 22 km from the base of Mount Natib.

*Geology*

Field mapping of the SW sector of the Natib Volcano from 390 m elevations down to the coast revealed siltstone–sandstone beds, deposits of lahars, pyroclastic flows and surges, and columnar jointed and autobrecciated lavas. These lithologies and their stratigraphy are described in this section according to the areas in which they are exposed (Figs 2 & 5).

*Lingatin quarry.* A quarry site adjacent to the Lingatin River south of Morong town proper exposed an 11–12 m-thick sequence of at least five deposits. The lowermost unit (NQPF1: Fig. 6a) is massive and composed of poorly sorted lithic clasts in a light-brown clayey matrix. Ranging in size from 2 to 40 cm, the clasts are mostly andesitic, normally

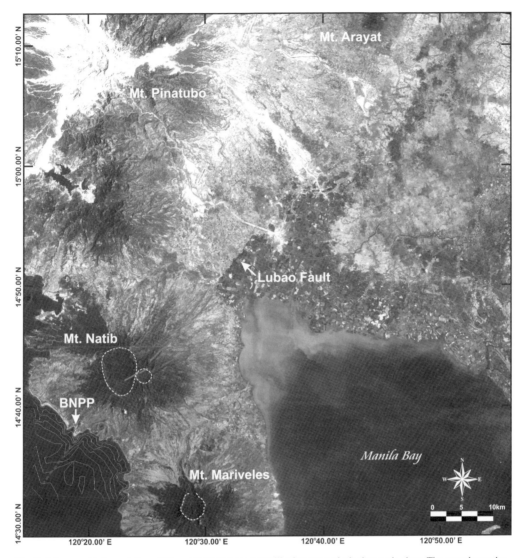

**Fig. 3.** Lineament interpretation of Mount Natib based on satellite images and a bathymetric chart. The map shows the Lubao Fault, interpreted lineaments on the surface of Mount Natib's edifice and offshore extension of the lineaments based on bathymetry. The two calderas of Mount Natib and the caldera of Mount Mariveles are outlined.

graded and typically angular, although the larger ones have been rounded by spheroidal weathering and have rotten cores. A network of holes, commonly with charred-grass stalks, distinguishes this deposit, which is a block-and-ash deposit.

NQPF1 is overlain by NQPF2, a 4 m-thick deposit that tapers at the edges (Fig. 6a, b). Massive and poorly sorted, it consists of devitrified pumice lenses (fiammes) 5–10 cm long and 1–5 cm thick, set in a pinkish-red ash matrix. Fewer welded-pumice fragments occur at the base but increase in abundance upwards. The pinkish-red colour of

the matrix and welding features indicate high-temperature emplacement. Angular–subangular polymictic lithic clasts, ranging in size from about 1 to 20 cm, along with mm-size crystals are dispersed throughout this unit, which is best interpreted as a pyroclastic-flow deposit.

Overlying NQPF2 in sharp contact, NQPF3 is a reddish brown, massive, poorly sorted and clast-supported 4 m-thick deposit. The clasts are lithic and angular–subangular, and range in diameter from 5 to 20 cm. This unit is also interpreted as a massive pyroclastic-flow deposit.

**Fig. 4.** Persistent scatterer interferometery of the NW flank of Mount Natib and the Lubao Fault. A notable change in line-of-sight (LOS) of the radar signal occurs at the boundary of the fault indicating differential movement of the western block relative to the eastern block. Transect A–A′ shows the most abrupt change in LOS across the Lubao Fault. The Y-axis corresponds to the change in LOS from March 2003 to March 2006. The centre of the X-axis in the cross-section is the approximate location of the Lubao Fault trace.

NQPF4, overlying NQPF3, is an approximately 4 m-thick, massive, poorly sorted deposit composed of lithic clasts and pumice fragments in a light-yellow, ashy matrix (Fig. 6c). Lithic clasts of variable composition range in size from 1 to 5 cm and are angular–subangular. Juvenile clasts are devitrified to white clay. NQPF4 is another distinct pyroclastic-flow deposit.

Overlying NQPF4 is NQPF5, a 3–4 m-thick sequence of reddish-brown parallel–subparallel layers that grade upwards into a more massive deposit (Fig. 6d). The reddish-brown ash layers contain lithic and pumice fragments that range in size from 2 to 5 cm. Minute crystals are present in the matrix. In the massive and poorly sorted portion of this unit are angular–subangular lithic fragments, 8–10 cm in diameter, and 1–2 cm-size pumice fragments that exhibit slight welding. A large brown rip-up clast about 6 m long and 2 m thick containing a smaller chunk of soil within the massive portion of this unit indicates en masse transport of eroded fragments (Fig. 6d). NQPF5 is

identified as a pyroclastic-surge deposit that grades into a more massive pyroclastic-flow unit.

NQPF1 and NQPF2 also crop out in a smaller adjacent quarry, and NQPF4 is exposed in 1.5 m-deep pits along the road between Lingatin River and the BNPP site. Beside the Lingatin River, NQPF5 overlies a 3 m-thick autobrecciated lava deposit.

*Cabigo and Yala points.* Thickly bedded, poorly sorted deposits are exposed in outcrops as high as 4–5 m along the coast of Cabigo Point. Variably weathered, the clasts range in size from pebbles to boulders, are rounded–subrounded, and are generally polymictic but are mostly andesitic–basaltic. Clasts in each bed typically are supported in matrixes of sand, typically very coarse. Discernable stratification is expressed in variable clast-size layer colours. Individual beds display normal grading (Fig. 7a). These are typical lahar deposits.

In fault contact and interbedded with lahar deposits is a 3 m-thick sequence of undulating and

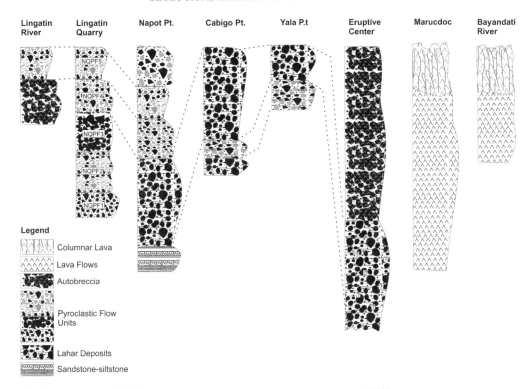

Lingatin River  Lingatin Quarry  Napot Pt.  Cabigo Pt.  Yala P.t  Eruptive Center  Marucdoc  Bayandati River

NQPF5
NQPF4
NQPF3
NQPF2
NQPF1

**Legend**

Columnar Lava

Lava Flows

Autobreccia

Pyroclastic Flow Units

Lahar Deposits

Sandstone-siltstone

**Fig. 5.** Stratigraphy of SW Natib based on detailed interpretations of outcrops at 1:2500.

cross-bedded layers of tephra ranging in thickness from 1 to 12 cm. The thicker beds containing larger lithic clasts, which range in size from a few millimetres up to 6 cm (Fig. 7b). Matrixes are generally composed of white ash containing millimetre-size crystals, and subangular clasts of pumice and lithic fragments. Pumice accumulations occur in some cross-bedded layers; other beds have reversely graded lithic clasts. All of these features, along with impact sags, are characteristic of pyroclastic-surge deposits. Similar but more massive white-coloured tephra deposits crop out further south along the coast of Yala Point. These whitish pyroclastic-flow deposits are overlain by a thick sequence of lahar beds.

*Napot Point.* The rocks exposed in cliffs and islets along the coast of Napot Point are indurated sands and silts, and lahar and pyroclastic-flow deposits. Pyroclastic-flow deposits crop out within the BNPP site itself. The sedimentary sequence is composed of several thick beds of brown–light-brown and well-sorted sandstone separated by thin–medium interbeds of sandstone and siltstone (Fig. 8a). This sequence of beds generally thins upwards. Parallel laminations are also preserved within the silty layers. These features indicate that

the sediments were most probably deposited in a low-energy, shallow-marine environment. Joints cut perpendicular to the strike of beds, displacing laminations by about 1 cm in some places.

Indurated lahar deposits 5–8 m thick are the most dominant rock type along the coast. They are massive to thickly bedded. Individual beds are poorly sorted and composed of cobble- to boulder-sized rounded–subrounded polymictic lithic clasts. Bases are commonly clast-supported but gradually become matrix supported towards their tops. In one outcrop, lahar beds exhibit normal grading.

An approximately 15 m-thick tuffaceous outcrop is exposed along a roadcut 200 m west of the BNPP office (Fig. 8b). The base of this outcrop is about 2 m thick, but only the upper part is well exposed. It is composed of clast-supported grey–light grey subrounded pebble- to cobble-size polymictic lithic fragments. Medium–coarse sand comprises the matrix. Overlying the bottom unit is a 5 m-thick, yellowish-brown, poorly sorted, matrix-supported layer. Resembling NQPF4 of the quarry section, its polymictic clasts range in size from 10 to 30 cm. Above this deposit is a 3.5 m stratified sequence of angular–subangular pumice and lithic clasts in an ashy matrix. Pumice sizes ranges from 1 to 2 cm, but the lithic clasts can be as large

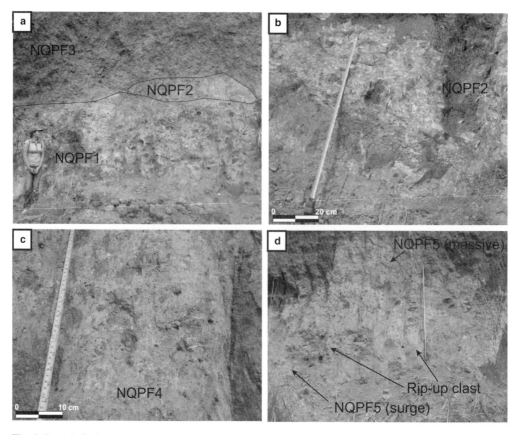

**Fig. 6.** Deposits in the quarry near the Lingatin River. (**a**) The oldest pyroclastic-flow deposit in the Lingatin Quarry (NQPF1) is overlain by an NQPF2 lens and massive NQPF3 layer. (**b**) Welded pumice fragments in NQPF2. (**c**) Yellowish pyroclastic-flow deposit. (**d**) NQPF5 deposit with a rip-up pyroclastic-flow deposit megaclast that in turn contains ripped-up soil.

as 15 cm. Individual strata range in thickness from 10 cm to 1 m and vary in colour from yellowish tan to reddish orange. A whitish pumice-rich layer 10 cm thick occurs in the upper-middle part of the sequence. Pumice clasts, some subwelded, are common in the reddish-orange tuffaceous layers (Fig. 8c, d), similar in appearance to unit NQPF5 of the quarry deposits.

The topmost unit is a poorly sorted light-brown ashy layer containing angular–subangular lithic clasts 1–20 cm in size and subangular white clay particles 1 cm or less in diameter. It filled a 0.4 m-wide channel and is about 4 m thick. All units in this outcrop, except for the basal layer, are interpreted as pyroclastic-flow deposits.

*Peak to the south of Metro Subic Highlands Resort.* A 390 m-high volcanic edifice juts out of the SW slope of the volcano about 5 km NE of Napot Point (Fig. 2). Four elongated ridges extend radially from the summit towards the south, SW and SE,

forming headlands on the coast. One ridge also extends NNE from the summit, forming a saddle as it joins the slope of Mount Natib.

Outcrops on the summit of this satellite cone are indurated, dark grey, massive breccias consisting of dominantly 1–8 cm-sized porphyritic andesite clasts set in a coarse-grained brecciated andesitic matrix. These massive breccias are exposed on a steep wall on one of the ridges, overlying what appears to be another massive layer composed of poorly sorted brecciated material that was inaccessible for closer inspection.

*Metro Highlands/Marucdoc.* Columnar lava deposits exposed on a steep slope at the side of one of the tributaries of the Marucdoc River and upstream of the Metro Subic Highlands Resort (Fig. 9) are composed of euhedral pyroxene and plagioclase laths in a fine-grained crystalline groundmass. Phenocryst sizes are 0.5–0.8 cm. Boulder-sized float of similar petrology are abundant along the Marucdoc

**Fig. 7.** Deposits along the coast of Cabigo Point. (**a**) Fractured lahar beds. (**b**) Pyroclastic-surge deposit showing undulating cross-bed structures, impact marks and reverse grading.

River and on slopes of the resort up to the gate of the BNPP property.

*Bayandati River.* Massive and autobrecciated lava deposits up to 5 m high and at least 50 m long crop out along the banks of the Bayandati River. The massive but jointed lava is dark grey in colour, and is composed of euhedral pyroxene and amphibole phenocrysts together with trachytic plagioclase laths in a fine-grained crystalline groundmass.

## Structures

A fault that cuts northwestwards across Natib Volcano was delineated by Wolfe & Self in 1983 from aerial images and topographic maps (Wolfe & Self 1983) (Fig. 10). The same fault was described in the environmental management report for the PNOC geothermal exploration of Mount Natib (PNOC 1988) and belongs to a set of subparallel faults superimposed on the other structures of the Natib Volcano, including its caldera (Cabato

*et al.* 2005). This NW-oriented fault follows the same trend as the Subic Bay Fault Zone interpreted from gravity and magnetic data by Yumul & Dimalanta (1997), and appears to control the northern coast of Subic Bay. A marine seismic reflection survey in the bay (Cabato *et al.* 2005) identified the feature as a fault cutting across 18–8 ka marine sediments, from the inconsistent thicknesses of the packages they disrupt. The focal mechanism solution for a 5.5 $M_w$ earthquake that occurred along this trend NW of Natib on 29 December 1982 is best interpreted as that of an oblique strike-slip fault (Fig. 1).

A lineament NE of Natib Volcano separates the dry alluvial fans of the mountains between Natib and Pinatubo from the low-lying coastal wetlands NW of Manila Bay (Fig. 3). First described by Siringan & Rodolfo (2003), localized ground subsidence was attributed to vertical movements across this lineament. Soria (2009) formally named it the Lubao Lineament after the municipality where it is best expressed and argued that despite high sedimentation due to the Holocene eruptions of Mt Pinatubo, the wetland–dryland boundary has been maintained because it is an active fault. Soria (2009) estimated that vertical components of motion at the lineament have dropped the southeastern block by as much as 3.5 m over the past 1.5 ka, based on palaeosea-level reconstructions from a peat layer taken in Lubao. Preliminary results of the persistent scatter interferometry of the Lubao area reveal differential ground movement, with a linear boundary corresponding to the trace of the lineament. The name Lubao Fault is thus more appropriate based on evidence of movement along the structure. US Geological Survey (USGS) epicentre data for $M_w$ 3.6 earthquakes from 1973 to 2008 include several shallow events that plot close to the fault (Fig. 1).

The lineaments SW of Natib Volcano identified in the remotely sensed images are exposed as faults at Cabigo and Napot points (Fig. 11a). At Cabigo Point, faults striking N20°–30°E and dipping 60°–70°SE truncate pyroclastic-surge deposits and bring them into contact with lahar deposits (Fig. 11b). Approximately 500 m NE along the coast, about 20 similarly oriented fractures cut indurated lahar deposits (Fig. 11b). At Napot Point, a cliff exposes indurated lahar deposits transected by faults that strike N13°–33°E and dip 28°–41°NW. Fault displacements, drag folding and rhomboid shear lenses along the fracture zones (Fig. 12) document thrust faulting. A scarp extends NE from the faulted outcrop at Napot Point into the fenced BNPP perimeter. This feature may be the morphological expression of the faulted rocks and needs further investigation through palaeoseismology (i.e. trenching studies).

**Fig. 8.** Deposits in the Napot Point area along the coast and within the BNPP site. (**a**) Sandstone–siltstone beds. (**b**) Alternating reddish-brown and yellowish-brown pyroclastic-flow deposits. (**c**) Baked contact of the upper layers of the pyroclastic-flow deposit. (**d**) Close-up view of the baked contact showing subwelded pumice clasts.

At SW Natib Point, values of $^{222}$Rn and $^{220}$Tn emitted from identified lineaments ranged from 4000 to 23 000 and from 25 to 4000 Bq m$^{-3}$, respectively (Fig. 13). Values peaked at sharp changes in topography. For comparison, $^{222}$Rn emitted from unfractured outcrops in the Lingatin Quarry were only 3000–3200 Bq m$^{-3}$. The Radon gas emitted from the lineaments are comparable to values of up to 30 000 Bq m$^{-3}$ that have varied only slightly ($\pm$1000 Bq m$^{-3}$) during repeated measurements of the Western Marikina Valley Fault, a known active fault that displaces paved roads in Pasig City, Metro Manila.

Following recent work describing faults that traverse volcanoes (Lagmay *et al.* 2000; Wooler 2003; Palomo *et al.* 2004; Norini *et al.* 2008; Watt *et al.* 2009; Tibaldi *et al.* 2010), the faults identified in the SW edifice of Natib are interpreted as the extension of the Lubao Fault of Siringan & Rodolfo

(2003) and Soria (2009). Both structures are collinear and have the same orientation.

## Discussion

### Volcanic hazard evaluation

The general procedure followed for the evaluation of volcanic hazards for the BNPP was the methodological approach (Fig. 14) outlined in the draft guidelines for volcanic hazards in site evaluation for nuclear installations (IAEA 2009). The approach involves four stages. Stage 1 is the initial assessment of volcanism of less than 10 Ma in the region of the BNPP. As volcanism less than this age was identified for Pinatubo, Natib and Mariveles we proceeded to stage 2, which characterizes sources of volcanic activity as initiating events. Current volcanic activity is identified for Pinatubo Volcano,

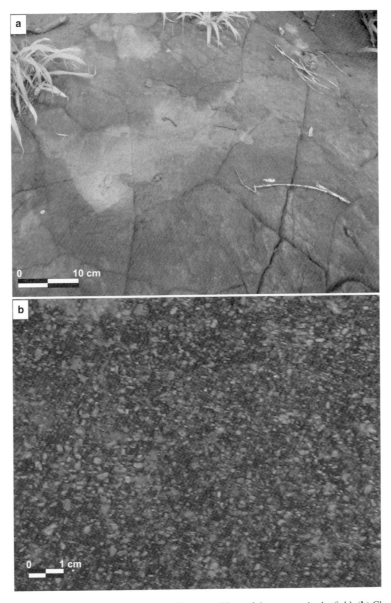

**Fig. 9.** Columnar jointed lava deposit near Marucdoc River. (**a**) View of the outcrop in the field. (**b**) Close-up view of the lava deposit.

which last erupted in 1990. Available age dates for Natib Volcano are 0.069–1.6 Ma (EBASCO 1977), 0.54–3.0 Ma (Wolfe 1983), 20–59 ka (EBASCO 1977, 1979), 27 ± 0.63 ka (Volentik *et al.* 2009) and 11.3–18 ka (Cabato *et al.* 2005). Deposits from Mariveles Volcano have dates of 0.19–4.1 Ma (Wolfe 1983) and as young as 5 ka (Siebert & Simkin 2002). Because the potential for future volcanic activity in the site region cannot be ruled out, hazards screening in stage 3 was

necessary and was determined using screening distance values (SDV), the maximum distance from the source to the site at which each phenomenon could be a hazard (McBirney *et al.* 2003). Numerical simulations by Volentik *et al.* in 2009 and the tephra fall experienced at the site in 1991 demonstrate that Pinatubo, Natib and Mariveles are volcanoes that produce hazards that are within screening distance values and, by definition, are capable volcanoes (Volentik *et al.* 2009). A capable volcano

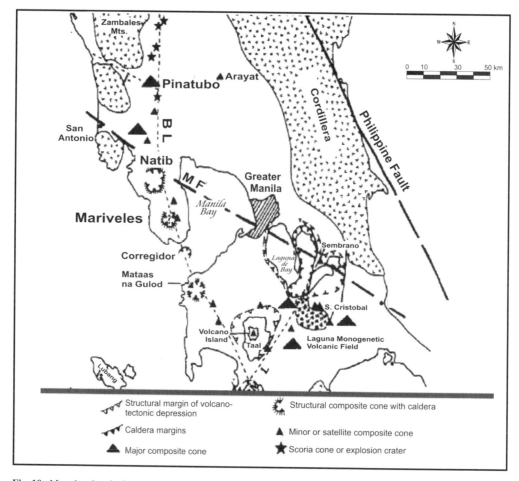

**Fig. 10.** Map showing the locus of volcanism along the Bataan Lineament (BL) and the trace of the Manila Fault (MF) according to Wolfe & Self (1983).

or volcanic field is one that: (1) may experience volcanic activity during the performance period of the nuclear installation; and (2) such an event has the potential to produce phenomena that may affect the site of the nuclear installation (IAEA 2009). The classification of all three volcanoes as capable prompted an evaluation of hazards at the BNPP site outlined in stage 4 of the guidelines.

In this work, the evaluation of hazards, development of site-specific models and assessment of site suitability is based on the geology of SW Natib. The stage 4 assessment of volcanic hazards at the BNPP site began with the identification of volcanic deposits in the field area. As early as the late 1970s, Newhall (1979) collectively described the deposits of lahars and at least six pyroclastic density currents (PDC) that underlie the SW sector of Natib as the 'Napot Point tephra'. Four are massive; the other two are stratified. Erosional contacts between the

PDC deposits, and their content of welded pumice fragments 5 cm in size and lithic clasts of up to 20 cm, indicate discrete large explosive events that originated from a nearby source or sources. The more likely candidates are Natib's two calderas and Mariveles Volcano. Pinatubo is an unlikely source, being separated from the deposits by 60 km of topographical barriers.

Lahar deposits atop, below and in fault contact with other volcanic deposits are widespread along the coastline of Napot Point. Frequent heavy rains in this humid tropical region can easily remobilize eruptive deposits on Natib's edifice. Several lava flow ridges were identified, including an eruptive centre located 5.5 km away from the nuclear site.

After recognizing the deposits, it is necessary to determine probabilistically the potential impacts of the volcanic processes that formed them should future eruptions occur at the Natib or Mariveles

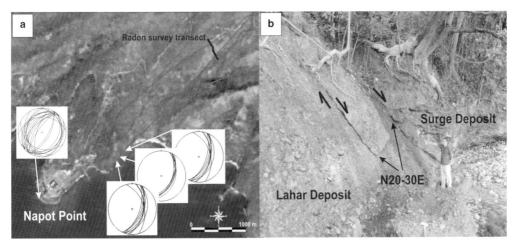

**Fig. 11.** Fractures measured along the Cabigo Point coast. (**a**) Stereoplot of fractures superimposed on the lineaments (red lines) identified from remotely sensed images. The black line refers to the radon survey transect. (**b**) Fault truncating pyroclastic-surge deposits and bringing them into contact with lahar deposits.

volcanoes. This can be achieved with good control on the age dates of eruptions, and stratigraphy to determine the frequency and rate of volcanic activity. The probability of a future Natib eruption was calculated by Ebasco (1977) at $3 \times 10^{-5}$ year$^{-1}$ and to be an order of magnitude greater by Volentik *et al.* (2009) at $1 \times 10^{-4}$–$2 \times 10^{-4}$ year$^{-1}$, with a confidence level of 95%. These

probabilities, together with Natib's active volcanic hydrothermal system (Ruaya & Panem 1991), means that Natib has credible potential for future eruption. Volentik *et al.* (2009) estimated an even higher probability for a VEI (Volcanic Explosivity Index) 6–7 eruption of Mariveles Volcano: $3.5 \times 10^{-4}$–$6 \times 10^{-4}$ year$^{-1}$, with a 95% confidence level. In some States a value for the annual

**Fig. 12.** Faults at Napot Point. (**a**) A 25 m-high outcrop of faulted indurated lahar deposits. (**b**) Truncated clasts with drag folding. (**c**) Rhomboid lenses along the shear plane. (**d**) Scarp extending in the NNE direction from the faulted outcrop into the BNPP fenced perimeter.

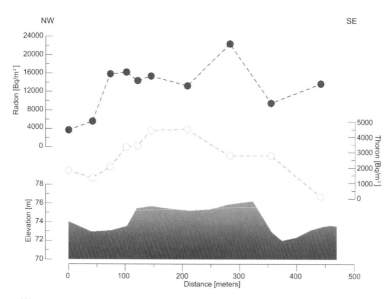

**Fig. 13.** Radon ($^{222}$Rn) and thoron ($^{220}$Tn) measurements traversing across identified lineaments (see Fig. 10a). Values of $^{222}$Rn peak at points near the lineaments and at sharp changes in relief.

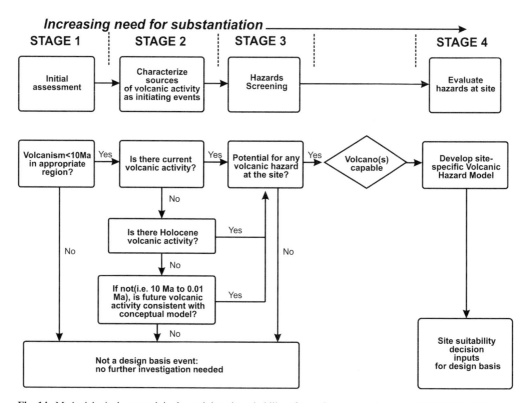

**Fig. 14.** Methodological approach in determining site suitability of a nuclear power plant site (IAEA 2009). This approach was followed in this study.

probability of $10^{-7}$ is used in the hazard assessment for external events as a reasonable basis to evaluate whether a volcano in the region could produce any type of activity in the future that could lead to serious radiological consequences (IAEA 2009). Although the probability assessment in this study can be improved with more age dates that would better constrain recurrence rates, the study already provides a conservative probability estimate that falls within the stated annual probability limit observed in some States (IAEA 2009), which assumes that future eruptions at Mount Natib and Mount Mariveles are possible.

After establishing the probabilities of Natib and Mariveles eruptions, the type of hazard responsible for each deposit present is assigned a screening distance value. Pyroclastic density currents generated by VEI 6–7 eruptions can affect the BNPP site, based on numerical models (Volentik *et al.* 2009). The presence of such deposits at Napot Point validates the runout of pyroclastic flows predicted by the energy cone model of Sheridan (1979) and thereby puts the BNPP site well within the screening distance value for this hazard (Volentik *et al.* 2009).

Lahar deposits are widespread along the coastlines of Napot, Cabigo and Emman points, but it is unclear whether the BNPP site is vulnerable to future lahars. Napot Point and adjacent headlands may have been raised high enough by the volcanic deposits to isolate them from lahar paths. At Pinatubo Volcano, however, lahars remobilize freshly deposited tephra to completely inundate channels (Rodolfo *et al.* 1996), and lahars erode and form new channels at Mayon Volcano (Paguican *et al.* 2009). Similarly, the Natib landscape could easily be altered, rendering obsolete any SDV analysis for lahars based on present topography. With regard to the hazard posed by lava flows, the presence of an effusive eruptive centre 5.5 km away from the BNPP, and lava deposits only a few hundred metres away, place the installation also within the screening distance value for lava flows.

The foregoing probability analyses will bear uncertainties until the frequency and timing of the past Natib and Mariveles volcanoes are established more precisely. There is more certainty about the physical characteristics of those past events, such as their volumes and spatial extents. Thus, the volcanic risk assessment for the BNPP leans more towards a deterministic analysis, focused on the geological characteristics of volcanic phenomena and their spatial extent, rather than an estimation of the likelihood of the occurrence of such hazards (IAEA 2009).

To determine whether a site should be excluded in the selection for a nuclear facility, the IAEA draft guidelines present the different volcanic phenomena that may pose potential hazards to a site (Table 1).

According to these guidelines, a 'Yes' in the site selection and evaluation column indicates that a significant hazard from this phenomenon generally constitutes an exclusion criterion, and a 'No' in the design column indicates that it is impractical to mitigate a potential hazard by either facility design or operational planning (IAEA 2009).

In the case of BNPP, the area is underlain by deposits of pyroclastic flows and surges, and lahars. Lava deposits and an eruptive centre are also proximal to the BNPP site. Of all these volcanic phenomena, the potentials for pyroclastic density currents and lava flows cannot be mitigated by engineering solutions. Lahar hazards, however, can be addressed by engineering design.

## Evaluation of seismic and tectonic hazards

The IAEA Safety Standard Series (IAEA 2003) suggest relevant coverage areas for different levels of investigation for seismic hazard evaluation. Typical radial extents are 150 km for regional investigation, 25 km for near-regional investigation, 5 km for the site vicinity and 1 km for the site area. Any geological structure within these coverage areas will have a corresponding impact on the nuclear power plant. The size, however, may vary depending on the geological and tectonic setting, and its shape may be asymmetric to include distant significant sources of earthquakes.

One of the most important elements for evaluating a nuclear plant site is surface faulting. *Capable faults* are structures that are most relevant when evaluating the geological features of the site. The IAEA provides criteria in identifying whether a fault is capable or not (IAEA 2002). The first criterion is that the fault shows evidence of significant past deformations or movements of a recurring nature during a period that is recent enough to infer reasonably that further movements at or near the surface could occur. In tectonically active areas like the Philippines, where both earthquake data and geological data consistently reveal short earthquake recurrence intervals, periods of the order of tens of thousands of years may be appropriate. The second criterion for a capable fault is a structural relationship with another known capable fault, such that movement at one may cause movement of the other at or near the surface.

Active faults determined by the Philippine Institute of Volcanology and Seismology (Phivolcs) within the region of the BNPP are the Manila Trench, East Zambales, Marikina Valley, Iba and Lubang faults, with distances from the site of 140, 90, 82, 75 and 66 km, respectively. In Subic Bay, active faults were also identified by Cabato *et al.* (2005) within 20 km of the BNPP site. The closest faults that have been identified are within 1 km of

**Table 1.** *Volcanic phenomena and associated characteristics that could affect nuclear installations, with implications for site selection and evaluation, and design (IAEA 2009)*

| Phenomena | Potentially adverse characteristics for nuclear installations | Site selection | Design/ operation |
|---|---|---|---|
| Tephra fall | Static physical loads, abrasive and corrosive particles in air and water | No | Yes |
| *Pyroclastic density currents: Pyroclastic flows, surges and blasts* | *Dynamic physical loads, atmospheric overpressures, projectile impacts, temperatures >300 °C, abrasive particles, toxic gases* | *Yes* | *No* |
| Lava flows and lava domes | *Dynamic physical loads, water impoundments and floods, temperatures >700 °C* | *Yes* | *No* |
| Debris avalanches, landslides and slope failures | Dynamic physical loads, atmospheric overpressures, projectile impacts, water impoundments and floods | Yes | No |
| Debris flows and lahars, floods | Dynamic physical loads, water impoundments and floods, suspended particulates in water | Yes | Yes |
| Opening of new vents | Dynamic physical loads, ground deformation, volcanic earthquakes | Yes | No |
| Ballistic projectiles | Projectile impacts, static physical loads, abrasive particles in water | No | Yes |
| Volcanic gases and aerosols | Toxic and corrosive gases, water contamination, gas-charged lakes | No | Yes |
| Tsunamis, seiches, crater lake failure, glacial burst | Water inundation | Yes | Yes |
| Atmospheric phenomena | Dynamic overpressures, lightning strikes, downburst winds | No | Yes |
| Ground deformation | Ground displacements >1 m, landslides | Yes | No |
| Volcanic earthquakes and seismic events | Continuous tremor, multiple shocks usually <$M$ 5 | No | Yes |
| Hydrothermal systems and groundwater anomalies | Thermal water >50 °C, corrosive water, water contamination, water inundation or upwelling, alteration, landslides | Yes | No |

Italicized entries are the hazards pertinent to BNPP without design solutions.

the BNPP, with one thrust fault cutting an outcrop at the tip of Napot Point just outside the fenced perimeter of the installation, with its trace only 200 m away from the nuclear reactor. Aside from very high radon measurements (Fig. 13), there is as yet no direct evidence of active fault movement within 1 km of the BNPP because the faulted rocks have not been dated. The second criterion, however, gives reason to believe that the faults within 1 km of the BNPP are active. The Lubao Fault NE of Natib (Soria 2009) is active, and has the same orientation and is collinear with the faults in the SW sector of Natib (Fig. 3).

Many faults that traverse volcanoes have been reported in the literature (Wooler 2003; Palomo *et al.* 2004; Norini *et al.* 2008; Watt *et al.* 2009; Tibaldi *et al.* 2010). A classic example is Mayon Volcano, which is traversed by the northern bounding fault of the Oas Graben (Lagmay *et al.* 2005; Lagmay & Zebker 2009). Named the Northern Oas Fault, the surface trace of this structure ends abruptly at the western margin of Mayon and re-emerges east of it, hidden by the active deposition of primary and reworked material on the conical edifice (Lagmay *et al.* 2000).

Capable faults are associated with earthquakes. A fault should be considered capable if the maximum potential earthquake associated with it is sufficiently large and at a depth where it is reasonable to infer that movement at or near the surface could occur (IAEA 2002). The length of the Lubao Fault, which according to the delineation of Soria (2009) terminates NE of the footslopes of Natib Volcano, is approximately 42 km. When extended to the SW part of Natib's edifice near Napot Point, the total length is 73 km. According to Wells & Coppersmith (1994), a 73 km fault length would be able to generate a magnitude 7.2 ($M_w$) earthquake. The IAEA suggests that where capable faults exist within 1 km of the nuclear facility, another site must be considered (IAEA 2005). Such is the case for the BNPP, where a capable fault based on the second criterion of the guidelines was identified within 1 km of the installation.

## Conclusions

Lavas, and the deposits of lahars, pyroclastic flows and pyroclastic surges, were mapped in the SW sector of Natib Volcano. At least six pyroclastic density current (PDC) deposits were mapped, three directly underlying the nuclear reactor facility. Deposits of at least six pyroclastic density currents were identified, with three of the units directly underlying the site of the BNPP. A previously unidentified eruptive centre is located 5.5 km from the main building of the plant.

Faults oriented N20°E–N30°E along the coast of Cabigo Point extend towards the SSW offshore in bathymetric charts as a linear change in relief. The continuation of these faults into SW Natib can be traced from lineaments oriented N30°E in ASTER images and aerial photographs. Radon emissions at these lineaments are as high as 22 000 Bq m$^{-3}$, against background values of 2000–4000 Bq m$^{-3}$. A thrust fault at the tip of Napot Point cuts up to the ground surface through lahars.

Natib is considered a capable volcano, based on its active volcanic hydrothermal system and a calculated probability of $1 \times 10^{-4}$–$2 \times 10^{-4}$ year$^{-1}$, with a 95% confidence level of a future VEI 6–7 volcanic eruption. The volcanic hazards posed to the site were assessed based on IAEA draft guidelines. Among the hazards identified, lava flows and pyroclastic density currents are within the screening distance value, the maximum distance from the source to the site at which the volcanic phenomenon could be a hazard. Of all the volcanic hazards, PDCs and lava flows do not have any engineering solutions. Lahar hazards, however, can be addressed by engineering design.

Faults were mapped in the SW sector of Natib. One at Napot Point cuts up to the ground surface through an indurated lahar deposit. These tectonic structures are evaluated as capable faults because they show a structural relationship with the Lubao Fault, which is considered active based on truncated recent fluviodeltaic sediments and palaeosea-level reconstructions recording as much as 3.5 m movement over the past 1.5 ka. When evidence shows the existence of capable faults within 1 km of the nuclear facility, another site must be considered. Such is the case for the BNPP, where capable faults associated with the Lubao Fault were identified within 1 km of the nuclear power plant.

The work on Natib Volcano is still in progress and further characterization of the volcanic deposits and faults is desired. The stratigraphy with corresponding age dates for each deposit will improve the understanding of eruption recurrence rates and probability estimates for future volcanic eruptions at Natib and Mariveles. Subsurface studies from numerous borehole data and geophysical surveys are also recommended to reduce uncertainties in surface geological mapping of vegetated and highly weathered terrain. With regard to seismic hazards, trenching studies of the faults within 1 km of the BNPP is the next logical step.

However, the study already provides conservative probability estimates to the hazard's assessment. Assuming such probabilities are sufficient to consider future eruptions as credible events, the presence of at least three PDC deposits clearly show that pyroclastic flows are well within screening distance and can affect the site. According to the IAEA draft guidelines, there is no engineering design that can address this type of hazard for a nuclear power plant.

Enough data have been gathered to use as one of the scientific bases for the decision of the Philippine government whether or not to activate the mothballed BNPP. These data will also be useful for general hazard preparedness of communities on the slopes of the volcano.

# References

AJARI, T. & ADEPELUMI, A. 2002. Reconnaissance soil–gas Radon survey over faulted crystalline area of ile-Ife, Nigeria. *Environmental Geology*, **41**, 608–613.

ALMERO, R. 1989. *Engineering Geology Aspects of Characterization: Study for a Radioactive Waste Disposal Site in PNPP-1, Morong, Bataan Province*. Master's thesis, University of the Philippines.

BURTON, M., NERI, M. & CONDARELLI, D. 2004. High spatial resolution radon measurements reveal hidden active faults on Mt. Etna. *Geophysical Research Letters*, **31**, L07618–L07627.

CABATO, J. A., RODOLFO, K. S. & SIRINGAN, F. 2005. History of sedimentary infilling and faulting in Subic Bay, Philippines revealed in high-resolution seismic reflection profiles. *Journal of Asian Earth Sciences*, **25**, 849–858.

COJUANCO, M. O. 2008. *House Bill No. 4631: An Act Mandating the Immediate Re-commissioning and Commercial Operation of the Bataan Nuclear Power Plant, Appropriating Funds Therefore, and for Other Purposes*. House of Representatives, Republic of the Philippines, Quezon City, Metro Manila.

CRENSHAW, W. B., WILLIAMS, S. N. & STOIBER, R. E. 1982. Fault location by radon and mercury detection at an active volcano in Nicaragua. *Nature*, **300**, 345–346.

DEFANT, M. J., BOER, J. Z. D. & DIETMAR, O. 1988. The western Central Luzon volcanic arc, the Philippines: two arcs divided by rifting? *Tectonophysics*, **145**, 305–317.

DZIEWONSKI, A. M. & GILBERT, F. 1976. The effect of small aspherical perturbations on travel times and a re-examination of the corrections for ellipticity. *Geophysical Journal of the Royal Astronomical Society*, **44**, 7–17.

EBASCO 1977. *Preliminary Safety Analysis Report, Philippine Nuclear Power Plant #1*. Technical report, Philippine Atomic Energy Commission Open-File Report and response to questions. Philippine Atomic Energy Commission, Manila.

EBASCO 1979. *Evidence Substantiating the Incredibility of Volcanism on the West Flank of Mt. Natib, and the Assessment of Volcanic Hazards at Napot Point*. Response to Philippine Atomic Energy Commission question #3. Philippine Atomic Energy Commission, Manila.

HILL, B. E., ASPINALL, W. P., CONNOR, C. B., KOMOROWSKI, J.-C. & NAKADA, S. 2009. Recommendations for assessing volcanic hazards at sites of nuclear installations. *In*: CONNOR, C. B., CHAPMAN, N. A. & CONNOR, L. J. (eds) *Volcanic and Tectonic Hazard Assessment for Nuclear Facilities*. Cambridge University Press, Cambridge, 566–592.

HOLDEN, N. E. 2004. Table of the isotopes. *In*: LIDE, D. R. (ed.) *CRC Handbook of Chemistry and Physics, Section 1*, 85th edn. CRC Press, Baton Rouge, LA.

HOOPER, A. J. 2006. *Persistent Scatterer Radar Interferometry for Crustal Deformation Studies and Modeling of Volcanic Deformation*. PhD Dissertation, Stanford University, CA.

IAEA 1978. *Report of the IAEA Safety Mission to the Philippines Nuclear Power Plant No.1*. Technical report. International Atomic Energy Agency, Vienna.

IAEA 2002. *Evaluation of Seismic Hazards for Nuclear Power Plants, Safety Standards Series*. Technical Report No. NS-G-3.3. International Atomic Energy Agency, Vienna.

IAEA 2003. *Site Evaluation for Nuclear Installations, Safety Standard Series*. Technical Report No. NS-R-3. International Atomic Energy Agency, Vienna.

IAEA 2005. *Geotechnical Aspects of Site Evaluation and Foundations for Nuclear Power Plants. IAEA Safety Standards Series No. NS-G-3.6*. Technical report. International Atomic Energy Agency, Vienna.

IAEA 2009. *IAEA Safety Standards for Protecting People and the Environment Volcanic Hazards in Site Evaluation for Nuclear Installations. DS405 Draft Safety Guide*. Technical report. International Atomic Energy Agency, Vienna.

KOYAGUCHI, T. & TOKUNO, M. 1993. Origin of the giant eruption cloud of Pinatubo, June 15, 1991. *Journal of Volcanology and Geothermal Research*, **55**, 85–96.

LAGMAY, A. & ZEBKER, H. 2009. *Permanent Scatterer Interferometry of Mayon Volcano, Albay, Philippines – Progress Report*. Technical report. European Space Agency, Earth Observation, Paris.

LAGMAY, A., TENGONCIANG, A. & UY, H. 2005. Structural setting of the Bicol Basin and kinematic analysis of fractures on mayon volcano, Philippines. *Journal of Volcanology and Geothermal Research*, **144**, 23–36.

LAGMAY, A. M. F., vanWYK DE VRIES, B., KERLE, N. & PYLE, D. M. 2000. Volcano instability induced by strike–slip faulting. *Bulletin of Volcanology*, **62**, 331–346.

MCBIRNEY, A., SERVA, L., GUERRA, M. & CONNOR, C. B. 2003. Volcanic and seismic hazards at a proposed nuclear power site in central Java. *Journal of Volcanology and Geothermal Research*, 11–30.

NASA 2009. The ASTER Volcano Archive (AVA). http://ava.jpl.nasa.gov/. Accessed August 2009.

NEWHALL, C. G. 1979. Review of volcanologic discussions in the PSAR and related documents, Philippine Nuclear Power Plant # 1. Technical report. US Nuclear Regulatory Commission, Washington DC.

NEWHALL, C. G. & PUNONGBAYAN, R. S. (eds). 1996. *Fire and Mud: Eruptions and Lahars of Mount Pinatubo,*

*Philippines*. University of Washington Press, Seattle, WA.

NORINI, G., GROPELLI, G., CAPRA, L. & LAGMAY, A. 2008. Quaternary sector collapses of Nevado de Toluca volcano (Mexico) governed by regional tectonics and volcanic evolution. *Geosphere Geological Society of America*, **4**, 854–871.

PAGUICAN, E. M. R., LAGMAY, A. *ET AL*. 2009. Extreme rainfall-induced lahars and dike breaching, 30 November 2006, Mayon Volcano, Philippines. *Bulletin of Volcanology*, **71**, 845–857.

PALOMO, A., MACAS, J. L. & ESPNDOLA, J. M. 2004. Strike–slip faults and Kalkaline volcanism at El Chichon volcano, southeastern Mexico. *Journal of Volcanology and Geothermal Research*, **136**, 247–268.

PAPASTEFANU, C. 2002. An overview of instrumentation for measuring radon in soil gas and groundwaters. *Journal of Environmental Radioactivity*, **63**, 271–283.

PAYOT, B. D., MAGLAMBAYAN, V. B. *ET AL*. 2008. Geology and hydrothermal alteration of the low sulfidation pantingan gold system, mount Mariveles, Bataan (Luzon), Philippines. *Resource Geology*, **55**, 155–162.

PNOC 1988. *Environmental Management Report for the PNOC Geothermal Exploration Project in Mt Natib, Bataan 1988*. Technical report. Philippine National Oil Company, Metro Manila.

RODOLFO, K., UMBAL, J. *ET AL*. 1996. Two years of lahars on the western flank of Mount Pinatubo, Philippines: initiation, flow processes, deposits, and attendant geomorphic and hydraulic changes. *In*: NEWHALL, C. G. & PUNONGBAYAN, R. (eds) *Fire and Mud: Eruptions and Lahars of Mount Pinatubo, Philippines*. University of Washington Press, Seattle, WA, 989–1013.

RUAYA, J. & PANEM, C. C. 1991. Mt. Natib, Philippines: a geochemical model of a caldera-hosted geothermal system. *Journal of Volcanology and Geothermal Research*, **45**, 255–265.

SCHMINCKE, H. & SUMITA, M. 2008. Volcanology in a changing world – the past 50 years. Plenary talk. *In*: *IAVCEI 2008 Conference, Iceland*. International Association of Volcanology and Chemistry of the Earth's Interior, Barcelona.

SEXTRO, R. G. 1994. Radon and the natural environment. *In*: NAGDA, N. L. (ed.) *Radon: Prevalence, Measurement, Health Risks and Control*. ASTM MNL, 15. American Society for Testing and Materials., Philadelphia, PA, 9–32.

SHERIDAN, M. 1979. Emplacement of pyroclastic flows: A review. *In*: CHAPIN, E. & ELSTON, W. (eds) *Ash-flow Tuffs*. Geological Society of America, Special Paper, **180**, 125–136.

SIEBERT, L. & SIMKIN, T. 2002. *Volcanoes of the World: an Illustrated Catalog of Holocene Volcanoes and their Eruptions*. Smithsonian Institution, Global Volcanism Program Digital Information Series, **GVP-3**.

SIRINGAN, F. & RODOLFO, K. 2003. Relative sea-level changes and worsening floods in the western Pampanga delta: causes and some possible mitigation measures. *Science Diliman*, **15**, 1–12.

SORIA, J. 2009. *Compaction Rates and Paleo-sea Levels Along The Delta Complex North of Manila Bay,*

*Luzon Island, Philippines.* MSc thesis, National Institute of Geological Sciences, University of the Philippines.

TIBALDI, A., PASQUARE, F. & TORMEY, D. 2010. Volcanism in reverse and strike-slip fault settings. *Earth and Environmental Science*, 315–348.

USGS 2004. *Shuttle Radar Topography Mission, 1 Arc Second scene SRTM_u03_n008e004, Unfilled Unfinished 2.0, Global Land Cover Facility.* US Geological Survey. University of Maryland Press, College Park, MD.

VOLENTIK, A. C., CONNOR, C. B., CONNOR, L. J. & BONADONNA, C. 2009. Aspects of volcanic hazards assessment for the Bataan nuclear power plant, Luzon Peninsula, Philippines. *In*: CONNOR, C. B., CHAPMAN, N. A. & CONNOR, L. J. (eds) *Volcanic and Tectonic Hazard Assessment for Nuclear Facilities.* Cambridge University Press, Cambridge, 229–256.

WATT, S. L., PYLE, D. M., NARANJO, J. & MATHER, T. A. 2009. Landslide and tsunami hazard at Yate volcano, Chile as an example of edifice destruction on strike–slip fault zones. *Bulletin of Volcanology*, **71**, 559–574.

WELLS, D. L. & COPPERSMITH, K. J. 1994. New empirical relationships among magnitude, rupture length, rupture width, rupture area, and surface displacement. *Bulletin of the Seismological Society of America*, **84**, 974–1002.

WESSEL, P. & SMITH, W. H. F. 1991. Free software helps map and display data. *Eos Transactions of the American Geophysical Union*, **72**, 441.

WOLFE, J. 1983. Origin of the Philippines by accumulation of allochthons. *Philippine Geologist*, **37**, 16–33.

WOLFE, J. & SELF, S. 1983. Structural lineaments and Neogene volcanism in southwestern Luzon. *In*: HAYES, D. (ed.) *The Tectonic and Geological Evolution of Southeast Asian Seas and Islands: Part 2.* American Geophysical Union, Geophysical Monograph, **27**, 157–172.

WOOLER, L. K. 2003. *Volcano Instability and Collapse from Basement Faulting*, Volume 5. European Geophysical Society, Munich.

YUMUL, G. P. JR. & DIMALANTA, C. B. 1997. Geology of the Southern Zambales Ophiolite Complex (Philippines): Juxtaposed terranes of diverse origin. *Journal of Asian Earth Sciences*, **15**, 413–421.

# Influence of the institutional and socio-economic context for responding to disasters: case study of the 1994 and 2006 eruptions of the Merapi Volcano, Indonesia

ESTUNING TYAS WULAN MEI[1,2]* & FRANCK LAVIGNE[2]

[1]Faculty of Geography, Gadjah Mada University, Bulaksumur Yogyakarta, Indonesia 55281

[2]Université Paris 1 Panthéon-Sorbonne, UMR 8591, Laboratoire de Géographie Physique, Meudon, France

*Corresponding author (e-mail: estu.mei@gmail.com)

**Abstract:** This article explores the institutional responses to the volcanic crises and related problems encountered during the 1994 and 2006 eruptions of the Merapi Volcano, Indonesia. It also illustrates traditional responses to the volcanic crisis led by the local community and provides recommendations to encourage a comprehensive institutional volcanic crisis management including community-based response. This study aims to understand and to explain the gap between institutional responses and the community's perception during pre- to post-crisis situations. Interviews, questionnaires and focus group discussions revealed that top-down institutional responses to the volcanic crisis are not fully appropriate in regions with a high cultural perception. Working with the community is an ideal solution to minimize the gap between the government, scientists, non-governmental organizations and the community itself. A community-based methodology combined with natural hazard studies generates comprehensive risk and crisis management.

Disasters are, by definition, extraordinary catastrophic events that can overwhelm normal coping strategies and resources (Reser 2007). Despite the fact that disaster management is complex in all its aspects, the government, the people and stakeholders need it in order to cope with disasters (Bermejo 2006). The number of studies on volcanic risk management has increased considerably in the last decade and deliberately so, because disasters come with the greater potential to affect growing populations. Thus, new theoretical perspectives and policy guides are required (McEntire *et al.* 2002).

Communities should be included in disaster management programmes in order for governments and communities to play complementary roles in coping with volcanic disasters (Paton *et al.* 2008). The role of governments and scientists is to anticipate volcanic eruptions and communicate about them to the population. Lack of knowledge about volcanic hazards can lead to low volcanic risk perception (Carlino *et al.* 2008). Information dissemination and education to the society at risk are key factors in correcting and improving the perception of volcanic threats (Leone & Lesales 2009). However, information dissemination and education implies passive absorption rather than active consultation (Eden 1996). So, the need for community participation and involvement in raising hazard awareness is crucial.

Top-down planning cannot be applied directly, and needs to be modified and adapted to the existing disaster situation and conditions. Differences in perception of disaster management issues by local communities and scientists or emergency planners can provoke a disruption of crisis management plans (Johnston & Ronan 2000). Human responses to disasters do not simply reflect individual patterns of behaviour. People's responses to disasters in the long term are expressed as a cultural adaptation by way of belief or warning messages (Reser 2007), and it is essential to consider the local and cultural factors in risk and crisis management (Lavigne *et al.* 2008). In order to create locally adapted crisis management, both institutional and traditional responses must merge through active participation of the community and institutions.

The study aims to understand and illustrate the gap between institutional responses and the community's way of thinking before, during and after crisis situations in the Indonesian context, using the Merapi Volcano as an example. This study is part of the FP 7 European programme 'Mitigate and Assess Risk from Volcanic Impact on Terrain and Human Activities' (MIAVITA), which seeks to develop tools and to integrate cost-effective methodologies to mitigate risks from various hazards on active volcanoes including Merapi.

*From*: TERRY, J. P. & GOFF, J. (eds) 2012. *Natural Hazards in the Asia–Pacific Region: Recent Advances and Emerging Concepts*. Geological Society, London, Special Publications, **361**, 171–186, http://dx.doi.org/10.1144/SP361.14
© The Geological Society of London 2012. Publishing disclaimer: www.geolsoc.org.uk/pub_ethics

This article focuses on the institutional responses, the problems encountered during the 1994 and 2006 Merapi volcanic crises management, and how the community led traditional responses to volcanic crises. It also suggests recommendations to encourage a comprehensive institutional volcanic crisis response that includes the traditional one. Merapi's 2010 eruption is not included in this article, owing to the incomplete data collection (work in progress). However, several important elements of crisis management of the 2010 Merapi eruption will be discussed and the chronology of the 2010 centennial eruption will be briefly presented.

## Merapi volcanic activity

Merapi is one of the most active volcanoes worldwide, with over 70 eruptions since 1548 (Voight *et al.* 2000*a*). During the last two centuries, this volcano has erupted explosively every 8–15 years and violently every 26–54 years, and the repose periods have not exceeded 3.5 years (Thouret *et al.* 2000). It lies approximately 25 km north of Yogyakarta, a city whose population is of over 1 million (BPS 2005). Approximately 1.1 million people live on the flanks of this volcano.

The eruptive activity during 1993–1994 encompassed a major phase of lava extrusion and dome growth that formed the 1994 dome, with a volume of $2.0 \times 10^{6}$–$2.6 \times 10^{6}$ m$^{3}$. Since February 1994, rock falls have produced a talus and rock-fall deposit build-up against the south run-out channel wall (Voight *et al.* 2000*a*). The dome became unstable upon reaching a critical volume and collapsed on 22 November 1994 (Ratdomopurbo & Poupinet 2000; Young *et al.* 2000). This VEI (Volcanic Explosivity Index) 2 eruption produced 7 km of pyroclastic flows along the Boyong River (Wilson *et al.* 2007). Because of the unpredictable nature of dome collapse and lack of short-term precursors (Voight *et al.* 2000*b*), 69 people were killed by the dome-collapse pyroclastic flows and associated ash-cloud surges.

The last eruption prior to the 2010 major eruption occurred in 2006. This eruption was categorized as typical Merapi-type pyroclastic flows due to dome collapse, similar to the 1994 eruption but over a longer period. The lava-dome growth started in March 2006 and it was rapidly followed by periods of numerous rock falls and dome-collapse pyroclastic flows during May and June 2006. A first eruption occurred on 5 May and was followed by a second eruption phase that was associated with a *M* 6.5 tectonic earthquake on 27 May 2006 in Bantul, approximately 30 km south of Merapi. On 14 June, two dome-collapse pyroclastic flows partly filled the Gendol River valley as far as 7 km. After 14 June, the volcanic activity

progressively decreased until the end of the eruption in early July 2006 (Charbonnier & Gertisser 2008). The long period of volcanic unrest caused an extended period of evacuation time, starting in late April and lasting until July (Table 1).

The 2010 eruption of Merapi lasted from late October until November 2010. This eruption was classified as a subplinian eruption with column-collapse pyroclastic flows (St Vincent type). On 20 September, authorities increased the alert level from level I (normally active) to level II (on guard), as recommended by the Centre of Volcanology and Geological Hazard Mitigation (CVGHM). One month later, the Indonesian government raised the alert to level III. On 25 October, the alert was raised to its highest level (IV) and the government warned villagers in threatened areas to move to safer grounds. People living within a 10 km radius were told to evacuate. The first casualties, including Mbah Maridjan, the volcano's gatekeeper, and 16 people in the Kinahrejo village, died on 26 October. The gatekeeper was the spiritual guardian of the volcano; and local people believed he had the power to speak to the spirits of the volcano. He also led annual sacrificial ceremonies called *labuhan* (Lavigne *et al.* 2008). Local people believed in him rather than government officials and volcanologists when it came to determining Merapi's danger level.

By the early morning of Saturday 30 October 2010, the volcano erupted again, for a longer period of time and more violently than the previous events. On Wednesday 3 November, the authorities decided to move the shelters 15 km away from the summit instead of the initial 10 km. By 4 November 4, Merapi had been erupting continuously for 24 h. The following day, owing to the strong persistent activity, the government decided to extend the safety zone to a radius of 20 km. The volcano continued to erupt until 30 November 2010. At least 320 000 people had been evacuated to emergency shelters and the death toll was over 353. On 3 December 2010, the official alert status was reduced to level 3 from level 4, as the eruptive activity had already waned.

## Methods

The methods used in this study include statistic data collection regarding the 1994 and 2006 eruptions; interviews with stakeholders; focus group discussions; and questionnaire-based surveys with villagers living in the area prone to pyroclastic flows and surges. Quantitative methods such as statistical analysis of questionnaire responses are known to be highly effective in measuring the 'cause and effect' of individual variables and have been successfully used in the volcanic risk perception domain

**Table 1.** *Chronology of the 2006 eruption of Merapi (Wilson* et al. *2007)*

| Date | Time | Event | Alert level |
|---|---|---|---|
| 12 April 2006 | | First pyroclastic flow (PF) | III |
| 25 April 2006 | | 198 multi-phase (MPT) earthquakes, four shallow volcanic tremors (SVT), one tectonic earthquake (TT) | III |
| 26 April 2006 | | 57 MPTs, one SVT | III |
| 3 May 2006 | | 84 MPTs, one SVT | III |
| 4 May 2006 | 02.00 | Lava erupted from summit | III |
| 7 May 2006 | | 133 MPTs, 88 TTs, one SVT | III |
| 8 May 2006 | | One SVT, 34 MPTs, 152 rock fall tremors (RFT) | III |
| 9 May 2006 | | Six SVTs, 142 MPTs, 152 RFTs | III |
| 10 May 2006 | | One SVT, 123 MPTs, 88 RFTs, four TTs. Evidence of new growing lava dome at summit reported | III |
| 12 May 2006 | | 90 MPTs, 214 RFTs, four TTs, 11 PFs upper Krasak and Boyong rivers | III |
| 13 May 2006 | | 27 MPTs, 24 RFTs, 14 PFs of uncertain distances | IV – evacuation order |
| 14 May 2006 | 00.00–00.06 | 23 ash/steam clouds erupted once every 15 min | IV |
| 20 May 2006 | | Pyroclastic flows | IV |
| 4 June 2006 | unknown | Geger Boyo collapses | IV |
| 13 June 2006 | | Alert level lowered from 4 (caution) to 3 (alert) | IV–III |
| 14 June 2006 | | Small dome collapse flow causes renewed evacuation of Kaliadem and surrounds | IV |
| 14 June 2006 | | Dome collapse, block-and-ash flow down the Woro Valley onto Kaliadem village. Two men were killed in a bunker where they tried to escape the flow | IV |
| 22 June–5 July 2006 | | Small dome collapse, block-and-ash flows continue, but decrease in intensity and frequency | |
| 12 July 2006 | | Lowering alert level | III – evacuees return home |
| 12 July–25 August 2006 | | Continued decrease in eruption activity | III |
| 25 August–30 September | | Decrease in eruption activity | II |
| By 1 October 2006 | | Return to baseline alert level | I |

(Johnston *et al.* 1999; Dominey-Howes & Minos-Minopoulos 2004; Gregg *et al.* 2004; Barberi *et al.* 2008; Carlino *et al.* 2008; Bird *et al.* 2010). Qualitative data collection methods were also used in order to understand and explain the community's way of thinking before, during and after crisis situations. Interviews were undertaken with people involved in the management process of volcanic crises; notably representatives from institutional organizations, municipality officials and community members, (Table 2).

The field data collection took place from April to August 2010 in the village of Turgo, which is part of the Purwobinangun and Ngargomulyo municipalities. Turgo is located on the southern side of the Merapi Volcano and Ngargomulyo on the western side (Fig. 1). The sites were chosen because they are located within the most hazard-prone areas. Both villages had experience of dealing with volcanic disasters; Ngargomulyo was damaged by pyroclastic flows and surges in 1930 and 1961, and Turgo in November 1994.

Focus group discussions (FGDs) were conducted in Turgo from 19 to 24 July 2010, and in Ngargomulyo on 28 and 29 July 2010. The aim of these FGDs was to analyse catastrophic events in the past (notably related to volcanic disaster), their impacts, problems and difficulties, vulnerability and capacities. The FGDs were moderated as advised by Krueger (1998) and conducted mostly in the Javanese language. In each village, four FGDs were achieved with 20 participants for each discussion: a group of women, a group of elderly people, a group of youths and a group of men, which also comprised local officials and villagers.

A questionnaire-based survey distributed to 143 respondents was carried out in May–July 2010 among 154 families in Turgo. Its goal was to

**Table 2.** *Interviewed people*

| Institutional organizations | | Village's officials and community member | |
|---|---|---|---|
| | Number | | Number |
| Provincial Disaster Coordinating Council (Yogyakarta Special Province) | 1 | Head of municipality (Purwobinangun; Ngargomulyo) | 2 |
| Municipal Disaster Coordinating Council (Sleman, Magelang, Klaten and Boyolali districts) | 4 | Village officers (Purwobinangun) | 2 |
| Merapi Volcano Observatory (BBPTK) | 2 | Heads of villages (Turgo village, Purwobinangun municipality) | 7 |
| Public Work (Sleman, Magelang and Klaten) | 3 | Head of cluster (Turgo) | 2 |
| | | School teacher (Turgo) | 1 |
| | | Local search and rescue operation volunteer group (Purwobinangun) | 2 |

study in depth the community's knowledge and individual perception of volcanic activity, experience in handling volcanic crisis, and traditional coping strategies to prevent or minimize future volcanic eruptions. Interviews were conducted face to face and in the local Javanese language.

## Responses to 1994 and 2006 eruptive crises

### Institutional responses

*Government responsibility.* There are four levels of government administration in Indonesia; that is, province (*propinsi*), district (*kabupaten/kota*), sub-district (*kecamatan*) and municipality (*kelurahan/ desa*). A municipality encompasses from five to 10 villages. Most organizations in Indonesia follow the government structure, with larger-size organizations having representatives at the provincial and district levels (Fig. 2). The local officials in municipalities and villages are also local villagers. Local leadership has a significant role in local capacity and their decision-making abilities.

Governments are mainly responsible for dealing with disasters and considering the roles played by stakeholders. Crisis management in

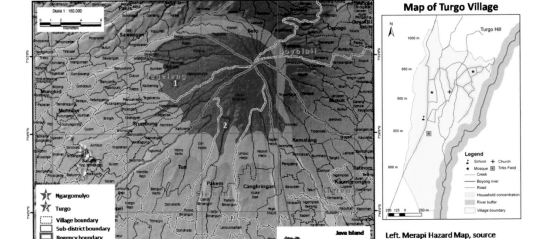

**Fig. 1.** Volcanic danger zone map of Merapi Ngargomulyo municipality, Turgo village and Tritis field.

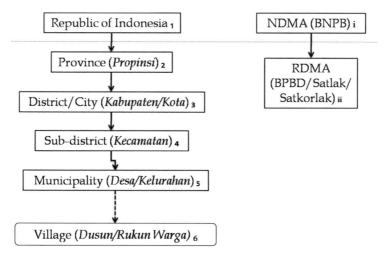

**Fig. 2.** Administrative divisions (1–6) and disaster management agency in Indonesia (i–ii).

Indonesia is based on a top-down hierarchical organization (President of the Republic of Indonesia 1990, 2008). The National Disaster Management Agency (NDMA: or, in Indonesian, BAKORNAS/ BNPB (*Badan Koordinasi Nasional Penanggulangan Bencana/Badan Nasional Penanggulangan Bencana* – Indonesian National Coordinating Agency for Disaster Management/Indonesian National Board for Disaster Management)) initiated in 1966, is a non-departmental body; its membership comprises up to 10 ministers and related governors. This agency's functions are to formulate, stipulate, and co-ordinate disaster management and its activities, pre-disaster, emergency response and post-disaster activities. To implement disaster management duties in Province and District/City regions, Regional Disaster Management Agencies (Satkorlak-Satlak/BPBD in Indonesian) have been established (Fig. 2).

A clear definition of a national disaster management policy is essential if a country is to establish and maintain adequate arrangements to deal with every aspect of its disaster threat, in all levels of the national structure and organization (from the national government through to local government or community level) (Carter 1991). If there is no policy to deal with disaster, arrangements to cope with it will be inadequate, and loss of material and human resources will occur.

The Centre of Volcanology and Geological Hazard Mitigation (CVGHM) is responsible for assessing and monitoring volcanic hazards (Fig. 3). Day-to-day conditions of the volcanic activity (*aktif normal, siaga, waspada, awas* – normally active; on guard; prepared; and beware conditions) are broadcast on the local radio. These four warning levels inform the community to get ready in case of an evacuation order (prepared and beware condition levels) (Fig. 4). CVGHM also provides maps that delineate three danger zones ranking from 3 to 1 (KRB 3, KRB 2 and KRB 1) judged unsafe for settlement. These maps are intended to support volcanologists in describing the pattern of past eruptions and to estimate the areas likely to be affected by various hazards (Suryo & Clarke 1985). The first danger zone map of Merapi at a 1:100 000 scale was published in 1978 by the VSI (Pardyanto *et al.* 1978). It is based on the lateral extent of the pyroclastic and lahar deposits from the 1930 and 1969 eruptions (Thouret *et al.* 2000). The most recent version of the hazard map, published in 2002, is based on volcanic deposits of the last 100 years, which is clearly limited with regard to Merapi's long eruption history (Hadisantono *et al.* 2002). Therefore, further volcanic hazard studies on Merapi should be undertaken in order to improve the official hazard map. A second problem for risk management is that this volcanic hazard map is not yet used for regional planning activities. Based on the volcano hazard map, the settlements situated within the hazard zone III should theoretically be permanently abandoned, whereas around 40 000 people inhabit this area on the whole volcano. For example, Turgo and Ngargomulyo municipalities encompass 922 houses for 3085 habitants. Another limitation of the official CVGHM map relates to the lack of data on potential damage and disaster prevention activities. In brief, a volcanic risk map would be very helpful in risk management, as well as in regional planning. Such a map is under construction in the frame of the MIAVITA FP 7 European project.

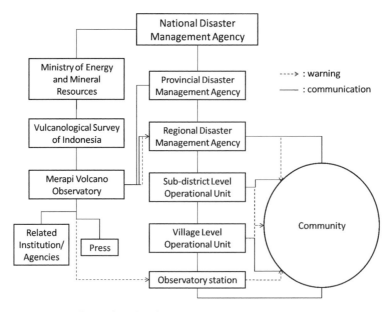

**Fig. 3.** Early warning system diagram in Indonesia.

*Relying on a short eruption history.* An ideal disaster management system needs to support the activities related to prevention, mitigation, preparedness, response, rehabilitation, reconstruction and development (Carter 1991). During the 1994 Merapi eruption, the lava dome collapsed, generating pyroclastic flows. On 22 November 1994, the *Kaliurang Post* reported flaming lava with hot clouds moving westward on Merapi's slope. The report reached Merapi Volcano Observatory (MVO) in Yogyakarta at 7:30 a.m. and was forwarded to the Sleman District, which relayed the information to the Pakem Subdistrict. By 10:00 a.m. the alert was given at

the Hargobinangun municipality, upon advice of the Pakem Subdistrict, but it was too late. Two hours before, dozens of houses were destroyed or heavily damaged by an ash-cloud pyroclastic surge, killing half of the 69 victims at a wedding party in Turgo. The other victims were buried by pyroclastic flows within the Boyong Valley at the same time.

Disaster preparedness encompasses actions undertaken before the event of a disaster to minimize its impacts. Local authorities and communities are highly vulnerable when the institution responsible for disaster lacks preparedness. Lacking

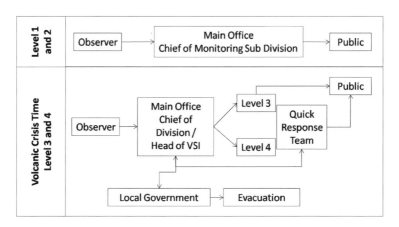

**Fig. 4.** Schematic diagram of volcanic activity and dissemination of information.

prevention, mitigation and preparedness response may explain the 1994 eruption. Prevention such as institutional support from the government in social protection was limited at that time. During the mitigation phase, land-use regulations prohibiting people from settling in the prone area were not well implemented. During the preparedness stage, the provision of warning systems, emergency communications, public education and awareness, as well as training programmes to reduce the volcanic risks, were also limited, if not inadequate. Before the 1994 eruption, there was no preparation or educational information on volcanic hazard, neither from government nor from non-governmental organizations. Without any preparation, local authorities were overwhelmed with the sudden eruptive crisis.

One aspect, which is not always given adequate priority, is individual and family preparedness. In many circumstances when government resources and emergency services are limited, such individual and family preparedness may be vital for survival (Carter 1991). Lack of first-aid knowledge and how to help the injured-burns victims became a challenge for local authorities, as well as for the community. As a result, many victims died on their way to the hospitals located in Pakem (12 km south of Turgo) and Yogyakarta City (20 km from Turgo). 'Most of the villagers who helped the burns victims did not have any knowledge of first aid. It was the first time we dealt with a volcanic crisis situation' (Suwaji, 52 years old, former head of Turgo village, interviewed on 30 June 2010).

Local authorities were not able to support rescue organization and emergency response, to organize effective evacuation, provide enough shelters and to facilitate the displacement of people. 'The conditions of shelters were very unpleasant, but at the time, what was most important for us was our safety. We brought nothing except the clothes on our backs. We were lucky to be able to run away from danger' (Sutirejo, a 78 year-old woman from Turgo, interviewed on 26 June 2010). Thousands of people evacuated through their own initiative, without their belongings (clothes, food, documents) settling in local shelters with limited facilities near the village office.

Aids for displaced people in local economic sectors were considerably low and not well organized. Since the majority of Turgo's inhabitants had at least one cow used for their income, the government offered a livestock shelter in Kaliurang. However, this solution was not helpful because there was no governmental support to feed the livestock. Villagers returned to their villages to collect grass for their cattle as they had no income to buy grass from the market. In many instances, villagers were forced to sell their livestock for a low price.

It shows that a disaster makes people more vulnerable.

During the 2006 eruption, after learning from past disasters, the local government tried to improve the disaster management system. In the prevention phase, information dissemination about volcano-related hazards was conducted. Vital infrastructure development was undertaken, upgrading the quality of evacuation routes by asphalting the roads before the 2006 eruption. An effort to conduct an effective evacuation was shown by the first evacuation on 13 May. Pregnant women and elderly people were the first to be moved, followed by children. Men chose to stay behind in their villages in order to look after their houses and farms. Trucks and vehicles provided by the authorities and local people were used to evacuate. By 19 May 2006, the Indonesian Red Cross reported a total of 20 080 people housed in emergency shelters. According to UNOCHA (2006a), 907 were sheltered in the Boyolali District, 6163 in the Sleman District, 8866 in the Magelang District and 4144 in the Klaten District. From 12 April until 13 June 2006, volcanic activity was still taking place but without the expected occurrence of pyroclastic flows. Merapi's behaviour induced villagers to think that staying in refugee camps was no longer necessary. The government and scientists failed to anticipate a long-onset eruption and then failed to communicate this fact to the local people. It resulted in a lack of trust between the local people, scientists and government. Despite daily warnings from the VSI of the continuing danger, people gradually trekked back to their villages. Some returned home daily from morning until afternoon, whereas others returned home discreetly and permanently regardless of the official order to evacuate. By 28 May 2006, up to 1800 people were believed to have returned to their villages (UNOCHA 2006a). Evacuees went home during the day and returned to evacuation camps at night. For example, in Turgo, 68% of the questionnaires' respondents declared having returned home every day in order to feed their cattle and clean their houses during the daytime (5 a.m. until 4 p.m.). 'Ever since I was young, every time there is a volcanic crisis, we go home almost every day during the evacuation period to feed the cattle and look after the farm land. We often come home very early in the morning, around 2 or 3 a.m. to avoid the police or guards' (Warno, a 62 year-old man from Ngargomulyo confirms during FGD on 28 July 2010).

Early in the morning of 27 May 2006, an earthquake with a magnitude of 6.2 on the Richter scale hit Bantul, 30 km south of Merapi (UNOCHA 2006b). This tectonic quake killed over 5800 people, injured more than 20 000 and demolished over 150 000 houses in Yogyakarta and central

Java provinces (UNOCHA 2006*b*). The earthquake swiftly increased the scale of emergency, and the volcanic eruption crisis and evacuation were overwhelmed by earthquake response. This tectonic earthquake did, indeed, correlate with an increase in pyroclastic flows in Merapi (Walter *et al.* 2007). The earthquake itself did not cause extensive damage to villages on Merapi. However, some problems arose when the evacuation camps on Merapi faced a shortage of relief supplies as efforts were directed to the earthquake-damaged areas in the south of Yogyakarta and Klaten, in the 10 day period following the earthquake (UNOCHA 2006*b*).

The statements above show that local authorities were not able to cope with two concomitant disasters occurring in the same area. Response to disaster is usually extensive and its success depends vitally on efficient preparedness (Carter 1991). The response operations usually have to be carried out under disruptive and traumatic conditions. Heavy demands of personnel, equipment and other resources are usually the main obstacles in disaster response. Without a basis of planning, organization and training, response operations are unlikely to achieve optimum success (Carter 1991).

The lack of anticipation during a long eruptive crisis by scientists and the government created a lack of trust and worsened the risks. On 13 June 2006, VSI lowered the alert level from level 4 (beware) to level 3 (prepared) a week after the partial collapse of the dome, which relieved pressure in Merapi's plumbing system (ESA 2006). Following the lowered alert level, refugees came back to their villages in trucks. However, they had to remain on guard and the trucks remained on standby in the villages. On 14 June, at around 12 p.m. a sudden increase in eruptive activity prompted sirens to be activated along the Gendol River (Fig. 5). Immediate evacuation was carried out and most people were able to evacuate on time. The same day, the largest block-and-ash pyroclastic flows reached a distance of 7 km from the summit, causing two fatalities and the total destruction of the Kaliadem village.

After this event, evacuation areas were redefined: including areas within an 8 km radius from the crater, as well as extending the forbidden zone within a 300 m on buffer of the valley rims of the Gendol, Boyong, Bedog, Krasak and Bebeng rivers (Fig. 6). The last evacuees began to return on 22 June in Magelang. The alert level was lowered to level I on 10 July, and by late July most evacuees had returned home (HA 2006*b*). The short period between the lowering and raising of the alert level on 13 and 14 June caused the villagers' uncertainty and distrust of both the government and scientists. Indeed, conditions to obtain a successful response to volcanic disaster include solid and well-coordinated efforts of local authorities, scientists and NGOs, and the use of an efficient early warning system.

*Multi-agency cooperation.* At Merapi, at least seven formal institutions and several non-governmental organizations (e.g. Kappala) work together on volcanic crisis management at each district level, namely the Regional/District Disaster Management Agency (RDMA), the Merapi Volcano Observatory (MVO), the army, the police, the Health Agency, the Public Works Agency and the Social Agency. The RDMA is in charge of stipulating and coordinating crisis-related activities with all institutions involved (e.g. evacuating the community, constructing evacuation shelters and providing food, logistics and health facilities). The functions of several institutions during a volcanic crisis were defined by a contingency planning, which the RDMA, MVO and UNICEF collectively created in 2009.

The multi-agency cooperation is not only needed during the crisis, but also before and after it. For example, the maintenance of evacuation roads becomes a major issue for post-crisis management. Following the 2006 eruption, the local government tried to enhance the quality of the roads by paving them with asphalt. However, after several years, the condition of the roads became worse due to trucks hauling volcanic material (De Belizal *et al.* 2011). The effort to maintain evacuation routes is

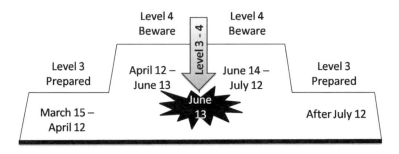

**Fig. 5.** Alert level of 2006 eruption.

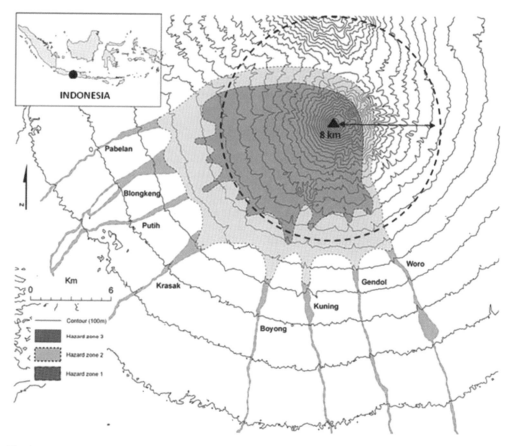

**Fig. 6.** Areas within a radius of 8 km from the crater, with several rivers on Merapi Volcano. *Source*: Hadisantono *et al.* (2002) and courtesy of BAKOSURTANAL, the National Agency for Survey and Mapping (Indonesia).

not uniform in each district; related institutions and society play an important role in this issue. For example, on the west flank of the Merapi Volcano, the chief of the Kemiren, Ngablak and Ngargomulyo municipalities refused to allow volcanic sand mining activity in their territory because they feared that the evacuation routes would be damaged by the trucks (De Belizal *et al.* 2011). In contrast, people and even the government of the Klaten District do not pay much attention to the condition of evacuation routes because sand mining is seen as a key sector of their economy. These examples illustrate how people's awareness and government support is essential in order to maintain infrastructure as a risk mitigation tool.

As mentioned by the BNPB (2010), the need for comprehensive disaster management planning is obvious, because during a disaster it is not clear who does what; every institution wants to help, but does not know what to do. In some cases, the same activities performed by different institutions results in overlapping planning. Therefore, a disaster management plan involving various stakeholders is needed.

## Responses of communities at risk

The community is the primary stakeholder and also the recipient of the direct impact of disasters. However, the role of communities in crisis management is often not taken into account. Volcanic crisis management should be carried within the framework of the socio-cultural background, involving national and local governments and non-governmental organizations.

*The influence of livelihood on local actions.* The community's volcanic risk perception plays a main role in crisis management; the perception of risk and success of response in minimizing volcanic risk are correlated (De la Cruz-Reyna & Tilling 2008). Socio-traditional responses towards disasters are common in Java (Oliver-Smith & Hoffman 1999). In the case of Merapi, the volcano is materially or spiritually significant to the local community; Javanese people consider the Merapi Volcano to be one of the sacred places, inhabited by spirits. It is the source of life, providing fertile soil for agriculture, and is the home of forests, fresh water and resources (Lavigne *et al.* 2008).

Social relationships between communities in Java are quite strong. It is reflected in their communal efforts ('*gotong royong*') in building mosques, churches, gates and portals, and during the planting season. During the 1994 volcanic disaster, this tradition of helping one another was exemplified during the evacuation of victims in Turgo. The evacuation process was initiated by the villagers after the first dome collapse, villagers fled by foot to the evacuation meeting point located at Tritis field in the southern part of Turgo (Fig. 1). During a second phase, the evacuation of victims was carried out using local resources such as motorcycles and cars owned by villagers. The poor condition of the roads and the lack of vehicles became major obstacles to evacuation. In the first days following the dome collapse, local people provided food and constructed temporary tents before the arrival of relief supplies from the government.

The influence of livelihood on local actions was also displayed during the 2006 eruption: apart from institutional responses, some villagers developed their own surveillance and warning system with their own observation teams. Similar attitudes have also been observed during post-eruptive lahars following the 2010 eruption of Merapi (Lavigne *et al.* 2011). Others prepared available local vehicles that could be used during evacuation. After the 26 May 26 2006 earthquake in Bantul, people from the still-erupting Merapi also helped earthquake victims, providing food and first aid, and even helping the reconstruction process. Societal interdependence in handling resources is quite important among the communities to reduce their vulnerability (Cashman & Cronin 2008). At the immediate aftermath of the earthquake, local people from the southern part of Yogyakarta fled toward Merapi because they feared a potential tsunami even though the status of the volcano was still at alert level IV. Such local response underlines the high level of traumatism due to the 2004 tsunami, which killed 170 000 people in Banda Aceh (Sumatra).

*Traditional responses.* Many legends and stories about the Merapi Volcano and its hazards are connected to the Javanese people's cultural and moral beliefs. As an example, according to a Pelemsari resident, the deaths of people in Turgo were due to a wedding ceremony that should not have been held during sacred days (Donovan 2010). Residents of Turgo disobeyed the rules and therefore suffered the consequences. Another example relates to the construction of a bridge connecting Turgo and Kaliurang in 1993. According to traditional belief, the bridge was not supposed to be built; hence, it was destroyed by post-eruptive lahars (Fig. 7). 'Oral history underlines that we are not allowed to cross the lahars road. Several workers who had built the bridge were killed by the eruption. It was a sign from unseen creatures and God that the bridge would impede the lahars flow and create higher risk to the community in Turgo'(Ninik, a 50 year-old woman from Turgo, interviewed on 26 July 2010). In Javanese nature, these religious–cultural worldviews and society are intrinsically interlinked (Schlehe 2010).

Traditional responses can become a source of difficulty for local authorities. When the Merapi Volcano's gatekeeper refused to evacuate during the 2006 eruption, some of the villagers, particularly in the Kinahrejo village, chose not to escape (Tempo Interaktif 2006). Based on their traditional belief and knowledge, they trusted Marijan, although they were highly exposed to the imminent danger. At the time, Marijan undertook a 3 day meditation with the intention of asking Merapi to limit the level of destruction. Marijan and hundreds of villagers believed that the 2006 eruption would not trigger a disaster. During the 2010 eruption, Marijan refused, as usual, to move out of his house prior to the eruption; he believed that his time to die in his village had come. The eruption on 26 October 2010 devastated the villages of Kaliadem and Kinahrejo; Marijan and 16 other people were found dead in his burnt house about 4 km from the Merapi summit.

As a result of the combined volcanic eruption and earthquake crisis in Java in 2006, several public rituals or ceremonies were conducted as a traditional response to the disasters. At that time, the Sultan of Yogyakarta, who is also the governor of the Yogyakarta Province, invited government representatives, religious leaders and also traditional spiritual leaders to a public meeting. Thousands of villagers attending this ceremony were included in the prayer. In 2006, the annual *labuhan* (auspicious ceremony or ritual) was held on the 30 day of Rejeb (Javanese lunar calendar) or on 26 August 2006 in the Gregorian calendar. Beside *labuhan*, communities in the NW part of Merapi's flank also have another form of ritual that they apply in their house; they offer food, perfume, clothes and other gifts to the unseen creatures each month. These *labuhan* and rituals seek to protect the people from disasters through their belief in God and unseen spirits on the Merapi Volcano (Lavigne *et al.* 2008).

**Fig. 7.** The bridge over the Boyong Valley between Turgo and Kaliurang. (Above) In December 1994. (Below) In February 1995 (photographs: F. Lavigne).

In some extreme circumstances, where there is great loss or change, human beings are confronted with difficult fundamental questions. In religious or traditional societies, the responses of disaster victims are varied and usually deal with morality, ethics, justice, sin and retribution, causality, liaison between the secular and the sacred, and the divine things (Bode 1977, 1989; Oliver-Smith 1979, 1996; Maida 1993; Cashman & Cronin 2008). This kind of reasoning behaviour exists almost everywhere, as explored by Bode (1977) after the 1970 Peruvian earthquake where myths and legends as well as the religious symbols and rituals sustained individual and cultural identity.

Public ceremonies were conducted as the communities' traditional response during and after the Merapi volcanic crisis in 2006. Traditional responses are not always local, as explained by Schlehe (2010). In Indonesia, a traditional ritual was held at the national level on 9 January 2008, attended by representatives of all religions, government officials, kings, sultans and royal families from 104 kingdoms across the Indonesian Archipelago. The purpose of the ritual was to protect the country against future disasters. These traditional responses can be viewed as an expression towards disaster, which includes social and cosmic justice. The fact that the government was involved in the ritual shows that traditional and institutional responses towards disasters are closely linked.

## Linking the community and institutional responses

*Unofficial warning.* Official statements regarding Merapi's activity should be made by the MVO or municipal disaster coordinating council in each district or province (Fig. 8). Volcanologists have the responsibility to deliver a timely and accurate assessment of the volcanic hazard. However, the challenge is to make sure that the information is not distorted. Rapid release of uncertain or inaccurate information can cause panic in communities. Here is one example of such an occurrence: a local community radio in Klaten interviewed someone who had little expertise in volcanology but who expressed his opinion and even predicted future activity during the 2006 eruptive period of Merapi. This created confusion amongst the residents and would have better been avoided. Better communication between the authorities, the media and also the population should be enhanced to improve crisis management.

*Raising public awareness.* The limitation of institutional response is when efforts to minimize risk do not involve the community. Information on volcano-related hazards is disseminated through the members of hazard mitigation offices at regional

or subdistrict levels. A major lesson was learned from the 1994 eruption: the national government stressed the immediate necessity to promote people's alertness to volcanic hazards and encouraged precautionary measures to be taken by local authorities to reduce vulnerability (UNDHA 1994).

'Shortly before the 2006 eruption and thereafter, there were many programmes related to disaster risk reduction committed by government or non-governmental organizations. The community plays an important role in disaster risk reduction. If they have better knowledge of volcanic hazards and their consequences on society, then in the future the expected risk could be reduced' (Yatin, 37 years old, Head of Ngargomulyo village, interviewed on 29 July 2010). After the 1994 eruption, the local hazard mitigation officers disseminated information about volcanic hazards and risks. However, this effort was not considered efficient because of the lack of community participation. Even though there were several participative programmes on disaster risk reduction, they were conducted in a fragmentary manner by non-governmental organizations. Then, on 26 May 2006, a cooperative network named Forum Merapi was initiated; it gathered local authorities from Sleman, Klaten, Magelang and Boyolali, the MVO, several local and international NGOs, academic institutions, and representatives of local communities. The forum's goal was to create a more comprehensive and participative disaster risk

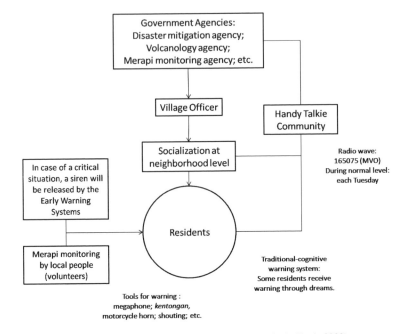

**Fig. 8.** Information flow during a volcanic crisis at Merapi Volcano (Sagala & Okada 2009).

reduction programme on the Merapi Volcano. Since 2006, several programmes on volcano-related disaster management were conducted under the forum's umbrella. For example, participative volcanic hazard mapping was conducted. Furthermore, local capacities to cope with disasters (Fig. 9) and community evacuation simulations were also integrated into disaster mitigation activities. Compulsory training programmes for hazard mitigation were applied in communities around Mount Merapi. Currently, the local authority of the Yogyakarta Province, in cooperation with the French Red Cross, is coordinating the disaster risk management and warning dissemination.

In 2006, before the eruption occurred, both the community and the government were well prepared in the four districts. In early April 2006, the government used four eruption scenarios prepared by volcanologists as part of their mitigation plans. The government and scientists used the third-case scenario (one level below the worst-case scenario, anticipating over 80 000 people to be displaced: UNOCHA 2006*a*). Logistics were prepared as early as April by local governments. An early warning system was also in place, which included a set of sirens and three CCTVs (close circuit televisions) to warn against incoming pyroclastic flows and lahars. An excellent example of pre-crisis management was carried out in the Sleman District, called the 'Sleman Disaster Information Network'. The scheme connects the regional disaster management agency, village offices, shelters, health centre and several schools within the high volcanic risk zone.

*Forced migration.* After the 1994 eruption, local authorities decided that 2700 evacuees from the five villages within the dangerous zone should be resettled in the *Sudimoro* (a Javanese word that means 'willing to come') village, located 8 km south of Turgo. Unfortunately, the plan to relocate was not accepted by the residents of Turgo, creating tension between local authorities and villagers who still wanted to live in their village. Several attempts were undertaken by the government to implement the resettlement plan. For example, the village of Turgo was erased from the government map and villagers were not recognized. 'It was difficult to relocate people from Turgo. The government even issued a statement that Turgo would be removed from official maps and its villagers would not be recognized. But this effort failed,

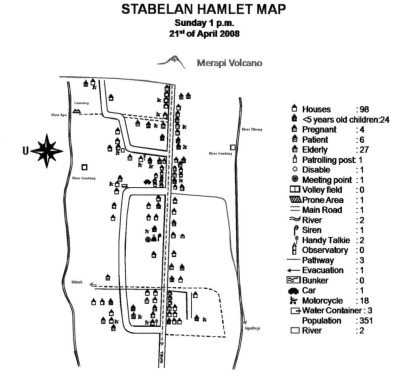

**Fig. 9.** Stabelan Hamlet map.

because many people finally returned to Turgo and remained there as before' (Misran, 44 years old, Head of Turgo village, interviewed on 28 April 2010).

New housing was built in the Sudimoro village. Although some villagers initially decided to move to the relocation area, most of them returned to Turgo (Dove 2008), even though the new houses were well constructed. Today, there are 111 households in the Sudimoro relocation site against 154 in Turgo, that is 40% of Turgo villagers are living in the resettlement. Attachment to their native village and easy access to resources from their land were the main reasons for wanting to return to live in Turgo after the 1994 eruption. 'Here (in Turgo), it is easier to make money. The access to the city is better in Sudimoro than here, but it is difficult for us to find a job in the city. Farming and cattle raising is our life. In Sudimoro, we do not have any land. If we live there, we have to go to Turgo every day, because our land is here' (Tukirah, 35 year-old woman from Turgo, interviewed on 10 May 2010).

The top-down structural mitigation effort to create resettlement was not well appreciated by the local community. Major issues were the lack of farming land and the difficulty to get food for their livestock. A sustainable post-disaster plan is one where victims participate in resettlement planning, which is an essential requirement (Oliver-Smith 1991). Similar resettlement problems also occurred in Mt Pinatubo's resettlement centre after the 1991 eruption (Gaillard 2008) or after the Skopje Earthquake in Macedonia (Davis 1977). Mitigation efforts should take into account the expectations, culture and socio-professional specificities of the affected people most concerned (Anderson 1993).

Without excluding the institutional modern mitigation measures, local knowledge and beliefs play an important role in disaster management, particularly in traditional societies. Communal perceptions of an event may be altered into myth-like stories and explanations (Cashman & Cronin 2008). In volcanic regions, local traditions and belief systems play an important role in motivating local reactions before, during and after a crisis (Swanson 2008). Thus, it is important to examine both hazards and culture in order to develop more-resilient communities.

Considering the fact that there are at least 5 million people living on the volcano slopes in Indonesia (BNPB 2010), the development of local capacity associated with volcanic disaster is absolutely necessary. Several approaches can be taken in order to gain more traditional knowledge of and responses to volcanic disaster, in the framework of a bottom-up disaster risk reduction programme. For example, participatory rural appraisal (PRA) or focused group discussion (FGD) allows scientists

to understand the main local perspective concerns (Cronin et al. 2004). The participatory three-dimensional mapping is scheduled to be carried out in the summer of 2011 in order to combine the spatial and time elements, as well as community knowledge and responses to volcanic hazards and risks.

## Conclusion

The gap between institutional responses and the community's way of thinking before, during and after crisis situations is the focus of this study. Institutional response to minimize risk is not as effective as when the community is involved. The fact that both people's awareness and the government are involved in ritual traditions shows that traditional and institutional responses towards disasters are closely linked.

Traditional responses towards disasters can provide an acknowledgement of the complexity of human response and a better understanding of the community's point of view on the disaster management process. Using top-down institutional responses to volcanic crisis is not sufficient in regions with a high cultural perception. Working with the community is an ideal solution to minimize the gap between the government, scientists, non-governmental organizations and the community itself. A community-based methodology combined with studies of physical hazards will generate a comprehensive risk and crisis management.

The following step that we propose in this study is to use participatory three-dimensional mapping for disaster risk reduction, where communities can express their knowledge and responses by combining spatial and time elements (Gaillard & Maceda 2009). However, it should be noted that these participative actions would be successful only if supported by at least four important stakeholders: society, government, scientific or academic institutions, and non-governmental organizations.

This study was held in the framework of the Mitigate and Assess Risk from Volcanic Impact on Terrain and Human Activities 'MiaVita', European Union programme under the Work Package 5 concerning 'Socio-economic Vulnerability and Resilience'. The authors wish to acknowledge the French Embassy in Jakarta and the Directorate General of Higher Education, Ministry of National Education Republic of Indonesia. We thank Dr Surono (Director of the Centre for Volcanology and Geological Hazard Mitigation, Indonesia), Dr Subandriyo (Head of the Merapi Volcano Observatory and his staff, especially I. Dewi, I. Sri Sumarti, B. M. Muzani and Nurcholik, local authorities (Sleman, Klaten, Magelang and Boyolali regencies), and people from the Turgo village and Ngargomulyo municipality. Special thanks to D. Grancher and A. Picquout for their help in data acquisition and processing. We also thank the two anonymous reviewers who assisted to improve the initial version of the paper.

# References

ANDERSON, M. B. 1993. Lessons in rehabilitation/resettlement efforts: implications for Mt. Pinatubo assistance programs. *Philippine Journal of Public Administration*, **37**, 351–374.

BARBERI, F., DAVIS, M. S., ISAIA, R., NAVE, R. & RICCI, T. 2008. Volcanic risk perception in the vesuvius population. *Journal of Volcanology and Geothermal Research*, **172**, 244–258.

BERMEJO, P. M. 2006. Preparation and response in case of natural disasters: cuban programs and experience. *Journal of Public Health Policy*, **27**, 13–21.

BIRD, D. K., GISLADOTTIR, G. & DOMINEY-HOWES, D. 2010. Volcanic risk and tourism in Southern Iceland: implications for hazard, risk and emergency response education and training. *Journal of Volcanology and Geothermal Research*, **189**, 33–48.

BNPB 2010. *Rencana Nasional Penanggulangan Bencana 2010–2014*. Badan Nasional Penanggulangan Bencana, Republik Indonesia.

BODE, B. 1977. Disaster, social structure and myth in the Peruvian Andes: the genesis of an explanation. *Annals of the New York Academy of Sciences*, **293**, 264–274.

BODE, B. 1989. *No Bells to Toll: Destruction and Creation in the Andes*. Sribners, New York.

BPS 2005. *Supas (Intercensal Population Census)*. Badan Pusat Statistik, Jakarta.

CARLINO, S., SOMMA, R. & MAYBERRY, G. C. 2008. Volcanic risk perception of young people in the urban areas of vesuvius: comparisons with other volcanic areas and implications for emergency management. *Journal of Volcanology and Geothermal Research*, **172**, 229–243.

CARTER, W. N. 1991. *Disaster Management: A Disaster Manager's Handbook*. Asian Development Bank, Manila.

CASHMAN, K. V. & CRONIN, S. J. 2008. Welcoming a monster to the world: myths, oral tradition and modern societal response to volcanic disaster. *Journal of Volcanology and Geothermal Research*, **176**, 407–418.

CHARBONNIER, S. J. & GERTISSER, R. 2008. Field observation and surface characteristics of pristine block-and-ash flow deposits from the 2006 eruption of Merapi Volcano, Java, Indonesia. *Journal of Volcanology and Geothermal Research*, **177**, 971–982.

CRONIN, S. J., GAYLORD, D. R., CHARLEY, D., ALLOWAY, B. V., WALLEZ, S. & ESAU, J. W. 2004. Participatory methods of incorporating scientific with traditional knowledge for volcanic hazard management on ambae Island, Vanuatu. *Bulletin Volcanology*, **66**, 652–668.

DAVIS, I. 1977. Emergency shelter. *Disaster*, **1**, 23–40.

DE BELIZAL, E., LAVIGNE, F. & GRANCHER, D. 2011. Quand l'aléa devient la ressource: l'activité d'extraction des matériaux volcaniques autour du volcan Merapi (Indonésie) dans la compréhension des risques locaux. [When the hazard becomes the resource: block and sand mining around Merapi volcano (Indonesia) in risk studies.] *Cybergeo : European Journal of Geography*, Environnement, Nature, Paysage, document 525, mis en ligne le 23 mars 2011, Consulté le 23 mars 2011. World Wide Web Address: http://cybergeo.revues.org/23555.

DE LA CRUZ-REYNA, S. & TILLING, R. I. 2008. Scientific and public responses to the ongoing volcanic crisis at Popocatépetl Volcano, Mexico: importance of an effective hazards-warning system. *Journal of Volcanology and Geothermal Research*, **170**, 121–134.

DOMINEY-HOWES, D. & MINOS-MINOPOULOS, D. 2004. Perceptions of hazard and risk on santorini. *Journal of Volcanology and Geothermal Research*, **137**, 285–310.

DONOVAN, K. 2010. Doing social volcanology: exploring volcanic culture in Indonesia. *Journal Compilation Royal Geographical Society Area*, **42**, 117–126.

DOVE, M. 2008. Volcanic eruption as agent of change on merapi volcano, central Java. *Journal of Volcanology and Geothermal Research*, **172**, 329–337.

EDEN, S. 1996. Public participation in environmental policy: considering scientific, counter-scientific and non-scientific contributions. *Public Understanding of Science*, **5**, 183–204.

ESA 2006. *Mount Merapi (Indonesia) Volcano June 2006*. European Space Agency, Paris. World Wide Web Address: http://earth.eo.esa.int/ew/volcanoes/Merapi_indonesia-june06/. Accessed 25 October 2009.

GAILLARD, J. C. 2008. *Differentiated adjustment to the 1991 Mt Pinatubo resettlement program among lowland ethnic groups of the Philippines*. The Australian Journal of Emergency Management, **23**, 31–39.

GAILLARD, J. C. & MACEDA, E. A. 2009. Participatory 3-dimensional mapping for disaster risk reduction. *Participatory Learning and Action*, **60**, 109–118.

GREGG, C. E., HOUGHTON, B. F., JOHNSTON, D. M., PATON, D. & SWANSON, D. A. 2004. *The perception of volcanic risk in Kona communities from Mauna Loa and Hualalai volcanoes, Hawaii*. Journal of Volcanology and Geothermal Research, **130**, 179–196.

HADISANTONO, R. D., ANDREASTUTI, M. C. H. S. D. ET AL. 2002. *Peta Kawasan Rawan Bencana Gung Api Merapi, Jawa Tengah dan Daerah Istimewa Yogyakarta scale 1:50 000*. Direktorat Vulkanologi dan Mitigasi Bencana Geologi, Bandung.

JOHNSTON, D. & RONAN, K. 2000. Risk education and intervention. *In*: SIGURDSSON, H. (ed.) *Encyclopedia of Volcanoes*. Academic Press, New York, 1229–1240.

JOHNSTON, D., BEBBINGTON, M. S., LAI, C. D., HOUGHTON, B. F. & PATON, D. 1999. *Volcanic hazard perceptions: comparative shifts in knowledge and risk*. Disaster Prevention Management, **8**, 118–126.

KRUEGER, R. A. 1998. *Focus Group A Practical Guide for Applied Research*. Sage, Thousand Oaks, CA.

LAVIGNE, F., BÉLIZAL, E., CHOLIK, N., NURNANING, A., PICQUOUT, A. & MEI, E. 2011. *Lahar Hazards and Risks Following the 2010 Eruption of Merapi Volcano, Indonesia*. Union General Assembly, Vienna, Austria, 03-08/04/2011 (abstract).

LAVIGNE, F., DE COSTER, B. ET AL. 2008. People's behaviour in the face of volcanic hazards: perspectives from Javanese communities, Indonesia. *Journal of Vulcanology and Geothermal Research*, **172**, 273–287.

LEONE, F. & LESALES, T. 2009. The interest of cartography for a better perception and management of volcanic risk: from scientific to social representations the case of Mt. Pelée volcano, Martinique (Lesser Antilles). *Journal of Volcanology and Geothermal Research*, **186**, 186–194.

MAIDA, C. A. 1993. Child and parent reactions to the Los Angeles area Whittier Narrows Earthquake. *In*: ALLEN, R. D. (ed.) Handbook of Post-Disaster Interventions (Special Issue). *Journal of Social Behaviour and Personality*, **8**, 421–436.

MCENTIRE, D. A., FULLER, C., JOHNSTON, C. W. & WEBER, R. 2002. *Acomparison of disaster paradigms: the search for a holistic policy guide. Public Administration Review*, **62**, 276–291.

OLIVER-SMITH, A. 1979. The crisis dyad: culture and meaning of medicine. *In*: ROGER, W. R. (ed.) *Nourishing the Humanistic: Essay in the Dialogue Between the Social Sciences and Medicine*. University of Pittsburgh Press, Pittsburgh, PA, 73–93.

OLIVER-SMITH, A. 1991. Successes and failures in post disaster resettlement. *Disasters*, **15**, 12–23.

OLIVER-SMITH, A. 1996. Anthropological research on hazards and disasters. *Annual Review of Anthropology*, **25**, 303–328.

OLIVER-SMITH, A. & HOFFMAN, S. 1999. *The Angry Earth: Disaster in Anthropological Perspective*. Routledge, New York.

PARDYANTO, L., REKSOWIROGO, L. D., MITROHARTONO, F. X. S. & HARDJOSUWITO, S. H. 1978. *Volcanic Hazard Map. Merapi Volcano Central Java Indonesia* (1/100 000). Geological Survey of Indonesia, Bandung, **II**, 14.

PATON, D., SMITH, L., DALY, M. & JOHNSTON, D. 2008. Risk perception and volcanic hazard mitigation: individual and social perspectives. *Journal of Vulcanology and Geothermal Research*, **172**, 179–188.

PRESIDENT OF THE REPUBLIC OF INDONESIA 1990. *Decree of the President of the Republic of Indonesia No. 43 1990 on the National Disaster Coordinating Agency*.

PRESIDENT OF THE REPUBLIC OF INDONESIA 2008. *Regulation of President of Republic of Indonesia Number 8 of 2008 Concerning National Disaster Management Agency*.

RATDOMOPURBO, A. & POUPINET, G. 2000. *An overview of the seismicity of Merapi volcano, Java, Indonesia 1983–1994. Journal of Volcanology and Geothermal Research*, **200**, 193–214.

RESER, J. P. 2007. The Experience of natural disasters: psychological perspectives and understandings. *In*: STOLTMAN, J. P., LIDSTONE, J. & DECHANO, L. M. (eds). *International Perspectives on Natural Disasters: Occurrence, Mitigation, and Consequences*. Advances in Natural and Technological Hazards Research, **21**. Kluwer, Dordrecht, 369–384.

SAGALA, S. & OKADA, N. 2009. *Policy Analysis for Hitting the Right Target: Risk Communication in Mt. Merapi*. Annals of Disaster Prevention Research Institute, Kyoto University, **52 B**.

SCHLEHE, J. 2010. Anthropology of religion: disasters and the representations of tradition and modernity. *Journal of Religion*, **40**, 112–120.

SURYO, I. & CLARKE, M. C. G. 1985. The occurrence and mitigation of volcanic hazards in Indonesia and exemplified at the Mount Merapi, Mount Kelud and Mount Galunggung volcanoes. *Quaternary Journal of Engineering Geology, Great Britain*, **18**, 79–98.

SWANSON, D. A. 2008. Hawaiian oral tradition describes 4000 years of volcanic activity at Kilauea. *Journal of Volcanology and Geothermal Research*, **176**, 427–431.

TEMPO INTERAKTIF 2006. *Mbah Maridjan Menolak Mengungsi, 13 May 2006*. World Wide Web Address: www.tempointeraktif.com/hg/nasional/2006/05/13/brk,20060513–77414,id.html. Accessed: 17 August 2010 (in Indonesian) .

THOURET, J. C., LAVIGNE, F., KELFOUN, K. & BRONTO, S. 2000. Toward a revised hazard assessment at Merapi Volcano Central Java. *Journal of Volcanology and Geothermal Research*, **100**, 479–502.

UNDHA 1994. *Indonesia Volcanic Eruption Nov 1994 UNDHA Information Reports 1–4*. United Nations Department of Humanitarian Affairs, Geneva. World Wide Web Address: http://www.reliefweb.int/rw/rwb.nsf/db900SID/ACOS-64CN8U?OpenDocument. Accessed: 28 August 2010.

UNOCHA 2006a. *OCHA Field Situation Report 1–17 Indonesia-Volcano-Update Mt. Merapi, Central Java Province 19 April – 26 May 2006*. United Nations Office for the Coordination of Humanitarian Affairs, Jakarta.

UNOCHA 2006b. *OCHA Field Situation Report 1–15 Indonesia-Earthquake-Update Central Java and Yogyakarta Provinces May – August 2006*. United Nation Office for the Coordination of Humanitarian Affairs, Jakarta.

VOIGHT, B., CONSTANTINE, E. K., SISWOWIDJOYO, S. & TORLEY, R. 2000a. Historical eruptions of Merapi Volcano, Central Java, Indonesia, 1768–1998. *Journal of Volcanology and Geothermal Research*, **100**, 69–138.

VOIGHT, B., YOUNG, K. D. *ET AL.* 2000b. Deformation and seismic precursors to dome-collapse and fountain-collapse Nuées Ardentes at Merapi Volcano, Java, Indonesia, 1994–1998. *Journal of Volcanology and Geothermal Research*, **100**, 261–287.

WALTER, T. R., WANG, R., ZIMMER, M., GROSSER, H., LÜHR, B. & RATDOMOPURBO, A. 2007. Volcanic activity influenced by tectonic earthquakes: Static and dynamic stress triggering at Mt. Merapi. *Geophysical Research Letters*, **34**, L05304.

WILSON, T., KAYE, G., STEWART, C. & COLE, J. 2007. *Impacts of the 2006 Eruption of Merapi Volcano, Indonesia, on Agriculture and Infrastructure*. GNS Science Report, **2007/07**.

YOUNG, K. D., VOIGHT, B., SUBANDRIYO,, SAJIMAN,, MISWANTO, & CASADEVALL, T. J. 2000. Ground deformation atmMerapi volcano, Java, Indonesia: Distance Changes, June 1988 – October 1995. *Journal of Volcanology and Geothermal Research*, **100**, 233–259.

# Exploratory spatial analysis of typhoon characteristics in the North Pacific basin

CHEN-CHIEH FENG* & JAMES P. TERRY

*Department of Geography, National University of Singapore, AS2, 1 Arts Link, Kent Ridge, Singapore 117570*

*Corresponding author (e-mail: geofcc@nus.edu.sg)*

**Abstract:** This paper analyses the spatial pattern of three tropical storm migratory behaviour parameters – track sinuosity, minimum pressure and duration of intense typhoons. The best-track data of the western North Pacific basin archived by the Regional Specialized Meteorological Center in Tokyo were used. The local Getis–Ord $G_i^*(d)$ statistic (where $d$ is distance) was employed in a geographical information system (GIS) environment to identify clusters of hot spots and cold spots of the three parameters. The analysis of storm-track sinuosity identified one dominant hot-spot cluster of sinuously tracking storms far from the continental margins of the North Pacific Ocean, with three small cold-spot clusters of straight-tracking storms relatively close to mainland SE Asia. The analysis of the second and third parameters revealed extensive overlap between the cluster of very intense typhoons (i.e. hot-spot cluster of minimum pressure, mean 926 hPa) and the cluster of long-duration typhoons (i.e. hot-spot cluster of duration at typhoon intensity, mean 5.4 days). The findings suggest that the Philippines and the Northern Marianas Islands are vulnerable to strike by both longer-lived and extremely violent typhoons. Overall, the technique highlights the strong potential for statistical clustering analysis to visualize and understand geospatial patterns in typhoon meteorological characteristics.

Over the past decades tremendous achievements in climatic observation research have advanced our understanding of typhoon (tropical cyclone) characteristics and equipped us with tools to predict their migratory behaviour more accurately than previously possible. Yet, in spite of the achievements, typhoons, tropical cyclones and hurricanes continue to wreak havoc in many countries around the world. Countries bordering the western North Pacific (WNP) –an area between the Equator and 60°N, and from longitude 100°E to 180°– and island nations therein are particularly vulnerable as approximately one-third of all tropical cyclones globally originate in this region. Moreover, many nations in the WNP basin have large and growing coastal populations, and are thereby specifically at risk of the impacts of severe storms and other storm-induced natural hazards (such as coastal inundation, river flooding and slope failure). Typhoon Morakot in August 2009, for instance, affected several Asian countries and wrought devastating damage in Taiwan, with the total cost of damage estimated unofficially at US$3.3 billion. This example highlights the importance of continual study on various typhoon characteristics, of which studies of their migratory behaviour is one priority in the WNP (Terry & Feng 2010).

Previous research on typhoon climatology has focused largely on the distribution, frequency and intensity of typhoons (McGregor 1995; Chan & Liu 2004; Emanuel 2004; Webster *et al.* 2005), as well as on a number of features of typhoon tracks (Harr & Elsberry 1991; Lander 1996; Ho *et al.* 2004; Camargo *et al.* 2007a). The track is the path that a typhoon follows as it matures and travels away from its original place of genesis. Nomenclatures for different track types have been suggested based on directions of movement, locations of maximum intensity, mathematical shape or sinuosity (Elsner & Liu 2003; Terry & Feng 2010), which offer objective and achievable means of categorizing storm tracks. However, relatively few studies have attempted analysis of the spatial clustering of parameters of the typhoon track characteristics.

In the present context, track sinuosity refers to how much the actual curving path followed by a typhoon deviated away from the straight line drawn directly between the start and finish points (which is referred to as the 'overall direction', and has a sinuosity value equal to 1). Motivation for investigating this particular feature of typhoon tracks is that it strongly influences whether individual typhoons enter different parts of the western North Pacific as they migrate away from their loci of original genesis; and so this also has a bearing on which coastlines are potentially at risk of landfall (i.e. typhoon crossing). Typhoons that follow

*From*: TERRY, J. P. & GOFF, J. (eds) 2012. *Natural Hazards in the Asia–Pacific Region: Recent Advances and Emerging Concepts.* Geological Society, London, Special Publications, **361**, 187–194, http://dx.doi.org/10.1144/SP361.15

sinuous tracks are also more complex in terms of forecasting their movement while active. Consequently, determining whether track sinuosity exhibits any spatial organization across the WNP basin, combined with a complementary investigation of where the most intense storms (i.e. typhoons) reach their maximum strength and how long they maintain typhoon intensity, therefore provides valuable information. This may be particularly useful for risk assessment and planning in those WNP nations that are frequently impacted by these violent storms.

Within the general framework of typhoon track studies begun in earlier work (Terry & Feng 2010), the goal of the present paper is to carry out an exploratory examination of the spatial clustering of several storm parameters using geographical information system (GIS) methodologies. Specifically, we analyse the available historical record of tropical storm tracks in the WNP and investigate the following three research questions. (1) Can any spatial clustering in terms of the sinuosity of tropical storm tracks be identified? (2) Is any spatial clustering recognized in locations of the most intense systems (typhoons) at their maximum strength (defined in terms of minimum central pressure at sea level)? (3) Is there evidence for spatial clustering of the duration at typhoon intensity?

## Methodology

### Study area

The study area falls under the responsibility of the Regional Specialized Meteorological Center (RSMC) for the western North Pacific, based at the Tokyo headquarters of the Japan Meteorological Agency (JMA). The JMA is the authority designated by the World Meteorological Organization to operate the RSMC-Tokyo (RSMC-Tokyo 2010), which is one of six RSMCs worldwide. The area monitored by the RSMC-Tokyo is demarcated in Figure 1. The WNP region is inhabited by over half a billion people and is characterized by tens of thousands of kilometres of coastline that is vulnerable to the impacts of tropical storms. The conventional WNP tropical storm season spans the boreal summer, extending for 7 months from May to November, although such storms also occur outside these months on occasion. Some summary statistics are presented in Table 1.

### Track data

The raw data of a tropical storm archived and provided by the RSMC-Tokyo (i.e. the best-track data) can be regarded to have two parts. The first

part is a header that provides information on the storm's name, international identifier, date, time and other control parameters. The second part is a series of storm-track points that contains, among other variables, time, maximum sustained wind speed, latitude, longitude and atmospheric pressure, all recorded at 6 h intervals (00:00, 06:00, 12:00, 18:00 GMT). To facilitate the retrieval of parameters critical to the quantitative description of the movement and intensity characteristics of the tropical storms, the raw data were first reformatted into track-based form, so that each record contains only the relevant information for each track and not a complete set of track points.

The data also underwent a filtering process to exclude track data points that fall outside the range of a tropical storm in its mature phase (sustained winds > 34 knots). In other words, the earlier phase while a tropical depression spins up into a nascent tropical storm and the later phase of decay after winds ease off below 35 knots are excluded from the analysis. Figure 2 illustrates a selection of typical storm tracks analysed. As wind speed in the dataset has been recorded in 5 knot increments, the first recorded position along a track with maximum sustained wind strength at 35 knots was therefore selected to identify the genesis location for each tropical storm. A similar procedure was used to identify the position of tropical storm decay and, thus, the terminating location.

The filtered data were then converted into a GIS-compatible format so that they could be analysed within GIS. Parameters of each tropical storm, including genesis location, terminating location, minimum pressure attained in hectopascals (hPa; where $1 \text{ hPa} = 100 \text{ Pa}$) to represent maximum intensity, and the location (latitude and longitude) where the minimum pressure was measured, were then extracted. Of the total 1555 tropical storms, a subset of 798 strengthened to become very intense systems; that is, typhoons – here defined by the central pressure falling below or equal to 970 hPa. (The 970 hPa minimum pressure threshold corresponds approximately to central maximum wind speeds (sustained over 10 min averaging times) of 65 knots ($120 \text{ km h}^{-1}$). Tropical storms attaining this strength are referred to as 'typhoons' or 'hurricanes' in different ocean basins, but represent category 12 on the Beaufort scale for wind force (Terry 2007).) For these storms we also extracted the duration (number of h) that the system remained at typhoon intensity ($\leq$970 hPa). Note that all but the sinuosity of storm tracks can be extracted directly from the raw data and, therefore, the way that the sinuosity parameter was measured warrants further explanation. The sinuosity value for each tropical storm track was calculated as the total 'meandering' distance travelled by a storm while

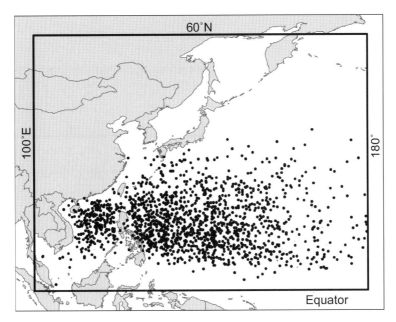

**Fig. 1.** Genesis points of all tropical storms in the western North Pacific from 1951 to 2009 ($n = 1555$) and boundaries of the RSMC-Tokyo area of responsibility (study area). Genesis refers to the location where tropical storms reached maturity, with maximum sustained winds above 34 knots (see the text).

in mature phase (maximum sustained wind speed >34 knots), divided by the direct (vector) length between the genesis and termination points. Using GIS, all distances were measured across the Earth-surface sphere using the law of haversines from spherical trigonometry.

## Spatial clustering

To identify spatial clustering of the variables under investigation, which include storm-track sinuosity,

**Table 1.** *Summary of tropical storm characteristics from 1951 to 2009 for the western North Pacific\**

| Tropical storm parameter | Mean | Range |
|---|---|---|
| Seasonal frequency | 26.4 | 16–39 |
| Start latitude (°N) | 16.2 | 1.5–37.6 |
| End latitude (°N) | 27.5 | 1.6–55.5 |
| Start longitude (°E) | 137.5 | 102.0–181.4 |
| End longitude (°E) | 132.0 | 97.5–187.0 |
| Duration (days) | 5.3 | 0.25–22.5 |
| Track length (km) | 2468 | 25–8137 |
| Track sinuosity | 1.27 | 1–7.68 |
| Minimum low pressure (hPa) | 963.5 | 870–1008 |

*Note that statistics represent the mature phase only (when maximum sustained wind speeds exceed 34 knots); that is, weaker phases in the formative and decay stages of a storm lifespan are excluded from the analysis.

location of typhoon minimum pressure and duration of time at typhoon intensity ($\leq$970 hPa), the local Getis–Ord statistic ($G_i^*(d)$) was employed, where $d$ is distance (Ord & Getis 1995). The $G_i^*(d)$ is an inferential statistic that considers the spatial relationships between data points within a chosen 'neighbourhood', and is capable of identifying the presence of significant spots (and then clusters) of high or low values of a chosen variable. In essence, the technique goes beyond simple visualization of the spatial distribution of chosen tropical storm parameters by uncovering hidden local clustering patterns in data that the global statistics average over. The null hypothesis of the $G_i^*(d)$ states that there is no spatial clustering of the values of a chosen variable. When the result of the $G_i^*(d)$ analysis indicates a small and significant $P$ value, 'hot spots' and 'cold spots' are identified as the null hypothesis has to be rejected. In this work, we choose 0.05 as the $P$ value under which hot spots or cold spots are identified. Hot spots (or cold spots) are therefore individual data points exhibiting significantly high (or low) values of the selected storm parameter that are similarly surrounded by high (or low) values, respectively. The method had been used elsewhere to identify hot spots in issues concerning climatology, such as the spatio-temporal distribution of snow cover (Farmer *et al.* 2009) and near-surface diurnal temperature trend (Peralta-Hernandez *et al.* 2009), as

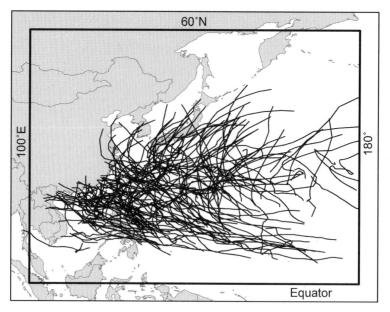

**Fig. 2.** Tracks of 160 tropical storms (about 10% of the recorded 1555 tracks) in the western North Pacific from 1951 to 2009. Only the mature phases of storms are shown; that is, while maximum sustained winds exceed 34 knots (see the text).

well as other environmental science domains (Zhang *et al.* 2008; Watters *et al.* 2010).

In this study, the location of the data points represent positions of the storm genesis or location of typhoon minimum pressure. The spatial relationship between the data points is described by $K$ nearest neighbours, where $K$ is a positive integer and the distances between neighbours are defined by a straight-line distance. $K$ nearest neighbours is therefore an area-variant descriptor that defines the neighbourhood of a storm genesis (or minimum pressure) point by an area bounded by $K$ closest points. The technique ensures that every data point is evaluated against a chosen number of neighbouring points, and is effective for evaluating data points that are distributed unevenly across the study area. For our analysis we use $K = 30$ nearest neighbours, following the suggestion of Getis & Ord (1996). The hot and cold spots in terms of selected storm parameter (track sinuosity, intensity or duration) amongst the population of data points are thus identified.

Following on, clusters of hot or cold spots can then be highlighted using standard deviational ellipses, with size capped at one standard deviation (1 SD); that is, an ellipse encloses approximately 68% of the hot or cold spots in a group, thus delimiting a 'hot-spot cluster' or 'cold-spot cluster'. The ellipses can then be used to visualize and measure (albeit in a rather qualitative way) the distribution

of a set of hot or cold spots, and show whether these clusters possess particular orientations or exhibit a certain spatial structure. In our case, the ellipses form 1 SD boundaries of hot- and cold-spot clusters of the following three attributes: (1) storm-track sinuosity (all 1555 tropical storms, plotted at genesis points); (2) typhoon maximum intensity (for a subset of 798 storms that strengthened to typhoon intensity below or equal to 970 hPa, plotted at the positions of minimum recorded pressure); and (3) the duration at typhoon intensity (798 storms, plotted following (2) above).

## Analysis and discussion

### Clustering of track sinuosity

From the analysis of storm-track sinuosity values, plotted at tropical storm genesis locations, multiple clusters of sinuosity hot and cold spots can be identified (Fig. 3). Three hot-spot clusters are seen, with the 1 SD ellipses enclosing areas where the majority of tropical storms generated subsequently followed more sinuous tracks than storms spawned elsewhere in the WNP region. The mean track sinuosities within the hot-spot clusters are similar: 1.46, 1.59 and 1.50 (left, middle-upper and lower-right red ellipses, respectively). This illustrates how tropical storms maturing in these clusters travel, on average, 46–59% further than

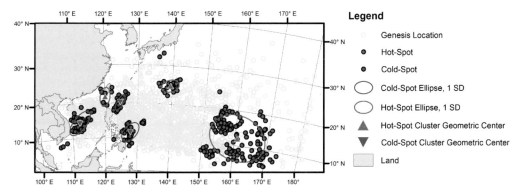

**Fig. 3.** Spatial clustering of tropical storm-track sinuosity values plotted at storm genesis points. Hot- and cold-spot ellipses define clusters of genesis locations for storms that subsequently followed relatively sinuous or straight tracks, respectively. Cluster mean values are given in the text.

straight-line distances between their start and finish points. Of these three clusters, one is clearly seen to be the dominant cluster in terms of area covered and number of hot spots contained (128 hot spots), while the others are subordinate (11 hot spots for the left ellipse and 22 hot spots for the middle-upper ellipse). The primary hot-spot cluster is located far from the Asian continental mainland, centred at 12.0°N, 160.8°E in the SE part of the WNP study area, covering a much larger area than the sum of the other two hot-spot clusters found further to the west and at higher latitudes. It has a spatial structure that extends roughly in a NW–SE direction, extending over Micronesia and the Marshall Islands. In contrast, the two subordinate hot-spot clusters are much smaller in size and exhibit different spatial structures. The smallest cluster is centred at 21.7°N, 120.2°E in the Luzon Strait south of Taiwan, and has a north–south alignment; while the other, located at 24.9°N, 139.5°E towards the centre of the study area in the open Pacific, is orientated approximately east–west.

The spatial analysis also identifies three cold-spot clusters positioned relatively close to one another on the western side of the WNP study area. These cold-spot clusters are centred, from left, middle-upper to lower-right, at: 14.5°N, 112.4°E; 20.2°N, 124.8°E; and 11.7°N, 127.9°E. The 1 SD cold-spot ellipses define clusters of tropical storm genesis points where, subsequent to formation, the storms followed straight tracks. The mean track sinuosity values of the three cold-spot clusters are 1.09, 1.12 and 1.09 (left, middle-upper and lower-right blue ellipses in Fig. 3), illustrating that storms generated here deviated little (travelling only 9–12% further) from the direct line between start and decay points. All cold-spot ellipses share four common features. First, they exhibit SW–NE structural

alignment. Second, they are small clusters of comparable size (similar also in size to the two subordinate hot-spot clusters found in the same part of the study area). Third, they are confined west of 130°E, occupying the South China Sea, Philippine Sea and western North Pacific Ocean. Fourth, they are located in relative proximity to land areas (Vietnam, Taiwan and the Philippines).

Climatological interpretation of the above findings is beyond the scope of this study, and so our work does not attempt to shed light on the physical mechanisms responsible for controlling tropical storm movement, and thus track morphometry, across the WNP. Nonetheless, investigations on this theme have been the focus of valuable research carried out by other researchers (e.g. Chan & Gray 1982; Lander 1996; Ho *et al.* 2004; Wu & Wang 2004, Camargo *et al.* 2007*a*, *b*). Yet, what the present study does provide, however, is evidence that tropical storms maturing in specific and identifiable parts of the WNP will either: continue in their preferred direction (straight tracks) and, therefore, should mostly be fairly predictable in terms of movement; or, alternatively, need closer monitoring (sinuous tracks) because they are likely to deviate, recurve or follow more complex paths over their lifespan.

*Clustering of maximum intensity*

The value of 970 hPa for minimum sea-level pressure was selected as the threshold to separate the subset of tropical storms from the complete record that strengthened into very intense systems (typhoons). The rationale for filtering out weaker tropical storms (>970 hPa) before spatial analysis is that it is within the context of identifying patterns in vulnerability to typhoon intensity-related impacts (violent winds, wave and surge damage) that this study is carried out, rather than meteorological conditions not so closely linked to strength (such as heavy rainfall). Thus, the filtered subset comprises the severe storms experienced within the WNP region. It was not possible to use measurements of maximum wind speed directly because the RSMC-Tokyo best-track data files contain information on winds only from 1977 onwards, whereas minimum pressure data are available for the entire dataset commencing in 1951. Of the 1555 tropical storms recorded from 1951 to 2009, 798 storms fall into our designated typhoon category.

Typhoon positions are plotted at the points where the minimum pressure was reached (Fig. 4). Because only typhoon-intensity systems are plotted and 'weaker' tropical storms already excluded, it was not meaningful to identify cold-spot clusters within this subset. Spatial analysis does, however, identify a single very large cluster of 256 hot spots, centred at 16.6°N, 135.5°E in the Philippine Sea. This cluster, therefore, represents the area where the most powerful typhoons achieved their maximum strength. The cluster has a structure that shows elongation in a roughly east–west direction, thus covering a large part of the Philippine Sea, but also extending westwards into the open Pacific Ocean. The mean minimum-pressure value for typhoons forming this cluster is 926 hPa. Such intense low pressure is capable of generating phenomenal sustained winds of 100 knots (185 km h$^{-1}$). It is also observed that near the western and eastern boundaries of the 1 SD ellipse, many typhoons reach their maximum intensity close to the Philippines or the Northern Mariana Islands.

## Clustering of typhoon duration

For the subset of 798 typhoons, their duration while at typhoon intensity can also be examined; that

is, the period of time while minimum pressure remained below or equal to 970 hPa. Similar to track sinuosity and minimum pressure described earlier, typhoon duration also needs to be plotted at single-point locations for cluster analysis to be performed on the data. This presents some challenges, but we chose to plot this parameter at the location of minimum pressure (Fig. 5). This choice is not ideal because, in reality, most typhoons, especially ones of longer duration, are not stationary throughout this time. Also, typhoon duration below 970 hPa may not necessarily be symmetrically distributed on either side of the position of maximum intensity. Nevertheless, plotting duration at minimum-pressure location is preferable to the main alternative of genesis location. This option is unsuitable because genesis location marks an earlier phase of storm lifespan that lies outside of our designated typhoon intensity. Furthermore, plotting typhoon duration at minimum-pressure location does permit direct comparison between spatial clustering patterns in typhoon maximum strength and longevity.

Figure 5 shows a single, very large cluster of 232 hot spots at 17.8°N, 141.0°E – centred near the middle of the WNP study area. This expansive cluster illustrates the region where typhoons generally survived longer than elsewhere, with a mean longevity at typhoon intensity of 130.4 h (5.4 days). The hot-spot cluster is elongated west–east, stretching from the eastern Philippine Sea out into the open Pacific Ocean. Similarly, a single cluster of 176 cold spots is identified, representing the zone where the duration at typhoon intensity is comparably short, averaging 44.1 h (1.8 days). The cold-spot cluster is centred at 18.1°N, 118.9°E but extends over both the South China Sea near Hainan Island and Vietnamese waters, and also over the western part of the Philippine Sea,

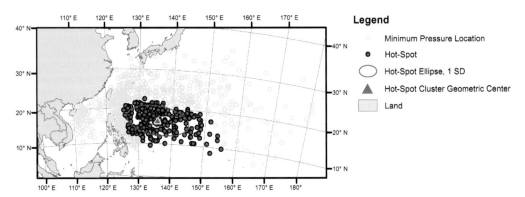

**Fig. 4.** Spatial clustering of the minimum pressure locations for 798 typhoons; that is, the subset of tropical storms that intensified to 970 hPa or below. The hot-spot ellipse therefore bounds the cluster of extremely intense typhoons (mean 925.6 hPa).

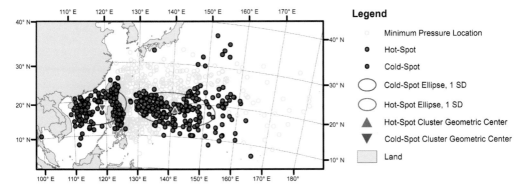

**Fig. 5.** Spatial clustering of the duration of typhoons (i.e. duration while below or equal to the 970 hPa threshold) plotted where minimum pressure was reached. Thus, hot- and cold-spot ellipses mark clusters of typhoons of longer or shorter duration, respectively. Cluster mean values are given in the text.

including the chain of islands that stretch from Taiwan to the central Philippines Archipelago.

Finally, by comparing Figures 4 and 5, some interesting overlap in clustering patterns of typhoon characteristics is observed. In the Philippine Sea and the adjacent part of the Pacific Ocean to the east, the hot-spot cluster of minimum-pressure locations (i.e. strongest typhoons) matches closely with the hot-spot cluster of typhoon duration (i.e. longest lifespans). The overlapping clusters emphasize unambiguously how this region of the WNP basin has a tendency to spawn both the most destructive typhoons and also those typhoons likely to survive many days at high intensity. Furthermore, the near coincidence of hot-spot clusters illustrates how the island states of the Philippines and the Northern Marianas are most vulnerable to these extreme typhoon systems.

## Conclusions

In order to visualize and gain greater comprehension of several spatial characteristics of tropical storms in the western North Pacific, this paper uses the local Getis–Ord $G_i^*(d)$ statistic within GIS to analyse best-track data of 1555 tropical storms that occurred between 1951 and 2009. The analysis provides evidence for the existence of spatial clusters in track sinuosity, maximum intensity and duration. More importantly, analysis locates hot- and cold-spot clusters for each parameter, some of which extend to the vicinity of highly populated coastlines. In this regard, the paper fills one gap in the existing literature in which tropical storm migratory characteristics are less explored, and should, therefore, contribute to hazard assessment as potentially vulnerable areas are identified in a new way.

Regarding track sinuosity, results show that sinuously moving tropical storms are mostly generated

far from continental margins of the North Pacific Ocean. The primary hot-spot cluster covers a large area in the SE WNP basin, so tropical storms developing there need careful monitoring over their lifespan because they tend to follow less predictable travel paths. In contrast, genesis loci for straighter-tracking storms form three small clusters, close to mainland SE Asia, where storm tracking is more certain after maturation.

For 798 storms attaining typhoon intensity ($\leq$970 hPa), a hot-spot cluster is identified for locations where the minimum pressure (i.e. maximum strength) is reached that is sited around the Philippine Sea and the adjacent part of the western North Pacific. This cluster of very intense systems (mean minimum pressure of 926 hPa) is found to overlap extensively with the hot-spot cluster for the duration of typhoon intensity (mean 5.4 days), thus indicating a strong similarity between the hot-spot distributions of these two parameters. This suggests that the islands of the Philippines and Northern Marianas are vulnerable to strike both by the longer-duration and the most violent typhoons. Conversely, the cold-spot cluster centred in the South China Sea illustrates how this part of the WNP basin sustains typhoon intensity for a shorter period (mean 1.8 days).

Understanding migratory behaviour is important for isolating (potentially) predictable features of tropical storms; and, hence, for risk assessment and planning in countries lying along their preferred paths. This paper thus sheds light on clustering patterns of track sinuosity, typhoon minimum pressure and duration. Yet, cluster analyses on further aspects of storm migratory behaviour are still needed. The analysis of migration velocity, for example, could assist disaster managers to approximate timings before typhoons spawned in different parts of the WNP region strike their coastlines. When combined with examination of actual typhoon travel paths, this may offer insights into the most vulnerable areas – even while nascent typhoons are still developing – that cannot be obtained by measuring track sinuosity alone. Similarly, examining cluster patterns in typhoon sizes may yield more precise spatial relationships between total areas affected and original cyclogenesis locations. The present work, illustrating the potential for typhoon parameter cluster analysis, is a first step in this process.

# References

CAMARGO, S. J., ROBERTSON, A. W., GAFFNEY, S. J., SMYTH, P. & GHIL, M. 2007a. Cluster analysis of typhoon tracks. Part I: general properties. *Journal of Climate*, **20**, 3635–3653.

CAMARGO, S. J., ROBERTSON, A. W., GAFFNEY, S. J., SMYTH, P. & GHIL, M. 2007b. Cluster analysis of typhoon tracks. *Part II: large-scale circulation and ENSO. Journal of Climate*, **20**, 3654–3676.

CHAN, J. C. & LIU, K. S. 2004. Global warming and western North Pacific typhoon activity from an observational perspective. *Journal of Climate*, **17**, 4590–4602.

CHAN, J. C. L. & GRAY, W. M. 1982. Tropical cyclone movement and surrounding flow relationships. *Monthly Weather Review*, **110**, 1354–1374.

ELSNER, J. B. & LIU, K.-B. 2003. Examining the ENSO-Typhoon Hypothesis. *Climate Research*, **25**, 43–54.

EMANUEL, K. 2004. Response of tropical cyclone activity to climate change: theoretical basis. *In*: MURNANE, R. J. & LIU, K.-B. (eds) *Hurricane and Typhoons: Past, Present, and Future*. Columbia University Press, New York, 395–407.

FARMER, C. J. Q., NELSON, T. A., WULDER, M. A. & DERKSEN, C. 2009. Spatial-temporal patterns of snow cover in western Canada. *The Canadian Geographer*, **53**, 473–487.

GETIS, A. & ORD, J. K. 1996. Local spatial statistics: an overview. *In*: LONGLEY, P. & BATTY, M. (eds) *Spatial Analysis: Modeling in a GIS Environment*. Wiley, New York, 261–277.

HARR, P. A. & ELSBERRY, R. L. 1991. Tropical cyclone track characteristics as a function of large-scale circulation anomalies. *Monthly Weather Review*, **119**, 1448–1468.

HO, C. H., BAIK, J. J., JIM, J. H., GONG, D. Y. & SUI, C. H. 2004. Interdecadal changes in summertime typhoon tracks. *Journal of Climate*, **17**, 1767–1776.

LANDER, M. A. 1996. Specific tropical cyclone track types and unusual tropical cyclone motions associated with a reverse-oriented monsoon trough in the western North Pacific. *Weather and Forecasting*, **11**, 170–186.

McGREGOR, G. R. 1995. The tropical cyclone hazard over the South China Sea 1970–1989. Annual spatial and temporal characteristics. *Applied Geography*, **15**, 35–52.

ORD, J. K. & GETIS, A. 1995. Local spatial autocorrelation statistics: distribution issues and an application. *Geographical Analysis*, **27**, 286–306.

PERALTA-HERNANDEZ, A. R., BALLING, R. C., JR. & BARBA-MARTINEZ, L. R. 2009. Analysis of near-surface diurnal temperature variations and trends in southern Mexico. *International Journal of Climatology*, **29**, 205–209.

RSMC-TOKYO 2010. *RSMC Tokyo - Typhoon Center*. Regional Specialized Meteorological Center (RSMC) Tokyo. Typhoon Center, Japan Meteorological Agency, Tokyo. World Wide Web Address: http://www.jma.go.jp/jma/jma-eng/jma-center/rsmc-hp-pub-eg/RSMC_HP.htm.

TERRY, J. P. 2007. *Tropical Cyclones: Climatology and Impacts in the South Pacific*. New York, Springer.

TERRY, J. P. & FENG, C. C. 2010. On quantifying the sinuosity of typhoon tracks in the western North Pacific basin. *Applied Geography*, **30**, 678–686.

WATTERS, D. L., YOKLAVICH, M. M., LOVE, M. S. & SCHROEDER, D. M. 2010. Assessing marine debris in deep seafloor habitats off California. *Marine Pollution Bulletin*, **60**, 131–138.

WEBSTER, P. J., HOLLAND, G. L., CURRY, J. A. & CHANG, H. R. 2005. Changes in tropical cyclone number, duration, and intensity in a warming environment. *Science*, **309**, 1844–1846.

WU, L. & WANG, B. 2004. Assessing impacts of global warming on tropical cyclone tracks. *Journal of Climatology*, **17**, 1686–1698.

ZHANG, C., LUO, L., XU, W. & LEDWITH, V. 2008. Use of local Moran's I and GIS to identify pollution hotspots of Pb in urban soil of Galway, Ireland. *Science of the Total Environment*, **398**, 212–221.

# Geovisualization of tropical cyclone behaviour in the South Pacific

GENNADY A. GIENKO[1]* & JAMES P. TERRY[2]

[1]*Department of Geomatics, School of Engineering, University of Alaska Anchorage, 3211 Providence Drive, Anchorage, AK 99508-4514, USA*

[2]*Department of Geography, National University of Singapore, AS2, 1 Arts Link, Kent Ridge, Singapore 117570*

*\*Corresponding author (e-mail: afgg@uaa.alaska.edu)*

**Abstract:** A combination of computational power, dynamic graphics and geographical information system (GIS) packages creates a powerful platform for advanced visualization tools to explore complex geographical phenomena in an interactive computer environment – known as geovisualization. Geovisualization is a relatively new computer-based approach that refers to a set of methods and techniques to support geospatial data analysis through the use of four-dimensional (4D), multi-variable and interactive visualization. In this paper, we illustrate and discuss the value of several spatialization techniques that are used to perform analysis of spatial structures of climatic and meteorological elements, especially through the geovisualization of characteristics and behaviour of tropical cyclones in the South Pacific Ocean. Preliminary findings are encouraging, allowing patterns and dependencies between chosen cyclone features to be identified, in turn indicating the enormous potential of geovisualization for analysing multi-variate spatial attributes within large tropical cyclone datasets.

Geographical information systems (GIS), originally developed for natural resource inventory and mapping, are now widely used in many scientific disciplines. Land information systems, environmental science, socio-economic studies and many other disciplines now use GIS to analyse and graphically represent geographically referenced processes and phenomena. One of these applications is climatological and meteorological studies, where visualization of spatial objects is important to understanding the underlying process and relations. Modern GIS packages provide powerful tools for advanced geovisualization as one of the steps in exploratory spatial data analysis. Geovisualization refers to a set of tools and techniques supporting geospatial data analysis through the use of four-dimensional (4D), multi-variable and interactive visualization.

Geographical information systems give possibilities to combine different georeferenced variables and parameters in such a way that it should also be possible to give consistently derived estimates of meteorological and climatological variables at any location at any time (Tveito 2007). Many climatological tasks are based on providing information about weather and climate by using observed values at fixed meteorological stations that are then adjusted for representativity, terrain and other effects affecting the local climatology. In many cases, GIS is primarily used as a tool to establish continuous maps of climate reference values of several elements. Many GIS packages offer built-in tools for spatial interpolation, which, being originally developed for stationary objects, are now used more and more for analysis of climatological data, such as tropical cyclones in particular.

The impacts of tropical cyclones on the environments of different types of islands across the tropical South Pacific (TSP) region are not so well understood compared to hurricanes and typhoons in other regions (e.g. the Caribbean Sea and North West Pacific) (Terry 2007). There are many factors associated with the characteristics and behaviour of cyclones, such as their relatively frequent occurrence and the weather effects they bring (intense and prolonged rainfall, storm surge, violent winds driving large erosive waves). Scientists have invested considerable effort to uncover and understand the variability of cyclone characteristics associated with El Niño events, ocean warming and climate change. One important feature is cyclogenesis position and the subsequent spatio-temporal behaviour of cyclones in tropical areas of the South Pacific. Such information is hidden in thousands of records of cyclone tracks, containing various data from satellite measurements for more than 340 cyclones since 1970 until present times.

Analysis of a large dataset (1970–2008) on tropical cyclone characteristics in the TSP region, recently provided by the Regional Specialized

*From*: TERRY, J. P. & GOFF, J. (eds) 2012. *Natural Hazards in the Asia–Pacific Region: Recent Advances and Emerging Concepts*. Geological Society, London, Special Publications, **361**, 195–208, http://dx.doi.org/10.1144/SP361.16

Meteorological Service (RSMC) at Nadi in Fiji, requires careful and thorough (time-consuming) checking for errors and accuracy before analysis can begin. This can be done using a combination of manual checks, mathematical tools and GIS. Once corrections have been made, investigation can commence on long-term historical trends in: tropical cyclogenesis positions (i.e. locations of origins); track length; storm duration; maximum intensity produced; and cyclone decay position. This work is amongst the first of its kind on the RSMC data for the TSP region, and thus provides insight into geographical patterns and changing temporal variability, possibly climate-change driven, in tropical cyclone behaviour for this region. Such research is already continuing in other cyclone-prone oceans of the world (e.g. the North Atlantic and North Pacific), but has lagged behind in the South Pacific owing the previous non-availability of (authenticated) data from the RSMC-Nadi. At this stage our research is focused on developing an advanced geovisualization methodology for exploratory analysis of spatio-temporal patterns of cyclones, which can also be used to carry out more demanding mathematical studies of storm movement.

In this paper, we discuss the value of several spatial interpolation and extrapolation techniques (spatialization) that may be used to perform the analysis of spatial structures of climatic and meteorological elements, for the overall purpose of geovisualization of tropical cyclone characteristics and behaviour using GIS.

## Mapping tropical cyclones

From mapping and visualization points of view, tropical cyclones (TCs) can be viewed as specific events occurring in particular places, but changing their spatial location and characteristics with time. Cyclones move at variable speeds, forming tracks with certain patterns and directions. Location and other parameters of cyclones are recorded at specific time intervals; thus, a tropical cyclone can be viewed as a single feature represented as sequence of co-ordinates (latitude and longitude) with recorded wind speed and atmospheric pressure. Such presentation makes it appropriate for using discrete GIS vector data models using points and polylines.

Mapping individual cyclone tracks as sequences of points connected by line segments and forming a polyline, is probably the best way to represent and study single occurrences of the phenomena. However, for the analysis of hundreds of cyclones recorded over decades, the entire dataset has to be processed using different spatial data models.

Overlaying all cyclone tracks in a single map results in a highly cluttered set of curved lines with little or almost no use for analysis. Alternatively, a point-based data structure can be used. The point data can be analysed as such (density and cluster analysis) or can be used to construct continuous surfaces. In this case, spatio-temporal visualization (geovisualization) can be considered as a valuable method for the systematic study of this hazardous climatological phenomenon. The next section describes the basis of the most commonly used techniques in spatialization. This is followed by a consideration of how these methods might be applied to the geovisualization of changing spatio-temporal characteristics of tropical cyclones, using data and individual examples of several recent storms in the South Pacific for illustration.

## Spatialization and visual analytics

Visual analytics is a general term used to describe the derivation of spatially continuous fields, using spatial interpolation (spatialization), and adding value to such products by combining and using several georeferenced information sources (Tveito 2007; Andrienko et al. 2010). The greatest challenge in spatialization of tropical cyclones is to balance the available information (both climatological data and other geographical information) with the specific needs of a particular study. The selection of the proper spatialization and visualization scheme for each individual purpose needs thoroughly worked out specifications concerning the requested spatial and temporal scales, as well as the desired accuracy.

Spatialization of data for tropical cyclones involves several steps: (a) rectification of linear features to a single point according to particular characteristic of a cyclone; (b) preliminary statistical data analysis (test for statistical distribution) and data normalization (if needed); (c) identification of a mathematical method of spatial interpolation, appropriate to a particular phenomenon, and constructing a spatial grid; and (d) validation of the interpolation.

### Rectification of a tropical cyclone track to a point

The source tropical cyclone records, available from Tropical Cyclone Regional Specialized Meteorological Centres (RSMCs), contain three major groups of quantitative information: date, location and wind speed (calculated as a function of atmospheric pressure). These source data can be used for spatialization alone or to derive a variety of secondary parameters, such as cyclone duration, length, sinuosity and velocity (moving speed of the cyclone eye). Whether the source or derivative data are used, the question is what particular location in geographical space should be used as a point to assign particular characteristics of a cyclone? Some points from the source data can be naturally used as such (e.g. genesis and decay of a cyclone are defined by magnitude of wind speed at 35 knots), but which point to use to assign, for example, sinuosity or duration of a cyclone? There might be several alternatives: use start or end (genesis or decay) points of a cyclone track; use one of the existing points from along a track (e.g. with the maximum wind speed); calculate the mean point on a track (e.g. half length or half duration); or calculate a centroid (geometrically weighted location, calculated using co-ordinates of all points of the track). Cyclone tracks are rarely straight lines, and it is assumed that centroids can be positioned off the track (often quite far from the track).

The choice of which point to use should also take into account the nature of the characteristic to be assigned to the point to allow for scientifically correct further analysis (e.g. azimuth of the cyclone can be assigned to the genesis point, while accumulated cyclone energy (ACE) or hurricane destruction potential (HDP) might better be assigned to the point of peak cyclone intensity). If multi-variable analyses are assumed, it is reasonable to make the 'point convention', when all cyclone characteristics are assigned to one designated point.

## Data accuracy and completeness

Data accuracy and completeness are important factors to consider while carrying out spatial analysis of cyclone data. Cyclone track records, provided by RSMCs, contain three groups of data: temporal, locational and atmospheric. Location and atmospheric pressure are recorded at fixed time intervals – 12 h for historical records and 6 h for more recent data. While the accuracy of time records is not questionable, the other parameters have a certain level of uncertainty that needs to be taken into account. Ambiguity in recording cyclone location and atmospheric pressure results in ambiguity of derived parameters. For example, the location of a cyclone is defined in geographical co-ordinates, where latitude and longitude values are shown in track records with one digit after the decimal point. This corresponds to approximately 11 km on the Earth's surface in equatorial areas. At the same time, identification of cyclone eye location can be inaccurate to 50 km (c. 0.45°) (Prasad 2008 pers. comm. RSMC-Nadi). Locational errors, ranging from ±10 to ±50 km, can significantly skew results of cyclone analysis, especially for those with short lengths (e.g. six cyclone tracks within the RSMC-Nadi database

have lengths of 120–180 km, four tracks are 220–280 km in length, and 10 tracks are between 320 and 500 km). Satellite systems, image analysis software and techniques for the identification of the cyclone eye location have changed over the last few decades, and reliability of the source data has improved.

Atmospheric data in cyclone track records comprise minimum barometric pressure at sea level and maximum sustained wind speed. These two parameters are indirectly derived using various methods, and the Dvorak technique is the one commonly used in practice. This satellite technique employs image-pattern recognition and empirically based rules to derive an estimate of tropical cyclone intensity in 'T-numbers', as a description of a cyclone in terms of cloud characteristics visible in satellite imagery. T-numbers are then used to compute the current intensity (CI number) using a few rules for redeveloping or weakening storms. The CI number is considered the best estimate of the current maximum winds and minimum sea-level pressure of the tropical cyclone; relationships between CI numbers, wind speed and atmospheric pressure are shown in Dvorak look-up tables (Dvorak 1975, 1984).

In this method, thermal infrared (IR) imagery is routinely employed in a subjective way to isolate discrete temperature levels and derive T-numbers from a combination of the temperature at the storm centre (usually a relatively warm eye) and the temperature of the cold convective cloud environment. In certain situations, image enhancement is used with the IR data to isolate discrete temperature levels. While this 'EIR' (Enhanced IR) variation of the standard technique yields reasonable estimates of intensity in most cases, analyst judgement on pattern or rule interpretation can occasionally lead to discrepancies between different tropical analysis centres estimating the same storm (Velden et al. 1998). The Tropical Cyclone Forecasters Reference Guide (2010) states that mean absolute errors inherent in intensities obtained through the Dvorak technique are large (approximately 15 hPa, where 1 hPa = 100 Pa), but these fixes are frequently treated as ground truth in many cyclone intensity forecast verification studies because these are the only data available (Tropical Cyclone Forecasters Reference Guide 2010). At the same time, atmospheric pressure in the Dvorak table ranges non-linearly from 1009 to 890 hPa, with incremental steps from 4 to 16 hPa for CI = 2.0 to CI = 8.0, respectively (Table 1 shows the look-up table for Dvorak current intensity (CI) v. maximum sustained wind speed (MWS) and minimum sea-level pressure (MSLP). Compare dMSLP with the mean absolute error of 15 hPa, where dMSLP is calculated as the

**Table 1.** *Dvorak current intensity (CI)*

| CI | MWS(knots) | MSLP (hPa) | dMSLP (hPa) |
|-----|-----|-----|-----|
| 1.0 | 25 | – | – |
| 1.5 | 25 | – | – |
| 2.0 | 30 | 1009 | 4 |
| 2.5 | 35 | 1005 | 5 |
| 3.0 | 45 | 1000 | 6 |
| 3.5 | 55 | 994 | 7 |
| 4.0 | 65 | 987 | 8 |
| 4.5 | 77 | 979 | 9 |
| 5.0 | 90 | 970 | 10 |
| 5.5 | 102 | 960 | 12 |
| 6.0 | 115 | 948 | 13 |
| 6.5 | 127 | 935 | 14 |
| 7.0 | 140 | 921 | 15 |
| 7.5 | 155 | 906 | 16 |
| 8.0 | 170 | 890 | |

difference between neighbouring MSLP values.) This introduces a certain level of ambiguity in identification of wind speed, and thus in genesis and decay points of cyclones (see a detailed discussion on evaluation of the Dvorak technique in Knaff *et al.* 2010).

## Exploratory spatial data analysis and geostatistics

Once the source data have been analysed and the 'point convention' has been made, the observed data need to be checked for dependency, stationarity and distribution. Spatial dependence is 'the propensity for nearby locations to influence each other and to possess similar attributes' (Goodchild 1992, p. 33). Atmospheric pressure, for instance, is more likely to be similar at points 5 km apart than at points 500 km apart. A statistical measure of the similarity of attributes of point locations is called *spatial autocorrelation*. In geostatistics, spatial variation is described in terms of a function (known as a correlogram) that shows how spatial autocorrelation decreases with increasing distance, finally reaching zero, or independence, at a certain distance (de Smith *et al.* 2009).

Spatial stationarity means that the statistical properties of data do not depend on exact locations of sample points. Therefore, the mean (expected value) of a variable at one location is equal to the mean at any other location, data variance is constant in the study area, and the correlation (covariance or semivariogram) between values in any two locations depends only on the vector distance that separates them, not on their exact locations (e.g. do not exhibit spatial autocorrelation). In other words, in spatial stationarity, residuals are identically distributed at all locations and the second order association between pairs of sites is assumed to depend only on the spatial distance between these sites (Perrin & Meiring 1999; Smith 2010).

Geostatistical methods are optimal when data are normally distributed and stationary. If the source data do not fit the normal distribution, then the data have to be normalized in order to obtain the assumption of spatial stationarity. To find the best way to normalize the data is the most challenging task. There are multiple options for dealing with non-normal data. First, the non-normality can be due to a valid reason (real observed data points). Invalid reasons for non-normality include mistakes in data entry and missing data values not declared missing. There are a great variety of possible source-data transformations for normalization, from adding constants to multiplying, squaring or raising to a power, converting to logarithmic scales, inverting and reflecting, taking the square root of the values, and even applying trigonometric transformations such as sine-wave transformations (Osborne 2002).

## Spatial interpolation

Spatial interpolation is used widely in the environmental sciences to estimate a spatial random field at unmonitored locations or to interpolate data onto a regular grid of points for use in subsequent analyses. Some geostatistical methods are based on simplifying assumptions such as spatial stationarity (Perrin 1999; Smith 2010). There is a wide choice of spatial interpolation methods to interpolate (or predict) spatially distributed data; among them are inverse distance, kriging, and various polynomial and spline techniques (Lam 1983; Li & Heap 2008).

The inverse distance method uses a 'simple' distance-weighted averaging method to calculate grid node values. Inverse distance-weighted methods are based on the assumption that the interpolating surface should be influenced most by the nearby points and less by the more distant points. The interpolating surface is a weighted average of the scatter points, and the weight assigned to each scatter point diminishes as the distance from the interpolation point to the scatter point increases.

Kriging is a group of geostatistical techniques to interpolate the value of a random field (e.g. the elevation, $z$, of the landscape as a function of the geographical location) at an unobserved location from observations of its value at nearby locations. Kriging is a set of linear regression routines that minimize estimation variance from a predefined covariance model. Kriging is based on the assumption that the parameter being interpolated can be treated as a regionalized variable. A regionalized

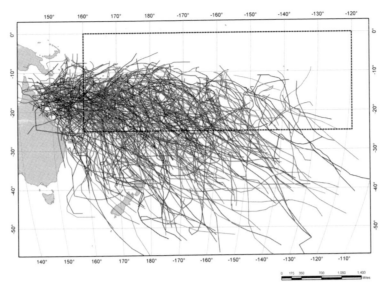

**Fig. 1.** Tracks of tropical cyclones from the RMSC-Nadi database between the 1969–1970 and 2007–2008 cyclone seasons. The tropical South Pacific (TSP) study area is shown as the dashed box.

variable is intermediate between a truly random variable and a completely deterministic variable in that it varies in a continuous manner from one location to the next and therefore points that are near each other have a certain degree of spatial correlation. However, points that are widely separated are statistically independent (the data being estimated are stationary) (Davis 2002). Over the past several decades kriging has become a fundamental tool in the field of geostatistics.

The local polynomial gridding method is most applicable to datasets that are locally smooth (i.e. relatively smooth surfaces within the search neighbourhoods) (Bresnahan & Dickenson 2008). Local polynomial interpolation can be seen as a combination of (global) polynomial methods and the moving average procedure. As with global polynomials, a least-square polynomial fit to the data is applied, with options for Order 1, 2 or 3 equations. However, instead of fitting the polynomial to the entire dataset, it is fitted to a local subset defined

by a window, as in the moving average model. The size of this window needs to be large enough for a reasonable number of data points to be included in the process (de Smith *et al.* 2009).

A spline is a special function defined piecewise by polynomials. In interpolating problems, spline interpolation is often preferred to polynomial interpolation because it yields similar results, even when using low-degree polynomials. Spline uses an interpolation method that estimates values using a mathematical function which minimizes overall surface curvature, resulting in a smooth surface that passes exactly through the input points (Franke 1982).

## Validation of interpolation

It is a common strategy to carry out an independent validation procedure when comparing the estimates with the observed values can assess the precision of spatialization. There are a few common similarity

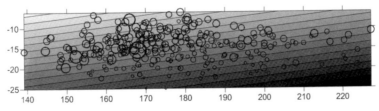

**Fig. 2.** Spatialization of tropical cyclone duration, plotted at the point of cyclogenesis. The circle diameter is proportional to duration. The overall trend in cyclone duration (shown as background shading) is calculated using linear polynomial regression. Darker shading means shorter durations.

G. A. GIENKO & J. P. TERRY

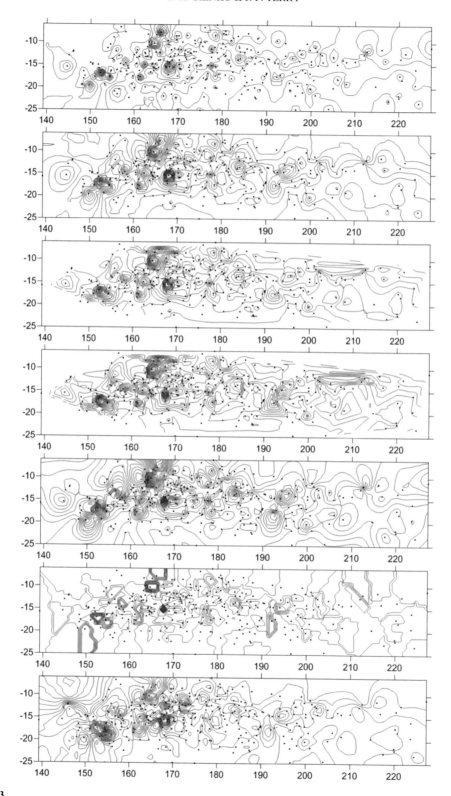

**Fig. 3.**

measures that can be used to validate estimates from almost any spatialization method, and there are basically two practical approaches for it. In the first method, the major part of the source dataset is used to construct a spatial interpolator, and the rest is used to estimate the accuracy of interpolation. This is probably the most accurate method, and can be applied when the original data sample is large and regularly sampled, and fulfils the criterion of stationarity.

The other approach is cross-validation, which considers all the data in the validation process. In a cross-validation procedure, one data point is left out of the data sample at a time. An estimated value for this point is derived by using all the other data points. This procedure is repeated until a value is estimated for all of the original data points. One possible drawback of using cross-validation is that the whole data sample is often used to define the interpolation model and, therefore, the validation might not be considered to be totally independent. However, this consideration is negligible when the dataset used is fairly large, and, therefore, cross-validation can be considered as an objective method of assessing the quality of interpolation. It is also used to compare the relative quality of two or more candidate methods. Results of cross-validation can also be used to assess the spatial variation in interpolation quality and to guide data sampling.

## Geovizualization of tropical cyclone attributes

Spatial data have a complex structure involving space, time and a number of thematic attributes, which poses significant challenges to geovisualization. The geovisualization of spatial data requires the use of maps or three-dimensional (3D) displays where at least two display dimensions are utilized to represent the physical space, which is different from information visualization dealing with abstract data spaces. This restricts the possibilities for the representation of the temporal and thematic components of the data. In modern geovisualization software, such data are represented using both traditional cartographic techniques based on the use of colours, textures, symbols and diagrams; and using computer-enabled techniques such as map animation and interactive 3D views. Moreover, maps are used in combination with

non-geographical visualization techniques such as scatterplots or parallel co-ordinates. The use of multiple interactively linked views providing different perspectives into the data has become a kind of standard in geovisualization. However, a number of problems have yet to be solved, such as the scalability of geovisualization tools and their usability.

Geovisualization is a set of innovative methods and tools for visualizing geospatial data, processes, analyses and models for synthesizing and understanding geospatial phenomena. Geovisualization is one of the main tools of advanced exploratory visual analysis, widely used by geographers and environmental scientists to outline strategy and tactics for further processing using numerical statistical and data-mining methods. The main objective of this section is to investigate methods and tools of geovisualization for exploratory visual analysis of spatio-temporal patterns of tropical cyclones, to uncover general tendencies and trends in selected storm features.

While tropical cyclones in the South Pacific region are observed during a certain period of year (the normal cyclone season spans from November through to May), their occurrences in space and time are mostly random. Thus, the cyclone dataset can be generally characterized as set of records of single events (rarely concurrent within the same region at the same time), irregularly distributed in 2D space (the spatial component) with certain cyclic patterns in time (the temporal component). Cyclones rarely occur at exactly the same location or move along exactly the same path, thus there is no repeatability of observations at the exact same location over time. Another issue is the spatial density of measurements. All of these issues result in uncertainty of the data both in space and time, which will have consequences for the homogeneity of gridded (interpolated) time series. One of the consequences of such biased input data is a high risk of performing extrapolation instead of interpolation. Thus, the representativity of the dataset is probably the most serious problem within the spatialization of tropical cyclones.

### Comparison of interpolation methods

Modern GIS and surface modelling packages provide a wide range of interpolation methods. Several interpolation functions were tested to spatialize various source and derivative tropical

---

**Fig. 3.** Spatialization of tropical cyclone duration. From top to bottom: inverse distance weighted, kriging, natural neighbour, triangulation with linear interpolation, minimum curvature, nearest neighbour and radial basis function. Points show the origins of tropical cyclones; south latitudes are negative. Note that all methods apart from the natural neighbour and triangulation with linear interpolation extend (extrapolate) the value surface well beyond bounding points from the source dataset.

**Table 2.** *Univariate cross-validation statistics for spatial interpolation of cyclone duration*

| Gridding method | Estimated Z value | | | Residual Z value | | | RMSE |
|---|---|---|---|---|---|---|---|
| | Min. | Max. | Range | Min. | Max. | Range | |
| Inverse distance to a power | 1.11 | 11.07 | 9.96 | −33.65 | 8.32 | 41.96 | 3.49 |
| Kriging | 0.16 | 18.15 | 17.99 | −33.07 | 15.15 | 48.22 | 3.90 |
| Natural neighbour | 0.72 | 19.49 | 18.77 | −33.22 | 16.49 | 49.71 | 3.96 |
| Triangulation with linear interpolation | 0.53 | 22.83 | 22.30 | −33.04 | 19.83 | 52.87 | 4.12 |
| Minimum curvature | −11.48 | 21.48 | 32.96 | −32.33 | 12.98 | 45.30 | 4.33 |
| Nearest neighbour | 0.38 | 39.00 | 38.62 | −30.50 | 36.00 | 66.50 | 4.53 |
| Radial basis function | −5.53 | 35.79 | 41.32 | −32.33 | 32.79 | 65.12 | 5.61 |

RMSE, root mean square error. All values are shown in days.

cyclone characteristics in the tropical South Pacific (TSP) region. Cyclone data were derived from the cyclone database, provided by RSMC-Nadi, comprising more than 340 cyclone track records from 1970 up to 2008 (Fig. 1).

Figure 2 shows the spatial distribution of cyclones and their duration in days (shown at cyclogenesis origins), with the general trend as background. Figure 3 illustrates results of spatialzation of cyclone duration using the following methods: inverse distance weighted, kriging, natural neighbour, triangulation with linear interpolation, minimum curvature, nearest neighbour and radial basis function.

While visual comparison of plots is useful to comprehend the entire picture of how duration of cyclones relates to their locations and how different techniques represent the phenomenon, it is useful to have a quantitative measure of how well one or another spatialization method reconstructs the source data. Table 2 shows cross-validation statistics for all methods employed, providing estimated and residual values (including root mean square error, RMSE). According to the cyclone dataset, the duration of cyclones range from 0.25 to 39.0 days, giving a range of 38.75 days. The nearest neighbour interpolation gives the most accurate presentation of the real range of the value (see estimated Z-value). Yet, at the same time, the residuals (maximum, minimum, range and RMSE) are not in agreement with the nearest neighbour method. Kriging is the most applied method, and has the advantage of being based on a spatial structure function that is founded on stochastic theory and not on trigonometric or curve-fitting techniques.

### Cyclogenesis

There are many features associated with the nature and behaviour of cyclones that make them an important natural hazard in affected regions, such as their

relatively frequent occurrence and the weather effects they bring (intense and prolonged rainfall, storm surge, and violent winds driving large and erosive waves). As mentioned earlier, the place and time of cyclogenesis (origin) is one of the critical characteristics of tropical cyclones that is often investigated, and is therefore worthy as a focus for applying geovisualization. Several geovisualization techniques have been used to explore different aspects of cyclogenesis in the TSP region based on cyclone track analysis from the RSMC-Nadi database.

### Spatial and temporal distribution and seasonality

Tropical cyclones in the TSP region have a clear seasonal pattern – the cyclone season starts in November and lasts until May (and sometimes until June). Figure 4 illustrates the occurrences of tropical cyclones from 1970 up to 2008 during the cyclone season. To explore temporal patterns

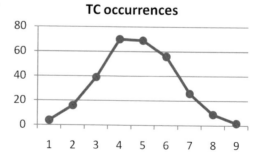

**Fig. 4.** Distribution of cyclone occurrences during the extended cyclone season (October–June, numbered from 1 to 9, respectively). The total number of analysed cyclones within the tropical South Pacific region from 1970 to 2008 is 291. Interpolation method: kriging.

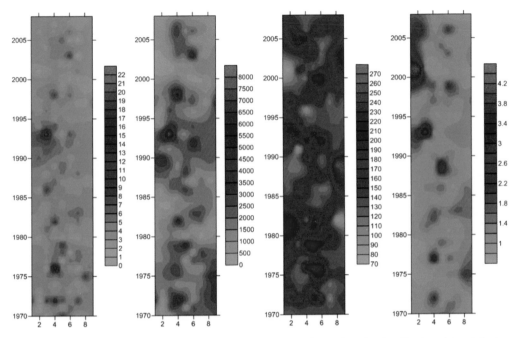

**Fig. 5.** Temporal representation of selected tropical cyclone characteristics: cyclone duration (days), track length (km), overall direction of travel or azimuth (degrees) and track sinuosity. Vertical axes are years; horizontal axes are months of the cyclone season. Interpolation method: kriging.

of cyclone characteristics over a number of years, this seasonal nature of the phenomena has been taken into account and used as a focus for geovisualization (Fig. 5). Figure 6 illustrates the spatial distribution of selected tropical cyclone characteristics.

## Spatial v. temporal presentation

The plot of the temporal distribution of cyclone wind speed at origins (Fig. 7, vertical plot, right) shows some difference in wind speed patterns between the periods 1970–1980 and 1981–2008. This is an interesting problem. As the point of cyclone origin is defined as the place where wind speed reaches 35 knots, if RSMC-Nadi officially names cyclones at this value, then the plot should have a uniform colour (light green, in our case). In reality, the plot shows clear evidence of non-uniformity of wind speed at designated origins, for which there might be several reasons. For example, some cyclones may have developed rapidly, quickly gaining intensity from 30 to 40–55 knots within a 6 h interval; that is, between one track fix and the next. Another explanation is that until the 1980s, cyclone tracks were recorded at 12 h intervals, resulting in the official designation of some cyclones with wind speeds already over 35 knots

at their origins. There may also be discrepancies in the data owing to technological limitations, methodology used, human factors or various other reasons. Visualization of temporal patterns therefore identified important inconsistencies in the source data, which, in turn, allowed for a clear differentiation of analysis of the spatial distribution in wind speed before and after 1980 (Fig. 7, plots at the bottom and in the middle).

## Volumetric geovisualization

Volumetric geovisualization is another powerful tool for exploratory spatial and temporal data analysis. Modern GIS packages provide several techniques for 3D visualization, including volumetric rendering and iso-surfaces. Figure 8 shows the result of volumetric interpolation of wind speed at cyclone origins. The attempt was made to visually explore variations of wind speed in space, with the purpose of identifying clusters at different thresholds of wind speed value. The plot represents the spatial location of the major cluster of wind speed at 65 knots, outlined as an iso-surface and a vertical cross-section, with contour lines representing the variation in wind speed along the longitude or latitude axis.

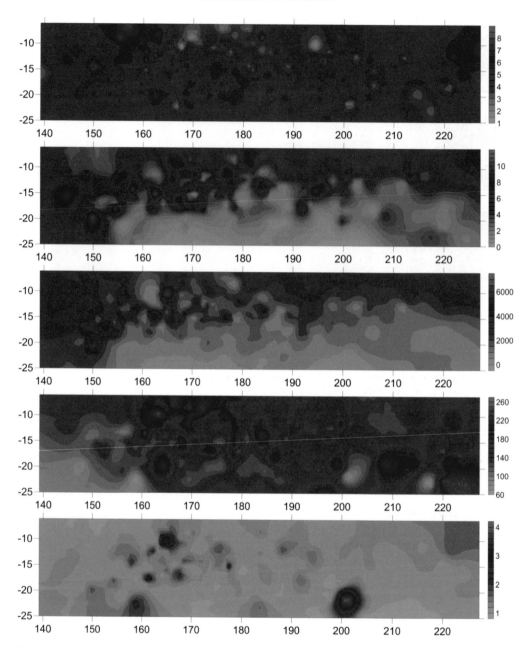

**Fig. 6.** Spatial representation of selected tropical cyclone characteristics: month of the year, duration (from 0.25 to 14 days), track length (km), overall direction of travel or azimuth (degrees) and track sinuosity (from 1.0 to 4.0). Vertical axes are latitudes; horizontal axes are longitudes. Interpolation method: kriging.

The plot in Figure 9 is an example of simultaneous 3D visualization of two cyclone characteristics: wind speed at the origin and cyclone duration. Wind speed is shown as volumetric density, calculated by 3D spatial interpolation. Cyclone duration is shown as an iso-surface.

Comparing such plots of iso-surfaces drawn from several viewpoints not only shows the spatial distribution of the chosen characteristic in geographical space (latitude and longitude) but also allows the study of dependencies between cyclone location, duration and wind speed at the origin.

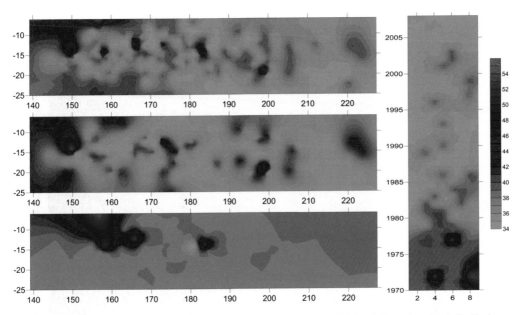

**Fig. 7.** Wind speed at the point of origin: spatial distribution from 1970 to 2008 (top left); and temporal distribution (vertical right). In the middle is spatial distribution from 1981 to 2008, and at the bottom is spatial distribution from 1970 to 1980. Interpolation method: kriging.

Owing to the obvious limitations of still pictures, it is not possible in this paper to illustrate the dynamic changes of shape and location of iso-surface in space (which would be possible by watching a film of time-sequenced images). However, the two sets of plots shown in Figure 9 nonetheless provide some idea of the tremendous functionality, power and scope of volumetric geovisualization.

### Individual track analysis

While the previous work was aimed at represen-tation of the entire set of available data to uncover general spatio-temporal patterns in cyclone activity in the TSP region, in other analysis the individual tracks were targeted for the exploration of cyclone behaviour. Figure 10 illustrates the results of itera-tive polynomial fitting of the track of Tropical Cyclone (TC) Percy, a category 4 intensity system that severely affected parts of the Cook Islands in early 2005. In this case, an attempt was made to use polynomial coefficients as one of the attributes of cyclone trajectories to be used for data mining using decision tree algorithms. Figure 11 serves as an illustration of 3D visualization of the track of TC Percy in 2005, when another attribute (wind speed) was used as the third dimension. These analyses incorporate the temporal nature of the phenomena but do not illustrate the time component explicitly.

### Conclusions

Considering the dangers associated with the occur-rence of tropical cyclones in affected ocean basins around the globe, it is incumbent on the scientific community to investigate the behaviour of these severe storms, and to assess whether future projec-tions associated with El Niño events, ocean warm-ing and climate change will influence cyclone numbers, frequencies, seasonality and other characteristics, such as duration, intensity and track shape. In spite of the enormous advances that have been made in understanding tropical cyclone processes over recent decades, a neglected step so far has been the geovisualization of cyclone spatio-temporal attributes. In response, the goals of this research were to illustrate and provide preliminary exploration of the wide range of methods and tools that may be of enormous value for the geovisualization and analysis of tropi-cal cyclone attributes, using the available dataset for the tropical South Pacific region. The main con-clusion is that, although geovisualization is cer-tainly not a trivial task in terms of either processes or interpretation of imagery produced, the first results have been encouraging. In particular, find-ings have allowed the uncovering of certain patterns and dependencies in cyclone behaviour, which helps to outline further strategy in advanced data analysis using appropriate statistical and data-mining methods.

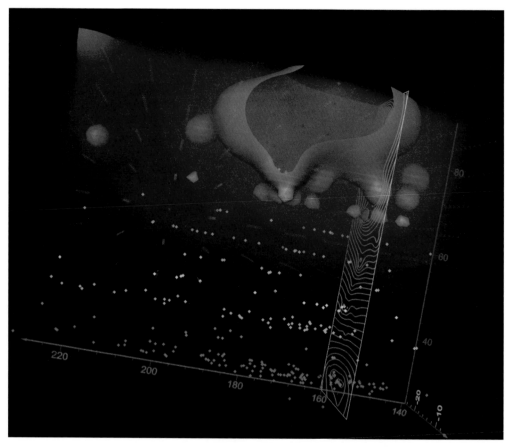

**Fig. 8.** Visualization of wind speed (volumetric density calculated using spatial 3D interpolation) with the iso-surface value set at 65 knots. The vertical cross-section contour lines represent variation of wind speed along longitude at 160°.

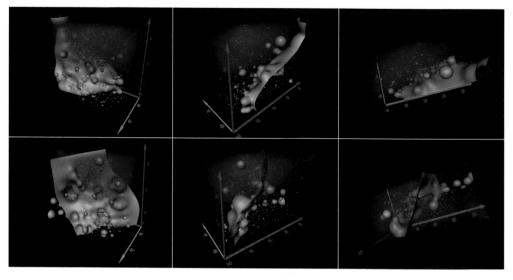

**Fig. 9.** Simultaneous 3D visualization of two characteristics of cyclones: wind speed at the origins (shown as volumetric density); and cyclone duration (iso-surface), shown from different viewpoints. The iso-value for cyclone duration is 3.8 days (top row) and 4.5 days (bottom row). These iso-values are chosen at random for illustration only.

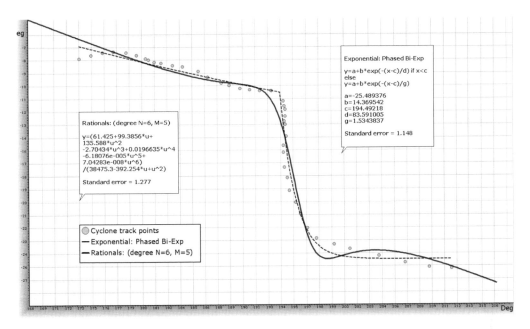

**Fig. 10.** Polynomial fitting of the track of TC Percy (2005). Fitting cyclone tracks using classical polynomial functions is not a trivial task as many cyclones follow complex meandering or looping trajectories.

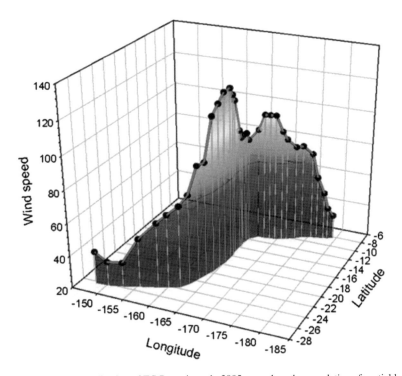

**Fig. 11.** Three-dimensional visualization of TC Percy in early 2005 to explore the correlation of spatial location and wind speed through all life phases of the storm (genesis, development, maturity and decay). Temporal behaviour can be implicitly reflected as the cyclone location is recorded at fixed time intervals of 6 h (black markers).

The authors thank the Fiji Meteorological Service for providing archived cyclone track data, and anonymous reviewers who recommended improvements on the original manuscript.

# References

ANDRIENKO, G., ANDRIENKO, N. *ET AL.* 2010. Space, time, and visual analytics. *International Journal of Geographical Information Science*, **24**, 1577–1600.

BRESNAHAN, T. & DICKENSON, K. 2008. *Surfer Training Guide*. Golden Software. World Wide Web Address: http://www.goldensoftware.com. Accessed September 2010.

DAVIS, J. C. 2002. *Statistics and Data Analysis in Geology*. 3rd edn. Wiley, New York.

DE SMITH, M. J., GOODCHILD, M. F. & LONGLEY, P. A. 2009. *A Comprehensive Guide to Principles, Techniques and Software Tools*, 3rd edn. Matador, Leicester.

DVORAK, V. F. 1975. Tropical cyclone intensity analysis and forecasting from satellite imagery. *Monthly Weather Review*, **103**, 420–430.

DVORAK, V. F. 1984. *Tropical Cyclone Intensity Analysis Using Satellite Data*. NOAA Technical Report, NESDIS 11. National Oceanic and Atmospheric Administration, Washington, DC.

FRANKE, R. 1982. Smooth interpolation of scattered data by local thin plate splines. *Computer and Mathematics with Applications*, **8**, 273–281.

GOODCHILD, M. 1992. Geographical information science. *International Journal of Geographic Information Systems*, **6**, 31–45.

KNAFF, J. A., BROWN, D. P., COURTNEY, J., GALLINA, G. M. & BEVEN, J. L., II. 2010. An evaluation of dvorak technique-based tropical cyclone intensity estimates. *Weather and Forecasting*, **25**, 1362–1379.

LAM, N. S. 1983. Spatial interpolation methods: a review. *The American Cartographer*, **10**, 129–149.

LI, J. & HEAP, A. 2008. *A Review of Spatial Interpolation Methods for Environmental Scientists*. Record 2008/23. Geoscience Australia, Canberra, 137.

OSBORNE, J. W. 2002. *Normalizing Data Transformations*. *ERIC Digest*, ED470204.

PERRIN, O. & MEIRING, W. 1999. *Identifiablility for Non-stationary Spatial Structure*. Technical report, NRCSE-TRS 020. National Research Center for Statistics and the Environment, Seattle, WA.

SMITH, T. 2010. *Notebook on Spatial Data Analysis*. Web book. World Wide Web Address: http://www.seas.upenn.edu/~ese502/#notebook. Accessed: February 2011.

TERRY, J. P. 2007. *Tropical Cyclones – Climatology and Impacts in the South Pacific*. Springer, New York.

TROPICAL CYCLONE FORECASTERS REFERENCE GUIDE 2010. *Tropical Cyclone Forecasters Reference Guide*. Naval Research Laboratory, Marine Meteorology Division, Monterey, CA. World Wide Web Address: http://www.nrlmry.navy.mil/~chu/chap6/ch6apb.htm. Accessed November 2010.

TVEITO, O. E. 2007. The developments in spatialization of meteorological and climatological Elements. *In*: DOBESCH, H., DUMOLARD, P. & DYRAS, I. (eds) *Spatial Interpolation for Climate Data: The Use of GIS in Climatology and Meteorology*. ISTE, London.

VELDEN, C. S., OLANDER, T. L. & ZEHR, R. M. 1998. Development of an objective scheme to estimate tropical cyclone intensity from digital geostationary satellite infrared imagery. *Weather and Forecasting*, **13**, 172–186.

# The value of a Pacific-wide tsunami database to risk reduction: putting theory into practice

JAMES R. GOFF[1]*, CATHERINE CHAGUÉ-GOFF[1,2] & JAMES P. TERRY[3]

[1]*Australia–Pacific Tsunami Research Centre, School of Biological, Earth and Environmental Sciences, University of New South Wales, Sydney 2052 NSW, Australia*

[2]*Australian Nuclear and Science Technology Organization, Locked Bag 2001, Kirrawee DC, NSW 2232, Australia*

[3]*Department of Geography, National University of Singapore, AS2, 1 Arts Link, Kent Ridge, Singapore 117570*

*\*Corresponding author (e-mail: j.goff@unsw.edu.au)*

**Abstract:** The recent 2011 Tōhoku Tsunami showed yet again the devastating impact that these events can have on coastal communities. Even prior to the 2004 Indian Ocean Tsunami there had been a growing awareness of the need to document a record of past tsunamis for risk reduction purposes. The bulk of such early databases were based on historical data. Only in recent years have palaeotsunami databases started to be collated. When one considers that the Pacific region accounts for 85% of known historical tsunamis worldwide, it is unsettling that we have only documented 11 palaeotsunamis throughout all Pacific Island countries (PICs). The way forward to enhance our understanding of palaeotsunamis, and to better understand the magnitude and frequency of events from local, regional and distant Pacific sources, is to gather data from each PIC. By collating data from each island it should be possible to map the spatial and temporal distribution of past events over the last several thousand years throughout the entire Pacific region. These data will provide the essential baseline information needed for achieving more effective disaster risk reduction for PICs.

There has been a growing recognition of the need for national tsunami databases to underpin risk reduction studies (Goff *et al.* 2010*b*). The message has been further reinforced by the recent 2011 Tōhoku Tsunami and the 2008 decision by the Fukushima Daiichi nuclear power plant's expert review panel on seismic resistance to ignore advice concerning evidence for historically larger tsunamis than their facility could currently withstand (Normile 2011). A number of historical tsunami databases were developed well before the 2004 Indian Ocean Tsunami (e.g. New Zealand: de Lange & Healy 1986; Indonesia: Latief *et al.* 2000; Greece: Papadopoulos 2000; Italy: Tinti *et al.* 2004;) but there have been several more developed since that event (Australia: Dominey-Howes 2007; China: Lau *et al.* 2010; New Caledonia: Sahal *et al.* 2010).

The most extensive historical tsunami database is the global collation provided on the National Oceanic and Atmospheric Administration (NOAA) Historical Tsunami Database at the National Geophysical Data Center (NGDC) (NGDC 2011). The NGDC database has been available since 2004, and is continually updated, rigorously cross-checked and validated for accuracy because of its recognized value for risk assessment. These historical databases are, however, always incomplete, although they most probably contain the majority of the larger events. For example, new data from Tasmania, Australia, have added several new events to the Australian historical record (Morris & Mazengarb 2009) and recent research has identified a January 1894 tsunami in New Caledonia (Anon 1894), adding to the recently published dataset (Sahal *et al.* 2010). These data are, however, yet to be incorporated into the global NGDC dataset.

From a total of around 7000 known historical tsunamis, about 85% have occurred in the Pacific Ocean (ITIC 2010*a*). While the database continues to grow, most of these historically documented accounts have occurred since 1800 AD. As an example, in New Zealand, the original historical database documented at least 32 tsunamis dating back to 1840 AD (de Lange & Healy 1986) but even in its most recent form it is limited to about 40 events over the past 190 years or so (Berryman 2005). However diligently the researcher collates information, historical databases will only ever extend back as far as the written record for a

*From*: TERRY, J. P. & GOFF, J. (eds) 2012. *Natural Hazards in the Asia–Pacific Region: Recent Advances and Emerging Concepts*. Geological Society, London, Special Publications, **361**, 209–220, http://dx.doi.org/10.1144/SP361.17

particular country. This is a particularly short period of time for much of the Pacific. None more so than for Pacific Island countries (PICs) (for the purposes of this paper, PICs are defined as countries or islands on the oceanic side of subduction zones associated with the Pacific Ring of Fire as opposed to circum-Pacific Island countries (CPICs) on the landward side, most notably in the Northern Hemisphere – the former therefore include the Hawaiian Islands, and the latter in particular include Japan, the Aleutian Islands and the Philippines). Few historical events in PICs extend back in time further than 1800 AD (NGDC 2011).

Geologically, this is an extraordinarily short record of events for the most tectonically active region of the world that provides little indication of the long-term magnitude and frequency of tsunamis, especially when the return period for large events can be hundreds to thousands of years. Palaeotsunami evidence, therefore, is the only way to try and capture the full return periods for large events, to characterize tsunami return periods, and provide the key underpinning data for risk reduction studies.

To extend our knowledge of past tsunamis further back in time we must rely on the prehistoric or unwritten record. Since 1987, researchers have continued to report on the sedimentary evidence of palaeotsunamis from most regions of the world, including countries in and around the Pacific Ocean (e.g. Burney *et al.* 2001; Goff *et al.* 2001; Pinegina *et al.* 2003; Cisternas *et al.* 2005; Kelsey *et al.* 2005; Nanayama *et al.* 2007). Several preliminary geological databases for palaeotsunamis have been collated, including those for the Cascadia subduction zone in the US Pacific NW (Peters *et al.* 2003), for Australia (Dominey-Howes 2007) and for New Zealand (Goff *et al.* 2010*b*). There are other forms of data, however, in the prehistoric record. Geomorphological (Goff *et al.* 2008*b*), archaeological (Aswani & Allen 2009) and traditional environmental knowledge (TEK) (Nunn *et al.* 2006; King *et al.* 2007; King & Goff 2010) data are equally useful in the search for evidence of palaeotsunamis in the Pacific Ocean.

In theory, it is simple to differentiate between a palaeotsunami and an historical one. A palaeotsunami has been defined as a 'tsunami occurring prior to the historical record or for which there are no written observations' (ITIC 2010*b*). In practice, the difference is not as clear-cut. This is particularly evident in countries surrounding the Pacific Ocean where there is a disjunct between the longevities of the national historical databases (e.g. Japan, 684 AD: NGDC 2011; Chile, 1562 AD: Berninghausen 1962). A palaeotsunami in one country can be an historical event in another (thereby called hybrid),

such as the 1700 AD Cascadia (Atwater *et al.* 2005) and 1604 AD Arica (Goff *et al.* 2010*a*) events. The advantage of such hybrid events for PICs is that the historical records from CPICs can supplement point-source geological data and improve the understanding of the tsunami risk (Goff *et al.* 2011*a*). This paper reports on the preliminary collation of PIC data into a useful dataset for use in tsunami risk reduction.

## Palaeotsunami data

The term 'palaeotsunami data' refers to geological, geomorphological, archaeological and TEK data sources. Archiving these data is problematic because they do not fit neatly within the adopted conventions for written historical tsunami information. A palaeotsunami has no measured run-up, no written eyewitness accounts and no specific calendar date (Goff 2008; Goff *et al.* 2010*b*). Unlike historically documented accounts, which are defined primarily by a specific date and then by a series of affected locations, palaeotsunamis are normally defined initially by site location and, ultimately, by an age range or approximate age. It is not until many sites have been studied that a better understanding of the affected locations for a single palaeoevent can be estimated (Goff *et al.* 2010*c*). This has implications for how a database is constructed.

Goff *et al.* (2010*b*) discussed the creation of a palaeotsunami database architecture, and we do not therefore propose to enter into a detailed explanation of the process. However, key points are summarized in Table 1. The database is listed under a series of headings with detailed descriptors to clarify the nature of the data contained within them. These adopt a standardized style similar to the NOAA Historical Tsunami Database at NGDC (NGDC 2011), but some are more specific to the nature of the palaeotsunami data. In particular, one row refers to a 'Proxy toolkit' of different criteria that have been used by various researchers to help provide evidence for palaeotsunamis. This does not however, imply that the criteria listed in Table 2 are 'diagnostic' of tsunami inundation. The list is a summary of the most common types of evidence synthesized from numerous tsunami studies (e.g. McFadgen & Goff 2007; Chagué-Goff *et al.* 2011; Goff *et al.* 2011*b*). The main focus is on the physical evidence of past tsunami inundation, but the value of TEK is also recognized as a key proxy record (King & Goff 2010). In general terms, it is assumed that the greater the number of criteria listed for a site (one line of data), the more likely it is to relate to tsunami inundation, and the higher the 'Validity' of the record. For many

**Table 1.** *Summary of palaeotsunami database architecture – headings and detailed descriptors (after Goff et al. 2010b, 2011a)*

| Heading | Detailed descriptor |
| --- | --- |
| Location | Geographical name, region, country |
| Latitude (S), longitude (E) | Site co-ordinates |
| Nature of evidence | *Primary* (P): Sedimentary/artefactual (archaeological) evidence |
| | *Secondary* (S): Geomorphic response – immediate/delayed |
| | *Cultural* (C): Oral record, anthropological interpretation |
| Site status | 1: Deposit present |
| | 2: Unknown |
| | 3: Deposit absent |
| | na: Not applicable |
| Dating technique | Technique(s) used to determine age/date of palaeotsunami – further details can be given in the Comments section (see below). Refer to the original reference for full details: |
| | • *Geochron*: one or more of; $^{14}$C, carbon-14 isotopic dating; OSL, optically stimulated luminescence dating; $^{137}$Cs, caesium-137 isotopic dating; $^{210}$Pb, lead-210 isotopic dating; Pollen, palynological biostratigraphy; Dendro, dendrochronology; SAR, sediment accumulation rates; Strat, stratigraphic correlation; Arch, archaeological information |
| | • *Currently Undated*: usually refers to TEK record |
| Inferred age/ year/range | AD or years BP, based on interpretation of relevant chronological data in cited references |
| Physical characteristics | Brief description of deposit (more details may be given in the Comments section) |
| Thickness (m – estimated) | Estimate of maximum deposit thickness (if available) |
| Elevation (m asl) | In metres above mean sea level – this is a palaeoproxy for run-up height. It is an approximation and underestimates true run-up. Based on estimated sea level at the time of inundation |
| Landward limit (m) | Estimated maximum inland distance of the deposit from the shoreline (estimated Mean High Water Spring) at the time of *inundation* – in metres. This is a palaeoproxy for inundation distance |
| Possible source(s) | Listed (i), (ii) … |
| | Location: name/location of the inferred/known tsunami source area |
| | Certainty: 1, known; 2, inferred |
| | Cause: possible nature of propagating event |
| Proxy tookit | Developed from criteria used to identify palaeotsunami deposits (after McFadgen & Goff 2007; Goff *et al.* 2010b). Refer to Table 2 for details |
| Comments | Summary of one or more of: chronological information (see 'Dating technique'), TEK record, physical characteristics, other data |
| References | One or more of: Published, Unpublished, Web page, Personal communication |
| Validity | Based on: (i) Nature of evidence; (ii) Tsunami criteria; (iii) Published/unpublished data; (iv) Context of site with regards to other sites of similar inferred age/year – an assessment of contemporaneous data |
| | 1: Excellent |
| | 2: Good |
| | 3: Moderate |
| | 4: Poor |
| | 5: Equivocal |

reasons, though, there are numerous sites with few criteria listed and caution is recommended with any interpretation based solely on a single site record. Each site needs to be viewed in the wider context of all possible contemporaneous records. Cross-correlation between local (tens of km from source), regional (hundreds of km from source) and more widespread (thousands of km from source) evidence often not only strengthens the case for palaeotsunami origin, but also provides indications of potential source areas (Goff *et al.* 2010b, c).

**Table 2.** *Toolkit of proxies used in the literature to identify palaeotsunamis and adopted for use in the Pacific database (after McFadgen & Goff 2007; Goff et al. 2010b ,2011a; Chagué-Goff et al. 2011)*

---

Proxy toolkit (numbers relate to those cited under the pertinent heading in Table 3)

---

1. Particle/grain sizes range from boulders to fine mud – palaeotsunami sediment grain sizes are source dependent
2. Sediments generally fine inland and upwards within the deposit, although coarsening-upwards subunits can be present. Deposits generally rise in altitude inland and can extend for several km inland and tens of km alongshore
3. Each wave *can* form a distinct sedimentary unit and/or there may be laminated subunits. Heavy mineral laminations often present – normally near base of unit/subunit
4. Distinct upper and lower subunits representing run-up and backwash can often be identified
5. Lower contact is unconformable or erosional – infilling of microtopography is visible in more recent deposits
6. Can contain intraclasts (rip-up clasts) of reworked (natural and anthropogenic) material
7. Often associated with loading structures at base of deposit
8. Generally associated with an increase in abundance of marine to brackish diatoms – generally a greater percentage of reworked terrestrial diatoms near the upper part of the deposit with more broken frustules near the base where higher-energy flows are experienced. Variations in diatom affinities often indicative of source areas and magnitude of event
9. Marked changes in foraminifera (and other marine microfossils) assemblages. Deeper water species are introduced and/or increase in foraminifera abundance and breakage of tests. Foraminifera size tends to vary with grain size
10. Pollen concentrations are often lower (diluted) in the deposit because of the marine origin and/or includes high percentage of coastal pollen (e.g. mangroves)
11. Increases in elemental concentrations of sodium, sulphur, chlorine, calcium, magnesium and other palaeosalinity indicators (including element ratios) occur in tsunami deposits relative to under- and overlying sediments. Indicates saltwater inundation and/or high marine shell content
12. Geochemical and microfossil evidence often extends further inland from the maximum extent of the sedimentary deposit
13. Individual shells and shell-rich units are often present (shells are often articulated and can be water-worn). Often more intact shells as opposed to shell hash. Small, fragile shells and shellfish can be found near the upper surface of more recent palaeotsunami deposits
14. Often associated with buried vascular plant material and/or buried soil and/or skeletal (human/animal) remains
15. Shell, wood and less dense debris often found 'rafted' near the top of the sequence
16. Often associated with archaeological remains (e.g. middens) and/or a TEK record. In many cases coastal occupation layers are often separated or extensively reworked at several sites along coastline
17. Known local or distant tsunamigenic sources can be postulated or identified
18. Geomorphology indicates tsunami inundation (e.g. an altered dune geomorphology, evidence of either uplift or subsidence)

---

## Theory into practice

The palaeotsunami dataset for PICs is sparse, with only 11 examples currently identified (Vanuatu: data are from two islands – refer to Goff *et al.* 2008*a* for details; New Zealand: data relate to North Island and some immediate offshore islands – refer to Goff *et al.* 2010*b* for details) (Fig. 1). While the full details of age-range constraints are contained in the relevant cited references, several points worth noting are presented below. The age range of 1500–1600 AD for the Cook Islands (Ckl) relates to uncertainty in dating based on an oral tradition (Kloosterman 1976) and maximum ages for radiocarbon dating of archaeological artefacts (Allen & Wallace 2007). Age ranges of 1450–1600 AD for the Austral Islands (A), 1260–1430 AD for Henderson Island (H), 1430–1570 AD for the Marquesas Archipelago (M) and 1300–2030 BP for American Samoa (S) all relate to maximum ages for possible events based on radiocarbon dating of archaeological artefacts (Di Piazza & Frimigacci 1991; Weisler 1994; Conte 2002; Bollt 2008; Crews 2008; Aswani & Allen 2009). A more recent (>) than 1650 AD date for the Society Islands (SI) relates to a minimum age for a possible event based on radiocarbon dating of archaeological artefacts (Wallin *et al.* 2008), and the ages of 1450–1480 AD, 1900–2250 BP, about 2800 BP and around 6500 BP for New Zealand are based on multi-proxy data from multiple sites (McFadgen 2007; Goff 2008). All BP

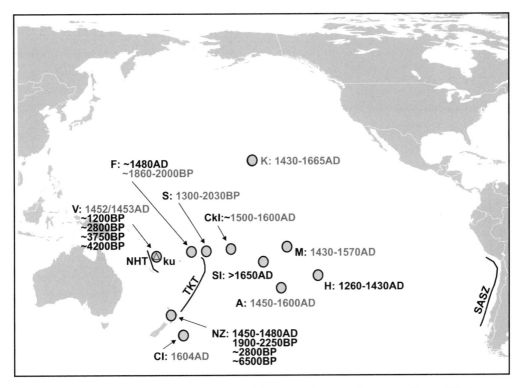

**Fig. 1.** Map of the Pacific Ocean showing palaeotsunamis in Pacific Island countries (after Goff *et al.* 2011*a*). A, Austral Islands; CI, Chatham Island; CkI, Cook Islands; F, Futuna; H, Henderson Island; K, Kaua'i; ku, Kuwae; M, Marquesas Archipelago; NHT, New Hebrides Trench; NZ, New Zealand (North Island); S, American Samoa; SI, Society Islands; SASZ, portion of South American Subduction Zone; TKT, Tonga–Kermadec Trench; V, Vanuatu. Light-blue filled black circles mark palaeotsunami locations: BP refers to calendar years Before Present (1950). Sites in red text are those detailed in Tables 3 and 4.

dates for Vanuatu are maximum age estimates based on radiocarbon dates of geological samples for possible palaeotsunamis (Goff *et al.* 2008*a*).

Examples of the nature and type of site records are given in Table 3 (geological, geomorphological and hybrid) and Table 4 (archaeological and TEK). Given the number of known historical tsunamis recorded in the Pacific Ocean, it is somewhat surprising that so few palaeotsunamis have been studied or identified. Acknowledging that there appears to be a relative dearth of research in the region, can the existing dataset be used to provide any pointers to assist with tsunami risk reduction?

First, the dataset has only a few *geological* examples. In addition to the three geological examples shown in Table 3, there are data from sites in Vanuatu (Goff *et al.* 2008*a*), Futuna (Goff *et al.* 2011*b*) and North Island, New Zealand (Goff 2008). At present, there are no more hybrid tsunamis or geomorphological sites other than those shown in Table 3, and the remainder of the dataset is composed entirely of archaeological and TEK evidence (refer to Fig. 1).

Most data points are concentrated in the southern half of the Pacific Ocean. This is primarily a function of the current extent of geological research coupled with the results of a preliminary archaeological literature search. This relative concentration of sites, however, provides a useful focus on potentially contemporaneous events in the Southern Hemisphere. While it is plausible that some palaeotsunami sources may be from the Northern Hemisphere, this seems unlikely given our understanding of the distant and regional effects of historically documented events in the Pacific Ocean (Iida *et al.* 1967; NGDC 2011). Recent work on the identification of sources from palaeotsunami deposits tends to confirm this suggestion (Goff *et al.* 2010*c*, 2011*a*).

Figure 2 summarizes a suite of scenarios that appear to effectively explain the spatial and temporal distribution of the limited number of sites

**Table 3.** *Examples of the nature and type of site records in the Pacific database (geological, geomorphological and hybrid)*

Examples: geological, geomorphological, hybrid

| | Māhā'ulepū Caves, Kaua'i | Tongoa, Vanuatu | Futuna, Wallis and Futuna archipelagos | Ua Huka, Marquesas archipelagos | Chatham Island, New Zealand |
|---|---|---|---|---|---|
| Location | | | | | |
| Latitude, longitude | N21°53'30", W159°25'17" | S16°55'07", E168°34'23" | S14°14'57", W178°10'46" | S08°56'19", W139°33'48" | S43°44'51", W176°48'18" |
| Nature of evidence | P (Geological) | P (Geological) | P (Geological) | S (Geomorphological) | P (Hybrid) |
| Site status | 1 | 1 | 1 | 1 | 1 |
| Dating technique | Geochron | Geochron | Geochron | Geochron | Geochron |
| Inferred age/year | 1430–1665 AD | 1452/1453 AD | 1860–2000 BP | 1430–1570 AD | 1604 AD |
| Physical characteristics | Boulders (>100 kg), to gravel, numerous peaty sand rip-up clasts. Fining inland – lower erosional contact | Carbonized tree rafted on a fining-upwards gravel, sand, pumice unit | Fining-upwards coarse – medium sand – lower erosional contact with underlying occupation layer | Coastal dune remobilization associated with prehistoric occupation | Fining-upwards sand and gravel with rip-up clasts and lower erosional contact |
| Thickness (m – est.) | Up to 1.00 | 0.40 | 0.08 | – | 0.20 |
| Elevation (m asl) | −0.50 to 0.50 (landward of 3.00 m high dune) | c. 5.00 | c. 6.00 | – | c. 0–0.5 |
| Landward limit (m) | 120 | 150 | 120 | 100 | 100 |
| Possible source(s) | (i) Local, 2, submarine landslide?; (ii) Kuwae, Vanuatu 1452/1453 AD, 2, caldera collapse;(iii) Chile 1575 AD, 2, earthquake | Kuwae, Vanuatu 1452/1453 AD, 1, caldera collapse | Tonga–Kermadec Trench, 2, earthquake | Unknown – South America?, 2, earthquake | 1604 AD Chilean Tsunami, 1 (from historical record in Chile, prehistoric in New Zealand), earthquake |
| Proxy tookit | 1, 2, 5, 6, 7, 14, 16, 17, 18 | 1, 2, 5, 15, 17, 18 | 1, 2, 4, 5, 6, 8, 9, 10, 13, 14, 15, 16, 17 | 16, 18 | 1,2,5,8,10,11, 15,16,17 |
| Comments | 14C and arch: event associated with Polynesian occupation. Comparison between other sites suggests event source is most likely local or distant Chilean | 14C: separates archaic (up to 1450 AD) and classic (17th century) | 14C: five dates bracket the deposit – contemporaneous deposits also found elsewhere on Futuna and in the South Pacific region | 14C: remobilized sand dated by underlying soil and overlying skeletons to between 1430 and 1570 AD | Pollen: age of event bracketed to between 1500 and 1800 AD using pollen changes associated with Moriori and subsequent European settlement |
| References | Burney et al. 2001 | Goff et al. 2008a, 2011a | Goff et al. 2011a, b | Conte 2002 | Goff et al. 2010a |
| Validity | 1 | 1 | 1 | 5 | 1 |

Refer to Table 1 for descriptors and Goff et al. (2011a) for full database.

**Table 4.** *Examples of the nature and type of site records in the Pacific database (archaeological and TEK)*

Examples: archaeological, TEK

| | Rururtu, Austral Islands | Aitutaki Island, Cook Islands | Aganoa, American Samoa | Pukapuka, Cook Islands | Kuwae, Vanuatu |
|---|---|---|---|---|---|
| Location | Rururtu, Austral Islands | Aitutaki Island, Cook Islands | Aganoa, American Samoa | Pukapuka, Cook Islands | Kuwae, Vanuatu |
| Latitude, longitude | S22°28'47", W151°20'19" | S18°51'49", W159°47'55" | S14°16'06", W170°33'54" | S10°51'07", W165°50'48" | S16°49'54", E168°31'43" |
| Nature of evidence | P (Archaeological) | P (Archaeological) | P (Archaeological) | C (TEK) | C (TEK) |
| Site status | 1 | 1 | 1 | na | na |
| Dating technique | Geochron | Geochron | Geochron | Arch | Arch |
| Inferred age/year | 1450–1600 AD | 1500–1600 AD | 1300–2030 BP | 1500–1600 AD | 1452–1453 AD |
| Physical characteristics | Fining-inland sand unit separates archaeological occupation layers | Fining-upwards coarse–fine sand unit separates archaeological occupation layers | 'Sterile sand' coarse, poorly sorted sand unit separating occupation layers | Cook Island oral record | Kastom story |
| Thickness (m – est.) | 0.90 | 0.25 | 0.80 | – | – |
| Elevation (m asl) | >2.00 | ?? | ?? | – | – |
| Landward limit (m) | 100+ | ?? | 40? | – | – |
| Possible source(s) | (i) Tonga–Kermadec Trench, 2, earthquake; (ii) South America, 2, earthquake | (i) Tonga–Kermadec Trench, 2, earthquake; (ii) South America, 2, earthquake | Tonga–Kermadec Trench, 2, earthquake | Tonga–Kermadec Trench, 2, earthquake | Kuwae, Vanuatu 1452–1453 AD, 1, caldera collapse |
| Proxy tookit | 1, 2, 5, 16, 17, 18 | 1, 12, 15, 16, 17 | 1, 5, 16, 17 | 16, 17 | 16, 17, 18 |
| Comments | $^{14}$C and Arch: Sand unit separates radiocarbon dated Archaic and Classic cultural units | $^{14}$C and arch: separates two distinct archaeological occupation layers – recognized site abandonment occurred – same event as Pukapuka (Cook Islands)? | $^{14}$C and arch: Sand unit separates two radiocarbon dated cultural layers | Arch: island settled c.1300 AD. About 250 years later island struck by tsunami. Only two women and 15 men survived – same event as Aitutaki? | Arch: the story of Pae and his revenge upon people who played a trick upon him |
| References | Bollt (2008) | Allen & Wallace (2007) | Crews (2008) | Kloosterman (1976) | Goff et al. (2008a) |
| Validity | 5 | 3 | 5 | 3 | 1 |

Refer to Table 1 for descriptors and Goff *et al.* (2011a) for full database.

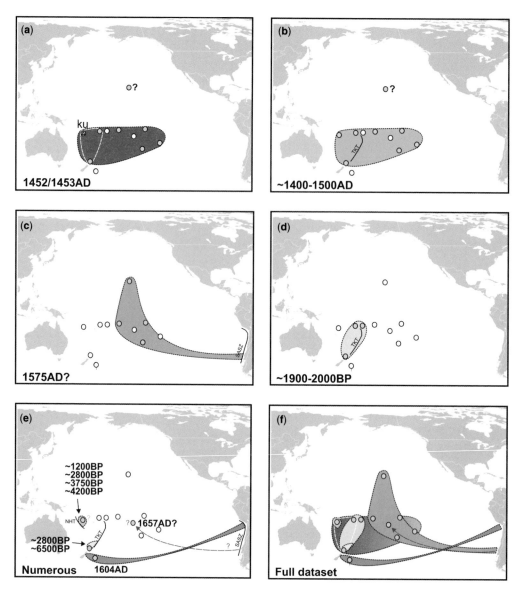

**Fig. 2.** Palaeotsunami source scenarios for age clusters in the dataset. (**a**) 1452–1453 AD Kuwae caldera collapse – the red shaded area bounded by the black dashed line represents the maximum possible extent of palaeotsunami; the area bounded by a white dashed line is an alternative interpretation (? = Kaua'i site outlier). (**b**) Potential 1400–1500 AD TKT event with areal extent shaded in pink (? = Kaua'i site outlier). (**c**) 1575 AD Chilean earthquake scenario. (**d**) 1900–2000 BP TKT event scenario. (**e**) Numerous single-site scenarios based around the NHT, TKT and SASZ scenarios. (**f**) Full dataset of possible scenarios (light-blue filled circles represent locations of contemporaneous age for the event being mapped, white filled circles indicate those locations where the age does not match the event being mapped).

currently identified. These scenarios build on recent research that has used multiple palaeotsunami deposits to identify potential Southern Hemisphere sources (e.g. Goff *et al.* 2010*a*–*c*, 2011*b*).

Figure 2a shows two shaded areas bounded by white and black dashed lines. The larger area

encloses all sites (shown as blue circles) except one (Kaua'i, Hawaii) with an approximate age range close to that of the proposed source, the Kuwae eruption of 1452–1453 AD. This VEI (Volcanic Explosivity Index) 7 eruption created a 12 km-long, 6 km-wide oval-shaped submarine caldera in central Vanuatu (Monzier *et al.* 1994; Self 2006). To put this in context, it was larger than the 1815 AD Tambora eruption, generated a minimum 100 km³ of pyroclastic deposits and had an eruptive mass of $1 \times 10^{14}$ kg (Gao *et al.* 2006; Self 2006; Witter & Self 2007). It has been proposed as a possible source for palaeotsunami deposits on Futuna (Fig. 1: F) and in North Island, New Zealand (Fig. 1: NZ), but it is unclear whether it could also have generated a large enough tsunami to have been recorded as far east as Henderson Island (Fig. 1: H). Nothing is currently known about possible palaeotsunami deposits to the west of Vanuatu and, as such, the possible regional extent of this source is largely unknown. The area enclosed by the white dashed line is therefore considered to be a more reasonable approximation of the possible regional extent of any palaeotsunami propagated from this source. While the Kaua'i (Fig. 1: K) site has an age range that covers the time period for this eruption, Kuwae seems an unlikely source. Conversely, some of the site age ranges do not span the 1452–1453 AD time period (Fig. 1: CkI, F, H) but have been included because of uncertainties in the chronological data (e.g. see discussion in Goff *et al.* 2011*b* for Futuna, F).

When studying potential sources for a cluster of palaeotsunami deposits in New Zealand, Goff *et al.* (2010*c*) noted that, while a Kuwae eruption was plausible, the degree of uncertainty in the age ranges made it more reasonable to consider an event that could have occurred between about 1400 and 1500 AD. This took the focus away from Kuwae and towards any potentially large subduction zone event in the region. More specifically, a case was made for a Tonga–Kermadec Trench event during this time period (Goff *et al.* 2010*c*). The addition of a cluster of potential contemporaneously aged sites within the South Pacific makes this more compelling (Fig. 2b). Waves would tend to propagate to the west and east away from the subduction zone and, therefore, the geographical spread of potential sites is a reasonable approximation of an area that could be affected by such an event. Once more, however, the Kaua'i site is an outlier.

While there appears to be numerous permutations and combinations of sources that could be proposed to explain the distribution of sites with age ranges of around 1400–1600 AD (Fig. 1), a paucity of data for potential sources markedly reduces the options. Based on modelled flow pathways for the catastrophic Pacific-wide 1960 Chilean Tsunami (Berryman 2005), its historical (in Chile) 1575 AD predecessor earthquake provides a plausible option that incorporates both Kaua'i and several South Pacific sites (Fig. 2c).

With the exception of a single site, there is a marked hiatus in the existing dataset between a clustering of dates around 1400–1600 AD and another cluster around 1900–2000 BP (Figs 1 & 2). We assume that this reflects the limited amount of research carried out in the region, but it could be indicative of the variability in magnitude and frequency of local, regional and distantly sourced events. As noted for all palaeotsunami databases, there is an increasing paucity of evidence for older events as taphonomic processes break down depositional records (e.g. Peters *et al.* 2003). This may well be the case for the 1900–2000 BP cluster that is centred on the Tonga–Kermadec Trench region (Fig. 2d).

Figure 2e depicts numerous single event records. Various authors have suggested probable palaeotsunami sources for several of the sites shown. Most recently, the hybrid 1604 AD event has seen a tangible link made between an historical South American earthquake and a palaeotsunami deposit in the Chatham Island, New Zealand (Goff *et al.* 2010*a*). Palaeotsunamis in Vanuatu (Fig. 2e: *c*. 1200–4200 BP) have been tentatively associated with possible palaeoseismic activity on the New Hebrides Trench (Goff *et al.* 2008*a*). Contemporaneously aged deposits around 2800 BP in both Vanuatu and New Zealand suggest that this may, however, be an oversimplification (Fig. 2e). Recently, both the circa 2800 BP and 6500 BP New Zealand events have been linked with activity on the Tonga–Kermadec Trench (Goff *et al.* 2010*c*). Given the proposed regional impact of a Tonga–Kermadec Trench event around 1400–1500 AD, this could be a plausible explanation for an earlier approximately 2800 BP palaeotsunami for which we currently have only two sites. The one remaining anomaly is the poorly constrained chronology for a possible event in the Society Islands. There are several South American source candidates. The 1657 AD earthquake is the closest in age, but equally an absence of other contemporaneously aged sites in the region points to this possibly being related to an unknown, local source, potentially a submarine landslide.

Collating the full dataset of possible palaeotsunami sites and sources is intriguing (Fig. 2f). It is possible to provide reasonable links between sites and sources without having to speculate unduly about potential unknown sources. It is, however, quite likely that these interpretations will change significantly as the database grows. It seems that the central South Pacific is exposed to numerous CPIC and local/regional sources. In the absence of a more comprehensive palaeotsunami database, it will be difficult to effectively gauge the tsunami risk faced by the many PICs in the region; a situation that is likely to be mirrored in the North Pacific. As a starting point, we deliberately chose to exclude many islands and countries on the landward side of the key subduction zones in the Northern Hemisphere. This has a more significant effect on the record for the North Pacific, which is only represented by one event in the Hawaiian Islands, making it difficult to assess the source for the Kaua'i palaeotsunami. While there is a well-researched palaeotsunami record for Japan that continues to be explored, it is more the effect of events from CPIC sources such as those off the Japanese coast on the oceanic islands of the Pacific with short tsunami histories that is of concern. Of particular note are the Commonwealth of the Northern Mariana Islands, the Federated States of Micronesia, and the Marshall Islands to the west and the Galapagos Islands to the east that sit astride the Equator, all of which have poor or short historical tsunami records (NGDC 2011).

## Where to from here?

In the wake of the recent 2009 South Pacific, 2010 Chile and 2011 Tōhoku tsunamis, it is hoped that the focus of attention will start to move once more to the Pacific Ocean. The 1960 Chilean earthquake and associated tsunami alone was a catastrophic Pacific-wide event that affected numerous PICs. To place this in context, in 2002 it was estimated that the potential costs of a one in 500 year event for an area comprising Fiji, Solomon Islands, Samoa, Tonga and Vanuatu would be in the order of A\$700 million (PIFS 2002). These estimates were based on minimal historical data and prior to the establishment of the NGDC historical database. Individual PICs, even with donor assistance, could not address these losses, and even a fraction of this cost is entirely unsustainable for PICs that are highly vulnerable because of their remoteness, isolation and limited capacity to absorb major disasters (PIFS 2002; Goff *et al.* 2011*a*).

The way forward is to use this remoteness to enhance our understanding of palaeotsunamis in the Pacific. Each PIC represents a point in the Pacific Ocean and by collating data from each island it should be possible to map the spatial and temporal distribution of past events over the last several thousand years throughout the region (Goff *et al.* 2011*a*). It is hoped that these accumulated data points will provide insights into the magnitude and frequency of local, regional and distantly sourced tsunamis, thus providing the essential baseline data needed for achieving more meaningful and effective disaster risk reduction for PICs.

J. R. Goff thanks the Pacific Islands Applied Geoscience Commission (SOPAC) for providing funding support for work in Vanuatu, and the Fonds de Coopération Economique, Sociale et Culturelle pour le Pacifique for research in Futuna.

## References

ALLEN, M. S. & WALLACE, R. 2007. New evidence from the east Polynesian gateway: substantive and methodological results from Aitutaki, southern Cook Islands. *Radiocarbon*, **49**, 1163–1179.

ANON 1894. Earthquakes in New Caledonia. *Hawera & Normanby Star*, **XXVI**, 2.

ASWANI, S. & ALLEN, M. S. 2009. Marquesan coral reef (French Polynesia) in historical context: an integrated socio-ecological approach. *Aquatic Conservation: Marine and Freshwater Ecosystems*, **19**, 614–625.

ATWATER, B. F., MUSUMI-ROKKAKU, S., SATAKE, K., TSUJI, Y., UEDA, K. & YAMAGUCHI, D. K. 2005. *The Orphan Tsunami of 1700 – Japanese Clues to a Parent Earthquake in North America.* US Geological Survey, Professional Paper, 1707.

BERNINGHAUSEN, W. H. 1962. Tsunamis reported from the west coast of South America, 1562–1960. *Bulletin of the Seismological Society of American*, **52**, 915–921.

BERRYMAN, K. (comp.). 2005. *Review of Tsunami Hazard and Risk in New Zealand.* MCDEM Report, 2005/104. Ministry of Civil Defence and Emergency Management, Wellington.

BOLLT, R. 2008. Excavations in Peva Valley, Rurutu, Austral Islands (east Polynesia). *Asian Perspectives*, **47**, 156–187.

BURNEY, D. A., JAMES, H. F. *ET AL.* 2001. Fossil evidence for a diverse biota from Kauài and its transformation since human arrival. *Ecological Monographs*, **71**, 615–641.

CHAGUÉ-GOFF, C., SCHNEIDER, J.-L., GOFF, J. R., DOMINEY-HOWES, D. & STROTZ, L. 2011. Expanding the proxy toolkit to help identify past events – Lessons from the 2004 Indian Ocean Tsunami and the 2009 South Pacific Tsunami. *Earth-Science Reviews*, **107**, 107–122, doi: 10.1016/j.earscirev. 2011.03.007.

CISTERNAS, M., ATWATER, B. F. *ET AL.* 2005. Predecessors to the giant 1960 Chile earthquake. *Nature*, **437**, 404–407.

CONTE, E. 2002. Current research on the Island of Ua Huka, Marquesas Archipelago, French Polynesia. *Asian Perspectives*, **41**, 258–268.

CREWS, C. T. 2008. *The Lithics of Aganoa Village (As-22–43), American Samoa: a test of chemical characterization and sourcing Tutuilan Tool-Stone.* Unpublished MA thesis, Texas A&M University.

DE LANGE, W. P. & HEALY, T. R. 1986. New Zealand Tsunamis 1840–1982. *New Zealand Journal of Geology and Geophysics*, **29**, 115–134.

DI PIAZZA, A. & FRIMIGACCI, D. 1991. A thousand years of gardening: a history of subsistence on Futuna. *Bulletin of the Indo-Pacific Prehistory Association*, **11**, 124–140.

DOMINEY-HOWES, D. 2007. Geological and historical records of tsunami in Australia. *Marine Geology*, **239**, 99–123.

GAO, C., ROBOCK, A. *ET AL.* 2006. The 1452 or 1453 A.D. Kuwae eruption signal derived from multiple ice core records: Greatest volcanic sulfate event of the past 700 years. *Journal of Geophysical Research*, **111**, D12107, doi: 10.1029/2005JD006710.

GOFF, J. R. 2008. *The New Zealand Palaeotsunami Database*. NIWA Technical Report, 131. National Institute of Water & Atmospheric Research, Auckland.

GOFF, J., CHAGUÉ-GOFF, C. *ET AL.* 2011*a*. Palaeotsunamis in the Pacific Islands. *Earth-Science Reviews*, **107**, 141–146, doi: 10.1016/j.earscirev.2010.10.005.

GOFF, J., CHARLEY, D., HARUEL, C. & BONTÉ-GRAPENTIN, M. 2008*a*. *Preliminary Findings of the Geological Evidence and Oral History of Tsunamis in Vanuatu*. SOPAC Technical Report, 416. Pacific Islands Applied Geoscience Commission, Suva, Fiji.

GOFF, J., LAMARCHE, G., PELLETIER, B., CHAGUÉ-GOFF, C. & STROTZ, L. 2011*b*. Predecessors to the 2009 South Pacific tsunami in the Wallis and Futuna archipelago. *Earth-Science Reviews*, **107**, 91–106, doi: 10.1016/j.earscirev.2010.11.003.

GOFF, J. R., CHAGUÉ-GOFF, C. & NICHOL, S. L. 2001. Palaeotsunami deposits: a New Zealand perspective. *Sedimentary Geology*, **143**, 1–6.

GOFF, J. R., MCFADGEN, B. G., WELLS, A. & HICKS, M. 2008*b*. Seismic signals in coastal dune systems. *Earth Science Reviews*, **89**, 73–77.

GOFF, J. R., NICHOL, S. L., CHAGUÉ-GOFF, C., HORROCKS, M., MCFADGEN, B. & CISTERNAS, M. 2010*a*. Predecessor to New Zealand's largest historic trans-South Pacific tsunami of 1868 AD. *Marine Geology*, **275**, 155–165.

GOFF, J. R., NICHOL, S. L. & KENNEDY, D. 2010*b*. Development of a palaeotsunami database for New Zealand. *Natural Hazards*, **54**, 193–208.

GOFF, J. R., PEARCE, S., NICHOL, S. L., CHAGUÉ-GOFF, C., HORROCKS, M. & STROTZ, L. 2010*c*. Multi-proxy records of regionally-sourced tsunamis, New Zealand. *Geomorphology*, **118**, 369–382.

IIDA, K., COX, D. C. & PARARAS-CARAYANNIS, G. 1967. *Preliminary Catalog of Tsunamis Occurring in the Pacific Ocean*. Data Report, 5. Hawaii Institute of Geophysics, Honolulu, HI.

ITIC 2010*a*. *Indian Ocean Tsunami 2004*. International Tsunami Information Center, Honolulu, HI. World Wide Web Address: http://ioc3.unesco.org/itic/contents.php?id=145. Accessed 10 September 2010.

ITIC 2010*b*. *IOC Tsunami Glossary*. International Tsunami Information Center, Honolulu, HI. World Wide Web Address: http://ioc3.unesco.org/itic/contents.php?id=19. Accessed 10 September 2010.

KELSEY, H. M., NELSON, A. R., HEMPHILL-HALEY, E. & WITTER, R. C. 2005. Tsunami history of an Oregon coastal lake reveals a 4600 yr record of great earthquakes on the Cascadia subduction zone. *Geological Society of America Bulletin*, **117**, 1009–1032.

KING, D. & GOFF, J. R. 2010. Benefitting from differences in knowledge, practice and belief: Māori oral traditions and natural hazards science. *Natural Hazards and Earth System Sciences*, **10**, 1–15.

KING, D., GOFF, J. R. & SKIPPER, A. 2007. Māori Environmental Knowledge and natural hazards in New Zealand. *Journal of the Royal Society of New Zealand*, **37**, 59–73.

KLOOSTERMAN, A. M. J. 1976. *Discoverers of the Cook Islands and the Names they Gave*. Cook Island Library and Museum, Raratonga.

LATIEF, H., PUSPITO, N. T. & IMAMURA, F. 2000. Tsunami catalog and zones in Indonesia. *Journal of Natural Disaster Science*, **22**, 25–43.

LAU, A., SWITZER, A., DOMINEY-HOWES, D., AITCHISON, J. & ZONG, Y. 2010. Written records of historical tsunamis in the northeastern South China Sea – challenges associated with developing a new integrated database. *Natural Hazards and Earth System Sciences*, **10**, 1793–1806.

MCFADGEN, B. G. 2007. *Hostile Shores: Catastrophic Events in Prehistoric New Zealand and Their Impact on Māori Coastal Communities*. Auckland University Press, Auckland.

MCFADGEN, B. G. & GOFF, J. R. 2007. Tsunamis in the archaeological record of New Zealand. *Sedimentary Geology*, **200**, 263–274.

MONZIER, M., ROBIN, C. & EISSEN, J.-P. 1994. Kuwae (~1425 A.D.): the forgotten caldera. *Journal of Volcanology and Geothermal Research*, **59**, 207–218.

MORRIS, M. K. & MAZENGARB, C. 2009. *Historical Accounts of Tsunamis in Tasmania*. Tasmanian Geological Survey Record, 2009/04.

NANAYAMA, F., FURUKAWA, R., SHIGENO, K., MAKINO, A., SOEDA, Y. & IGARASHI, Y. 2007. Nine unusually large tsunami deposits from the past 4000 years at Kiritappu marsh along the southern Kuril Trench. *Sedimentary Geology*, **200**, 275–294.

NGDC 2011. *NOAA/WDC Historical Tsunami Database at NGDC*. National Geophysical Data Center, Boulder, CO. Wide Web Address: http://www.ngdc.noaa.gov/hazard/tsu_db.shtml. Accessed 10 September 2010.

NORMILE, D. 2011. Scientific consensus on great quake came too late. *Science*, **332**, 22–23.

NUNN, P. D., BANIALA, M., HARRISON, M. & GERAGHTY, P. 2006. Vanished islands in Vanuatu: new research and a preliminary geohazard assessment. *Journal of the Royal Society of New Zealand*, **36**, 37–50.

PAPADOPOULOS, G. A. 2000. *Historical Earthquakes and Tsunamis in the Corinth Rift, Central Greece*. Institute of Geodynamics, NOA Publication, **128**.

PETERS, R., JAFFE, B., GELFENBAUM, G. & PETERSEN, C. 2003. *Cascadia Tsunami Deposit Database*. USGS Open-File Report, **03-13**.

PIFS. 2002. *Catastrophe Insurance*. Session 3 Paper, Forum Economic Ministers Meeting, Vanuatu. PIFS(02)FEMV.12. Pacific Islands Forum Secretariat, Suva, Fiji.

PINEGINA, T. K., BOURGEOIS, J. & MELEKESTSEV, I. V. 2003. A millennial-scale record of Holocene tsunamis on the Kronotskiy Bay coast, Kamchatka, Russia. *Quaternary Research*, **59**, 36–47.

SAHAL, A., PELLETIER, B., CHATELIER, J., LAVIGNE, F. & SCHINDELÉ, F. 2010. A catalog of tsunamis in New Caledonia from 28 March 1875 to 30 September 2009. *Comptes Rendus Geoscience*, **342**, 434–447.

SELF, S. 2006. The effects and consequences of very large explosive volcanic eruptions. *Philosophical Transactions of the Royal Society A*, **364**, 2073–2097.

TINTI, S., MARAMAI, A. & GRAZIANI, L. 2004. The new catalogue of the Italian tsunamis. *Natural Hazards*, **33**, 439–465.

WALLIN, P., ÖSTERHOLM, I., ÖSTERHOLM, S. & SOLSVIK, R. 2008. Chapter 27. Phosphates and bones: An analysis of the courtyard of marae Manunu, Huahine, Society Islands, French Polynesia. *In*: CLARK, G., LEACH, F. & O'CONNOR, S. (eds) *Islands of Inquiry. Colonisation, Seafaring and the Archaeology of Maritime Landscapes.* Terra Australis, **29**. Australian National University E Press, Canberra, 423–434.

WEISLER, M. I. 1994. The settlement of marginal Polynesia: new evidence from Henderson Island. *Journal of Field Archaeology*, **21**, 83–102.

WITTER, J. B. & SELF, S. 2007. The Kuwae (Vanuatu) eruption of AD 1452: potential magnitude and volatile release. *Bulletin of Volcanology*, **69**, 301–318.

# Index

Page numbers in *italics* refer to Figures. Page numbers in **bold** refer to Tables.